D1597450

MATHEMATICAL LOGIC AND PROGRAMMING LANGUAGES

Prentice Hall International
Series in Computer Science

C.A.R. Hoare, Series Editor

Published

BACKHOUSE, R.C., *Syntax of Programming Languages, Theory and Practice*
de BAKKER, J.W., *Mathematical Theory of Program Correctness*
BJORNER, D. and JONES, C., *Formal Specification and Software Development*
CLARK, K.L. and McCABE, F.G., *micro-PROLOG: Programming in Logic*
DROMEY, R.G., *How to Solve it by Computer*
DUNCAN, F., *Microprocessor Programming and Software Development*
ELDER, J., *Construction of Data Processing Software*
GOLDSCHLAGER, L. and LISTER, A., *Computer Science: A Modern Introduction*
HEHNER, E.C.R., *The Logic of Programming*
HENDERSON, P., *Functional Programming: Application and Implementation*
HOARE, C.A.R. and SHEPHERDSON, J.C., eds. *Mathematical Logic and Programming Languages*
INMOS, LTD., *The Occam Programming Manual*
JACKSON, M.A., *System Development*
JONES, C.B., *Software Development: A Rigorous Approach*
JOSEPH, M., PRASAD. V.R. and NATARAJAN, N., *A Multiprocessor Operating System*
MacCALLUM, I., *Pascal for the Apple*
REYNOLDS, J.C., *The Craft of Programming*
TENNENT, R.D., *Principles of Programming Languages*
WELSH, J. and ELDER, J., *Introduction to Pascal, 2nd Edition*
WELSH, J., ELDER, J. and BUSTARD, D., *Sequential Program Structures*
WELSH, J. and McKEAG, M., *Structured System Programming*

MATHEMATICAL LOGIC AND PROGRAMMING LANGUAGES

Edited by

C.A.R. HOARE and **J.C. SHEPHERDSON**

The papers in this book were first published in the Philosophical Transactions of the Royal Society, Series A, Volume 312, 1984.

Englewood Cliffs, New Jersey London New Delhi Rio de Janeiro
Singapore Sydney Tokyo Toronto Wellington

0-13-561465-1

PRENTICE-HALL INTERNATIONAL, INC., *London*
PRENTICE-HALL OF AUSTRALIA PTY., LTD., *Sydney*
PRENTICE-HALL CANADA, INC., *Toronto*
PRENTICE-HALL OF INDIA PRIVATE LIMITED, *New Delhi*
PRENTICE-HALL OF JAPAN, INC., *Tokyo*
PRENTICE HALL OF SOUTHEAST ASIA PTE., LTD., *Singapore*
PRENTICE-HALL, INC., *Englewood Cliffs, New Jersey*
PRENTICE-HALL DO BRASIL LTDA., *Rio de Janeiro*
WHITEHALL BOOKS LIMITED, *Wellington, New Zealand*

Printed in Great Britain by A. Wheaton & Co. Ltd, Exeter

1 2 3 4 5 89 88 87 86 85

Contributors

ABRIAL, J.R.
26 rue des Plantes, 75014 Paris, France
CLARKE, E.M., Jr.
Carnegie-Mellon University, Pittsburgh, Penn., USA
DIJKSTRA, E.W.
The University of Texas at Austin, USA
GOOD, D.I.
The University of Texas at Austin, USA
HOARE, C.A.R.
Oxford University Computing Laboratory, UK
KOWALSKI, R.
Imperial College, London, UK
MARTIN-LÖF, P.
University of Stockholm, Sweden
MILNER, R.
University of Edinburgh, UK
TURNER, D.A.
University of Kent, Canterbury, UK
VALIANT, L.G.
Harvard University, Cambridge, Mass., USA

MATHEMATICAL LOGIC AND PROGRAMMING LANGUAGES

A Discussion organized and edited by Sir Michael Atiyah, F.R.S., C. A. R. Hoare, F.R.S., and J. C. Shepherdson

(*Discussion held* 15 *and* 16 *February* 1984 – *Typescripts received* 2 *April* 1984)

CONTENTS

'*It is reasonable to hope that the relationship between computation and mathematical logic will be as fruitful in the next century as that between analysis and physics in the last. The development of this relationship demands a concern for both applications and for mathematical elegance.*'

(J. McCarthy, 1967)

PREFACE

This book reports a Discussion Meeting of the Royal Society of London, held on 15 and 16 February 1984. The meeting was organized by Sir Michael Atiyah, F.R.S., John Shepherdson, and myself; and Elizabeth Fielding organized a very successful exhibition to accompany it.

The strong connection between the formalization of mathematical logic and the formalization of computer programming languages was clearly recognized by Alan Turing as early as 1947, when, in a talk on 20 February to the London Mathematical Society, he reported his expectation

> '*that digital computing machines will eventually stimulate a considerable interest in symbolic logic and mathematical philosophy. The language in which one communicates with these machines, i.e. the language of instruction tables, forms a sort of symbolic logic*'.

The central problems facing the computer scientist as a software engineer are the formulation of valid specifications, the construction of efficient programs, together with a proof that the programs meet their specifications. The design of suitable notations and formal proof methods can make a significant contribution to the solution of these problems, provided that the designs are based on 'the results, methods, and spirit of formalization in mathematical logic' (Hao Wang 1967).

Four of the contributions to this book describe such designs. Robert Kowalski recommends use of the formal language of predicate logic for the expression of specifications, and looks forward to the development of more powerful mechanical theorem-provers that will directly execute these specifications. Meanwhile, we should use a sub-language (for example Horn clauses), for which theorem-provers are currently available. Mathematical reasoning must be used to prove the equivalence of the more efficient Horn clause program with its possibly clearer specification expressed in a richer language. Jean-Raymond Abrial recommends for specifications the full language of (typed) set theory, and shows how the conventional notations of sequential programming may be defined within this framework. My contribution follows these suggestions: it shows how programs expressed in a procedural programming notation can be regarded as predicates describing the behaviour of a machine executing the program; and for their total correctness it is sufficient to show that they imply their specifications.

David Turner suggests that the language of functional programming is a compromise, suitable both for specification and for executable programs: in expressive power it is nearly as good as logic; and in execution efficiency it approaches a conventional procedural language. Where necessary, algebraic laws can be used to optimize a specification before execution.

Once a logical system and language have been properly formalized, it is possible to program a computer to conduct proofs within the system, or at least check such proofs. This was also predicted by Alan Turing in 1947:

> '*Some attempts will be made to get machines to do actual manipulations of mathematical formulae. To do so will require the development of a special logical system for the purpose*'.

Two such systems are reported here. The first is Gypsy, designed by Don Good, which aids the proof that programs expressed in a conventional notation will meet their specifications expressed as predicates which are true before and after execution of the program. This system has already been used in practice on certain critical programs. The second is Robin Milner's LCF, designed to check and help construct proofs in Dana Scott's Logic of Computable Functions. The outstanding achievement of this system is its use of secure type-checking to ensure correctness of more sophisticated proof methods.

Two of our contributors show how the study of the needs of programmers has inspired new and fruitful developments in logic. Ed Clarke has studied the problem of constructing complete axiom systems for proof of partial correctness, and describes the implications of this for programming language design. Per Martin-Löf reports on the design of a programming language together with its proof system, in a manner that is strongly related to intuitionistic logic and constructive mathematics. I expect both these researches will have a profound influence on our understanding of the relation between mathematical logic and programming languages.

The remaining two papers offer relief from the pursuit of formalization. Edsger W. Dijkstra gives a beautiful example of a mixture of formal and informal reasoning in the design of an algorithm to solve a problem in distributed computing. Les Valiant considers the prospect of teaching computers by example to do what we want, thus avoiding altogether the rigours of formal specification and programming. He applies methods of complexity analysis to evaluate the promise of this approach.

In conclusion, it is my hope that this book will be seen as a worthy advance in directions advocated and pursued by Christopher Strachey; and summarized by him:

> '*Mathematical Logic has inspired many of the most elegant and useful advances in Computing Science of the last fifteen years. Their usefulness lies in their promise for improving the quality of the program specifications, and the reliability of their development. Their elegance is displayed in the design of simple programming languages for the expression of mathematical and logical ideas in a form capable of direct execution on a stored-program computing machine.*'

June 1984 C. A. R. HOARE, F.R.S.

The relation between logic programming and logic specification

By R. Kowalski

Department of Computing, Imperial College, 180 Queen's Gate, London SW7 2BZ, U.K.

Formal logic is widely accepted as a program specification language in computing science. It is ideally suited to the representation of knowledge and the description of problems without regard to the choice of programming language. Its use as a specification language is compatible not only with conventional programming languages but also with programming languages based entirely on logic itself. In this paper I shall investigate the relation that holds when both programs and program specifications are expressed in formal logic.

In many cases, when a specification *completely* defines the relations to be computed, there is no syntactic distinction between specification and program. Moreover the same mechanism that is used to execute logic programs, namely automated deduction, can also be used to execute logic specifications. Thus all relations defined by complete specifications are executable. The only difference between a complete specification and a program is one of efficiency. A program is more efficient than a specification.

Logic programming

The use of logic as a specification language may be more familiar than its use as a programming language. A short introduction may therefore be appropriate.

Logic programming (Kowalski 1974, 1983) is based upon (but not necessarily restricted to) the interpretation of rules of the form

A if B and C and ...

as procedures

to do A,
do B and do C and ....

This interpretation is equivalent to 'backwards reasoning' and is a special case of the resolution rule of inference (Robinson 1965). It is the basis also of the programming language PROLOG (Colmerauer *et al.* 1973; Clark & McCabe 1984).

Example 1.

(*a*) x is mortal if x is human.

This is interpreted as the procedure

'to show x mortal
show x human'

or

'to find x mortal
find x human'

depending whether x is given or not.

(*b*) Socrates is human.

This is interpreted as a procedure that solves problems without introducing further subproblems.

The notation of (*a*) and (*b*) is one we have used to simplify the syntax of logic for teaching children (Ennals 1982). This syntax is translated by a PROLOG program into more conventional symbolic notation:

Mortal(x) if Human(x)
Human(Socrates).

To find a mortal we pose the *query*

Find x where Mortal(x).

This is equivalent to proving the theorem:

there exists an x such that x is mortal, i.e.
$\exists$ x Mortal(x).

The procedural interpretation answers the query by reasoning backwards from the theorem to be proved by using 1 (*a*) to reduce the problem to the subproblem of showing

there exists an x such that x is human,

which is solved directly by 1 (*b*). As a byproduct, the solution

x = Socrates

can be extracted from the proof. In this way 1 (*a*) and 1 (*b*) behave as a program and backwards reasoning behaves like procedure invocation.

In this example we are given declarative statements of classical logic, and the procedural interpretation turns them into a program. The following example is more obviously related to computing.

A LOGIC SPECIFICATION OF THE SORTING PROBLEM

Example 2.

Sort(x y) if Permutation(x y)
and Ordered(y).

The rule can be read both declaratively:

'y is a sorted version of x
if y is a permutation of x
and y is ordered'

and procedurally:

'to sort x into y
find a permutation y of x and
show y is ordered'.

Given complete definitions of the lower-level Permutation and Ordered relations, the rule for Sort *completely* specifies the notion of sorting. The procedural interpretation turns the specification into an executable, although very inefficient, non-deterministic program.

Notice that the specification of sortedness can be used both to test given x and y and to generate y as output, given x. It can even be used to generate pairs of x and y that satisfy the Sort relation. This is the same flexibility that we have with database queries. The mechanization of theorem-proving makes it possible to query program specifications.

Note also that the specification of sortedness contains no assignment statements or other side effects. The purpose of assignment is to re-use space for the purpose of efficiency. It has no place, therefore, in program specifications where the emphasis is on clarity.

A LOGIC PROGRAM FOR THE SORTING PROBLEM

Example 3.

Sort(x x) if Ordered(x)
Sort(x y) if $i < j$
and $x_i > x_j$
and Interchange(x i j z)
and Sort(z y).

The declarative reading of the rules is obvious:

If x is ordered
then x is already a sorted version of itself.
If x contains some out of order pair
$x_i > x_j$ where $i < j$
and these are interchanged giving an intermediate sequence z
and y is a sorted version of z
then y is also a sorted version of x.

But it is the procedural interpretation of the rules that makes them useful. Taken together the two rules behave as a procedure. Given x as input and y as output

to sort x,
repeatedly interchange out of order pairs
$x_i > x_j$ where $i < j$
until x is ordered.

Here we have used functional syntax with relational semantics. The single condition

$x_i > x_j$,

which employs a form of functional syntax, would need to be replaced by three conditions in relational syntax:

Contains(x i u) and
Contains(x j v) and
$u > v$.

We shall have more to say about the relation between functional and relational syntax later.

Notice that the procedural reading of the rules suggests a destructive assignment operation that replaces the sequence x by the result of interchanging x_i and x_j. Such an assignment that destroys the preceding value of x is an efficiency-improving operation that should not be allowed to affect the semantics of the rules as determined by their declarative reading.

Verification of logic programs

A *complete logic specification* defines a collection of relations in the same way that a *logic program* does. Given a set of sentences S containing a predicate, say P(x y), S defines P in the sense that

> (s t) is in the relation P
> iff
> S logically implies P(s t)
> or equivalently
> for first-order logic
> iff
> P(s t) can be proved from S.

This notion of 'definition' accords with our intuition in the case where S is a logic program. Because it is so hard to distinguish between programs and complete specifications, we use the same notion of definition for both. But notice that, according to this, any relation defined by a finite set of sentences of first-order logic is semi-computable (i.e. recursively enumerable). This conflicts with the usual notion of semantic definition in which even very simple sentences of first-order logic 'define' uncomputable relations.

We shall now prove that the sort program of example 3 meets the specification of example 2. To do this we shall show that if (s t) is in the relation defined by the program then it is also in the relation defined by the specification.

Proof by induction on the length n of a proof (computation) of Sort(s t) by means of the program. We shall show that

> if the program implies Sort(s t) then
> t is a permutation of s and
> t is ordered.

n = 1. Sort(s t) can be proved by using the first rule of the program alone.

> Therefore s = t and s is ordered.
> So t is a permutation of s and t is ordered.

n = k+1. There is a backward proof of Sort(s t), the first step of which uses the second rule of the program to reduce the goal Sort(s t) to the subgoals

> $i < j$
> $s_i > s_j$
> Interchange(s i j r)
> Sort(r t),

for some concrete i, j and r. Obviously, the proof of the subgoal Sort(r t) takes fewer than k+1 steps. Therefore we may assume by the induction hypothesis that

> t is a permutation of r and
> t is ordered.

But Interchange(s i j r) implies that

> r is a permutation s.

Therefore

t is a permutation of s and
t is ordered.

The relation between the specification of sortedness and various logic programs for sorting lists has been studied in detail by Clark & Darlington (1980).

The inductive method of proof, which works in this example to show that a program meets its specification, works whether the specification is partial or complete. The same proof, in particular, shows that the program meets the *partial* specification that

t is ordered whenever Sort(s t) is logically implied by the program.

Notice, however, as this example shows, there is no purely syntactic distinction between complete and partial specifications. A definition of orderedness is a complete specification for the problem of testing or generating ordered sequences, but it is only a partial specification for the sorting problem.

A PROGRAM WITHOUT A SPECIFICATION

The following example, due to Peter Hammond (Hammond & Sergot 1983), is a logical reconstruction of a small part of a medical expert system implemented in the expert system shell EMYCIN. It can be regarded either as a program without a specification or as a complete specification that runs efficiently enough not to need a separate program.

Example 4.

```
x should take y if x has complained of z
                  and y suppresses z
                  and Not y is unsuitable for x
y is unsuitable for x if y aggravates z
                         and x has condition z
aspirin suppresses inflammation
aspirin suppresses pain
    etc.
aspirin aggravates peptic ulcer
lomotil aggravates impaired liver function
    etc.
```

This example is characteristic of many others whose main objective is to represent some aspect of human knowledge or expertise. It has no specification besides the informal constraint that it reflects such knowledge and expertise as faithfully as possible. In this respect it bears more resemblance to a program specification than it does to a program. On the other hand, because it runs with tolerable efficiency, it is impossible not to regard it as a program as well. Similar examples can be found in the field of expert systems, in the formalization of legislation (Cory *et al.* 1984) and in data processing, where database queries, for example, can be regarded as specifications that behave like programs. This example also illustrates two other features of 'logic programs': negation by failure and declarative input–output.

Negation by failure

In our previous examples we have restricted ourselves to the use of rules and queries with positive atomic conditions. This is equivalent to the *Horn clause* subset of logic. In example 4 we have extended the Horn clause subset to allow negated conditions. The procedural interpretation of Horn clauses can be extended to deal with such conditions. For example, a negated condition such as

Not y is suitable for x

is judged to hold if the positive condition

y is unsuitable for x

fails to hold. Such negation by failure is consistent with classical negation (Clark 1978) provided the implicit only-if half of 'definitions' is made explicit, i.e. in this case provided the second rule is re-expressed as

y is unsuitable for x
iff there exists z such that y aggravates z
and x has condition z.

Moreover, negation by failure can only be used to test conditions and not to generate solutions. For example, given the additional assumption

John has condition peptic ulcer,

the negated goal

Find y where Not y unsuitable for John

incorrectly fails because the unnegated goal.

Find y where y unsuitable for John

succeeds. Thus, although negation by failure is correct and efficient, it is also incomplete. The limitations of negation by failure are discussed in Kowalski (1983).

Declarative input–output

In example 4 the relations

x has complained of z

and

x has condition z

are not defined. The appropriate parts of their 'definitions' can be provided dynamically by 'the user' as they are required by the system. This makes input–output *declarative* in the sense that it can be understood entirely in logical terms: the output is a logical consequence of the information initially contained in the system together with any information provided by the user (Sergot 1982). The input can be given in any order, provided it does not affect the logical implication of the output.

THE EXTENDED HORN CLAUSE SUBSET OF LOGIC

The Horn clause subset of logic, even if it is extended to allow negated conditions, lacks the expressive power of the standard form of logic. For example, the natural *specification* of the subset relation requires the use of a condition that itself has the form of a universally quantified Horn clause.

Example 5.
(*a*) $X \subseteq Y$ if For all z [$z \in Y$ if $z \in X$].

We call this generalization of the Horn clause subset of logic, in which conditions can have the form of universally quantified Horn clauses, the *extended Horn clause subset of logic*. This extension has great expressive power and many examples such as the definition of subset, the definition of greatest common divisor and the definitions of ordered sequence given later in the paper can be formalized naturally within this language. The use of conditions that are universally quantified Horn clauses often makes it possible to avoid the use of recursion. For the definition of subset, recursion is unavoidable if we restrict ourselves to the use of Horn clauses:

(*b*) Nil $\subseteq$ Y
cons(u v) $\subseteq$ Y if $u \in Y$ and $v \subseteq Y$.

The Horn clause definition of subset is the obvious recursive *program*, given that sets are represented by lists. It is very like a program in a functional programming language and it can be directly executed in PROLOG.

Given an appropriate definition of the membership relation $\in$, 5 (*a*) is a complete specification of the subset relation. It is executable in the sense that if $s \subseteq t$ is implied by 5 (*a*) together with the associated definition of $\in$ then $s \subseteq t$ can be proved by means of a mechanical theorem-proving procedure. With today's general-purpose theorem-proving procedures, however, this will be very inefficient. But by translating 'For all' into double negation and interpreting negation by failure, universally quantified Horn clause conditions can be executed both correctly and efficiently. The specification 5 (*a*) of subset, in particular, will run as an iteration:

> given s and t it will attempt to show $s \subseteq t$ by consecutively generating the elements of s and showing that they belong to t (by *failing* to show that there is any element of s that does *not* belong to t).

Such iterative execution of the specification can be more efficient than recursive execution of the program. Thus much of the work that has previously gone into the derivation of programs from specifications may have been wasted. Moreover, it has also distracted attention from the problem of designing theorem-provers that efficiently execute program specifications.

The 'specification' of subset can benefit more than the recursive program from being executed by means of different strategies. For example, an 'or-parallel' theorem-prover that can explore alternatives in parallel could, conceptually at least, attempt to show $s \subseteq t$ by exploring the elements of s in parallel, perhaps using associative look-up to show that they all belong to t. Thus we obtain different algorithms simply by changing the mode of execution (Kowalski 1979).

On the other hand, the translation of 'For all' into double negation and the interpretation of negation as failure, although correct and efficient, is incomplete. Certain logical consequences cannot be proved by these means. In particular, although 5(*a*) can be used to test that the subset relation holds for given s and t, by using these methods it cannot be used to generate s from t or t from s. Moreover, it will succeed only when s has finitely many members.

The derivation of logic programs from logic specifications

Given a logic program and a complete logic specification, it is often possible to derive the program from the specification. Such programs are derived by using the rules of logic and as a consequence are guaranteed to be correct.

Although in the subset example it may be better to execute the 'specification' than the 'program', in other cases no execution strategy can render a specification as efficient as a program. It is instructive, therefore, to show how 5 (*b*) can be derived from 5 (*a*), if only because it is a simple example and because such derivation is useful in other cases. For this we need to replace the if-half of the specification by its full iff form:

$$X \subseteq Y \text{ iff For all z } [z \in Y \text{ if } z \in X]; \qquad (s1)$$

we also need auxiliary definitions to specify how sets can be represented by lists:

$$\text{Not Exists z } [z \in \text{Nil}] \qquad (s2)$$
$$z \in \text{cons}(u\ v) \text{ iff } z = u \text{ or } z \in v. \qquad (s3)$$

These three sentences, together with the axioms of equality, constitute a *complete specification*, which logically implies the program.

Proof.

(*a*) The specification implies the recursive clause of the program:

$$X \subseteq Y \text{ if For all z } [z \in Y \text{ if } z \in X] \qquad \text{(by (s1))}$$
(the if-half of the specification)
$$\text{cons}(u\ v) \subseteq Y \text{ if For all z } [z \in Y \text{ if } [z = u \text{ or } z \in v]] \qquad \text{(by (s3))}$$
$$\text{cons}(u\ v) \subseteq Y \text{ if For all z } [z \in Y \text{ if } z = u] \text{ and For all z } [z \in Y \text{ if } z \in v]$$
$$\text{cons}(u\ v) \subseteq Y \text{ if } u \in Y \text{ and } v \subseteq Y \qquad \text{(by (s1))}$$

(*b*) The specification implies the basis of the program:

$$\text{Nil} \subseteq Y \text{ if For all z } [z \in Y \text{ if } z \in \text{Nil}] \qquad \text{(by (s1))}$$
(an instance of the if-half of the specification)
$$\text{Nil} \subseteq Y \text{ if For all z } [z \in Y \text{ if False}] \qquad \text{(by (s2))}$$
$$\text{Nil} \subseteq Y \text{ if True}$$
$$\text{Nil} \subseteq Y.$$

Note that the proof of (*a*) can be regarded as generalizing the fold–unfold method of Burstall & Darlington (1977). It can be viewed both as logical proof and as symbolic execution of the specification. This method of deriving logic programs from logic specifications has been developed by Clark (Clark & Sickel 1977; Clark *et al.* 1982); Hogger (1978*a*, *b*) and others (Hanson & Tarnlund 1979; Winterstein *et al.* 1980).

We have shown that the program is partially correct by showing that it is logically implied by its specification. This may be counter-intuitive, and therefore requires explanation. Suppose a set of sentences S defines a relation P(x y). (In a typical application, x might be input, y output and P(x y) an input–output relation.) This means that

> (x y) is in relation P
> iff
> $S \vdash P(x\ y)$.

Where $X \vdash Y$ means that conclusion Y can be proved from assumptions X. Thus not only does S imply P(x y), it also 'computes' it, in the sense that its instances can be derived by means of a mechanical theorem-proving procedure. Suppose Spec and Prog are a complete specification and a program, respectively, defining a relation P(x y). Then to say that the program is *partially correct* relative to the specification is to say that every instance of P that is a consequence of Prog is also a consequence of Spec, i.e.

> if Prog $\vdash$ P(x y) then Spec $\vdash$ P(x y).

But this holds if

> Spec $\vdash$ Prog

by the transitivity of the proof predicate. If the converse holds, i.e.

> if Spec $\vdash$ P(x y) then Prog $\vdash$ P(x y),

then the program is *complete* in the sense that the program derives every instance of P that is defined by the specification. This holds if

> Prog $\vdash$ Spec.

Notice that to prove correctness or completeness we can replace either Spec or Prog by any stronger set of sentences that implies the same atomic relations. This justifies the use of the iff form of definitions and induction in such proofs. Thus it is closely related to Hoare's identification of a program (this symposium) with the *strongest* predicate that describes its behaviour.

Notice also that to prove a specification implies a program, we need to show that the specification logically implies each clause in the program. Thus the *complexity* of proving partial correctness is linear in the number of clauses in the program, and the complexity of proving completeness is linear in the number of clauses in the specification.

Verification of the Euclidean algorithm

The Euclidean algorithm can be verified by the same technique of deriving programs from specifications that was used to verify the recursive program for subset. For the Euclidean algorithm, however, the program is significantly more efficient than the specification. Here we use functional notation for the sake of clarity.

Example 6.

```
(a)    gcd(x y) = z if z divides x
                    and z divides y
                    and For all u [u ≤ z if u divides x
                                            and u divides y].
```

Notice that, like the definition of subset, this definition is expressed in the extended Horn clause subset of logic. However, the Euclidean algorithm for gcd can be expressed in Horn clause form:

(*a*) gcd(x y) = z if x divides y
gcd(x y) = z if x $\leqslant$ y
and x divides y with remainder r
and r $\neq$ 0
and gcd(r x) = z.

As for example 5, it can be shown that the specification (in iff form together with auxiliary properties of 'divides', '$\leqslant$' and the axioms of equality) logically implies the program. However, unlike example 5, the derivation requires genuine mathematical ingenuity. Although both specification and program are executable, the program is significantly more efficient.

Note.

(1) The functional notation gcd(x y) = z can be rewritten in relational notation as Gcd(x y z).

(2) By exploiting functional notation, the second clause of the program can be written more compactly as

gcd(x y) = gcd(r x) if x $\leqslant$ y
and x divides y with remainder r
and r $\neq$ 0.

(3) For the sake of completeness we need to add a third clause

gcd(x y) = gcd(y x) if y $\leqslant$ x.

The use of functional notation simplifies the program, but is inefficient if the equality symbol, =, is defined by means of the axioms of equality. We shall show later how functional notation can be transformed into relational notation without equality. Thus we can have the convenience of functional notation while retaining the semantics of relations. Relational semantics gives us both partial functions and non-deterministic functions as special cases.

Alternative specifications of orderedness

In our next and last example we show that the technique of deriving programs from specifications also applies when both the specification and the program are formulated in the extended Horn clause subset of logic. Moreover, it applies when both program and specification can be regarded as alternative specifications.

Example 7.

A *specification–program* of ordered sequence:

(*a*) Ordered(x) if For all i j [$x_i \leqslant x_j$ if i < j].

Another *specification–program*:

(*b*) Ordered(x) if For all i [$x_i \leqslant x_{i+1}$].

Executed by means of an extended Horn clause theorem-prover, 7 (*b*) is significantly more efficient than 7 (*a*). Given a sequence x of finite length n, it takes time/space proportional to n to test whether x is ordered; 7 (*a*) takes time/space proportional to n^2. Both 7 (*a*) and 7 (*b*) are more flexible than a conventional algorithm in that the elements of the sequence x can be accessed either in sequence or in parallel. Either way, 7 (*b*) can be executed at least as efficiently as a conventional program.

It is instructive to compare 7 (*b*) with the corresponding Horn clause program, where sequences are represented by lists

Ordered(Nil)
Ordered(cons(u Nil))
Ordered(cons(u cons(v w))) if u $\leqslant$ v
and Ordered(cons(v w)).

This is less natural than 7 (*b*) and less flexible. Not only is it restricted to sequential exploration of the sequence, but it is committed to exploring it in one particular order.

It is harder to compare 7 (*a*) and 7 (*b*) as specifications than it is to compare them as programs. What is clear, however, is that it is much easier to show that 7 (*b*) implies 7 (*a*) than it is to show the converse.

THEOREM. *Example* 7 (*b*), *with appropriate properties of* $\leqslant$, *implies* 7 (*a*).

Proof. Assume

	For all i j [$x_i \leqslant x_j$ if i < j],	
then	For all i [$x_i \leqslant x_{i+1}$]	(since i < i+1),
then	Ordered (x)	(assuming 7 (*b*)),
therefore	7 (*a*).	

This can be interpreted as showing either that 7 (*a*) is a *correct program* relative to 7 (*b*) as specification or that 7 (*b*) is a *complete program* relative to 7 (*a*) as specification.

THEOREM. *Example* 7 (*a*), *with induction and appropriate properties of* $\leqslant$, *implies* 7 (*b*).

Proof. We shall show 7 (*a*) implies 7 (*b*) by showing that

For all i [$x_i \leqslant x_{i+1}$]

implies

For all i j [$x_i \leqslant x_j$ if i < j].

The proof is by induction on j.

j = 0. For all i [$x_i \leqslant x_0$ if i < 0] is vacuously true on the assumption that sequence indices are non-negative.

j = k+1. Assume i < k+1. We need to show $x_i \leqslant x_{k+1}$.

Case 1. i = k.

Then	$x_i \leqslant x_k$,	
	$x_k \leqslant x_{k+1}$	(assuming 7 (*a*)),
therefore	$x_i \leqslant x_{k+1}$.	

Case 2. i < k.

Then	$x_i \leqslant x_k$	(by induction hypothesis),
	$x_k \leqslant x_{k+1}$	(assuming 7 (*a*)),
therefore	$x_i \leqslant x_{k+1}$.	

The relation between functional and relational notation

Perhaps the main alternative to the use of logic for program specification is some form of functional language with equality. The semantics of such languages are usually defined by means of algebra or category theory, and rewrite or reduction rules are usually used to execute them.

If we restrict attention to first-order functional languages (in which functions are not allowed as arguments to functions) then it is possible to transform equations into Horn clauses, providing them with a model theoretic semantics and predicate logic proof rules. This is done by treating functions as a special case of relations. We use the schemas

f(x) = y iff F(x y), (E1)
P(f(x)) iff For all y [P(y) if f(x) = y], (E2)

where with every function symbol f there is associated a predicate symbol F and P(y) is any formula with free variable y. For simplicity we consider functions of one argument. Functions of several arguments can be treated in the same way.

Consider the simple example of a functional program for computing the length of lists:

length(Nil) = 0
length(cons(u v)) = length(v) + 1

We can use (E1) and (E2) to transform this into a Horn clause program.

(*a*) length(Nil) = 0
Length(Nil 0) (by (E1))
(*b*) length(cons(u v)) = length(v) + 1
Length(cons(u v) length(v) + 1) (by (E1))
Length(cons(u v) y) if length(v) + 1 = y (by (E2))
Length(cons(u v) y) if Plus(length(v) 1 y) (by (E1))
Length(cons(u v) y) if Plus(z 1 y)
and length(v) = z (by (E2))
Length(cons(u v) y) if Plus(z 1 y)
and Length(v z) (by (E1))

Notice that the application of (E2) in the penultimate step involves treating the whole formula

Length(cons(u v) y) if Plus(length(v) 1 y)

as P(length(v)). By using (E2) this becomes

[Length(cons(u v) y) if Plus(z 1 y)] if length(v) = z,

which simplifies to

Length(cons(u v) y) if Plus(z 1 y) and length(v) = z.

In Kowalski (1983) this step was performed more directly by using an additional schema (E3)

P(f(x)) iff Exists y [P(y) and f(x) = y],

which unnecessarily assumes that the function f is total.

The schema (E1) and (E2) have been used in effect as a higher-order program that transforms equations into Horn clauses. This transformation, moreover, provides the basis for a simple *proof* that any recursively enumerable function can be computed by means of Horn clauses. Take any set of recursion equations defining a recursively enumerable function and apply (E1) and (E2) to produce a Horn clause program that computes the same function. It is straightforward to verify that each computation step, which uses the recursion equations as rewrite rules, can be mimicked by backwards reasoning by using the corresponding Horn clauses to get the same result. (The proof, which is given in greater detail in Kowalski (1983), uses (E3) in addition to (E1) and (E2), and therefore incorrectly assumes that recursively enumerable functions are total.)

Conclusion

The examples investigated in this paper show how hard it is to distinguish logic programs from complete logic specifications. The only criterion that can be used to discriminate between them seems to be relative efficiency, but this applies just as much to pairs of programs as it does to pairs of programs and specifications.

Given a distinction between program and specification, however, verification of the program reduces to a demonstration of logical implication. Given a complete specification, in particular, it is often possible to verify the program by showing that it can be derived from the specification by using the rules of logic.

Logic sufficiently blurs the distinction between program and specification that many logic programs can just as well be regarded as executable specifications. On one hand, this can give the impression that logic programming lacks a programming methodology; on the other, it may imply that many of the software engineering techniques that have been developed for conventional programming languages are inapplicable and unnecessary for logic programs.

References

Burstall, R. M. & Darlington, J. 1977 Transformation for developing recursive programs. *J. Ass. comput. Mach.* **24**, 44–67.

Clark, K. L. 1978 Negation as failure. In *Logic and data bases*, pp. 293–322. New York: Plenum Press.

Clark, K. L. & Darlington, J. 1980 Algorithm classification through synthesis. *Computer J.* 61–65.

Clark, K. L. & McCabe, F. 1984 *Micro-PROLOG: programming in logic.* Englewood Cliffs, N.J.: Prentice-Hall.

Clark, K. L., McKeeman, W. M. & Sickel, S. 1982 Logic program specification of numerical integration. In *Logic programming* (ed. K. L. Clark & S.-A. Tarnlund), pp. 123–139. London: Academic Press.

Clark, K. L. & Sickel, S. 1977 Predicate logic: a calculus for deriving programs. *Proc. 5th Int. Joint Conf. on Artif. Intell. Cambridge, Mass.*

Clark, K. L. & Tarnlund, S.-A. 1977 A first order theory of data and programs. In *Proc. IFIP 1977*, pp. 939–944. Amsterdam: North-Holland.

Clark, K. L. & Tarnlund, S.-A. (eds) 1982 *Logic programming.* London: Academic Press.

Colmerauer, A., Kanoui, H., Pasero, R. & Roussel, P. 1973 Un Système de Communication Homme–machine en Français. Groupe Intelligence Artificielle, Université d'Aix Marseille, Luminy.

Cory, H. T., Hammond, P., Kowalski, R. A., Kriwaczek, F., Sadri, F. & Sergot, M. 1984 *The British Nationality Act as a logic program*, Department of Computing, Imperial College, London.

Ennals, J. R. 1982 *Beginning micro-PROLOG*, Computers in education. London: Heinemann.

Hammond, P. & Sergot, M. 1983 A PROLOG shell for logic-based expert systems. In *Proc. 3rd BCS Expert Systems Conference*, pp. 95–104.

Hansson, A. & Tarnlund, S.-A. 1979 A natural programming calculus. In *Proc. 6th IJCAI, Tokyo, Japan*, pp. 348–355.

Hogger, C. J. 1978*a* Program synthesis in predicate logic. In *Proc. AISB/GI Conf. on Artif. Intell., Hamburg*, pp. 18–20.

Hogger, C. J. 1978*b* Goal oriented derivation of logic programs. In *Proc. MFCS Conf., Polish Academy of Sciences, Zakopane*, pp. 267–276.
Hogger, C. 1981 Derivation of logic programs. *J. Ass. comput. Mach.* **28**, 372–422.
Kowalski, R. A. 1974 Predicate logic as programming language. In *Proc. IFIP*, pp. 569–574. Amsterdam: North-Holland.
Kowalski, R. A. 1979 Algorithm = logic + control. *J. Ass. comput. Mach.* **22**, 425–436.
Kowalski, R. A. 1979 Logic for problem solving. New York, Amsterdam: Elsevier.
Kowalski, R. A. 1983 Logic programming. In *Proc. IFIP*, pp. 133–145. Amsterdam: North-Holland.
Robinson, J. A. 1965 A machine oriented logic based on the resolution principle. *J. Ass. comput. Mach.* **12**, 23–41.
Sergot, M. 1982 A query-the-user facility for logic programming. In *Proc. ECICS, Stresa, Italy* (ed P. Degano & E. Sandewall) pp. 27–41 Amsterdam: North-Holland.
Warren, D., Pereira, L. M. & Pereira, F. 1977 Prolog – the language and its implementation compared with Lisp. In *Proc. Symp on Artif. Intell. and Programming Languages. SIGPLAN Notices* (no. 8) **12** and *SIGART Newsletter* **64**, 109–115.
Winterstein, G., Dausmann, M. & Persch, G. 1980 Deriving different unification algorithms from a specification in logic. In *Proceedings of Logic Programming Workshop, Debrecen, Hungary* (ed. S.-A. Tarnlund), pp. 274–285.

Discussion

M. A. Jackson (101 *Hamilton Terrace, London, U.K.*). Professor Kowalski spoke more than once of the 'efficiency' of a specification. Does he interpret efficiency with respect to some operational definition of his semantics?

R. Kowalski. The execution of a logic program or specification is made by means of a mechanical proof procedure. Given a fixed proof procedure, different specifications–programs behave with different efficiency. The efficiency of a specification, therefore, can only be evaluated relative to some proof procedure. Such a proof procedure can be regarded as defining an operational semantics. Model theoretic semantics defines a denotational semantics.

M. J. Rogers (*Department of Computer Science, University of Bristol, U.K.*). Programs written in PROLOG seem in practice to be very much more difficult to check for correctness than those written in a procedural language. Part of this difficulty appears to stem from tracing the actions in taking the first matching clause and then following the program through nested loops. The problem is further complicated by the action of assert and retract clauses.

R. Kowalski. In the paper I have restricted my attention to logic programming with Horn clauses and various extensions. I have not considered PROLOG and its relation with logic programming.

Pure logic programs can be verified without taking their behaviour into account. This makes it possible to use increasingly sophisticated proof procedures to execute logic programs without complicating correctness proofs.

It is possible to write pure logic programs in PROLOG, but because of its depth-first search, this can give rise to infinite loops and other less extreme forms of inefficiency, especially when executing specifications rather than programs. To avoid such loops the 'programmer' may need to control the order in which clauses are executed. The verification of such programs then needs to take behaviour into account; and, because PROLOG's behaviour includes back-tracking and is more complicated than conventional program execution, verification of such programs can be more complicated than verification of conventional programs.

The dynamic assertion and retraction of clauses in PROLOG programs introduces a form of destructive assignment, for the purpose of improving efficiency. This further complicates behaviour and, what is worse, destroys the behaviour-independent semantics of the program and significantly complicates program verification.

There are two main ways to improve this undesirable situation. (1) Insist on greater logic programming discipline within PROLOG programs. Where this leads to inefficiency, transform the logic program in a correctness-preserving way so that it runs efficiently without using the extralogical features of PROLOG. The resulting program will be less obviously correct, but at least its correctness can be demonstrated declaratively without needing to consider its behaviour. (2) In the longer term, we need to develop improved logic programming languages, which do not rely on extralogical features for the sake of efficiency. Special attention needs to be paid, in particular, to combatting the worst cases of inefficiency, which arise as a result of not being able to use programmer-controlled destructive assignment.

J. C. SHEPHERDSON (*School of Mathematics, University of Bristol, U.K.*). Can Professor Kowalski explain why one often says 'if' when one means 'if and only if'?

R. KOWALSKI. The 'if-' half of the 'if-and only if' half of definitions is the computationally useful part. On the one hand, the explicit use of 'if and only if' syntax obscures the pragmatic intention conveyed by using 'if'; on the other hand, using 'if' obscures the fact that 'only if' is also intended.

The use of 'if' syntax facilitates incremental program and specification development. It makes it easy to add more clauses to a definition, without explicitly retracting an explicitly stated 'only-if' assumption.

The use of 'if' when 'if and only if' is intended can be regarded as a special case of default reasoning, where some assumption is made 'by default'. Default reasoning is common in artificial intelligence, especially in systems based on frames, where it is generally regarded to be in conflict with classical logic. It can be argued that replacing 'if' halves of definitions by 'if and only if' gives a logical reconstruction of default reasoning.

D. SANNELLA (*Department of Computer Science, University of Edinburgh, U.K.*).

(1) I do not see why Professor Kowalski's logic program for subset is more amenable to parallel execution than an equivalent functional program would be. Functional programs offer the same opportunities for parallel execution as logic programs, and for exactly the same reasons.

(2) In his gcd example, Professor Kowalski seemed to indicate that the search for gcd(x, y) would be limited to numbers less than x and y. Putting a limit on the search requires either a careful choice of the specification of divides (which must state more or less explicitly that divides (x, y) is false if $x > y$) or else a lot of cleverness on the part of the compiler. The fact that some specifications lead to non-terminating programs suggests that the relation between specifications and programs is not as close as Professor Kowalski says.

R. KOWALSKI. (1) Logic programs provide for two main kinds of parallelism, and-parallelism and or-parallelism. And-parallelism is the analogue of parallel evaluation of subterms in functional programming languages. The opportunity for or-parallelism, however, results from the non-deterministic computation of relations instead of functions. It is the analogue of parallel search for answers to queries in relational databases. This combination of opportunities for both and-parallelism and or-parallelism reflects the fact that logic programming can be regarded as generalizing and unifying functional programming and relational databases. The resulting unification also encompasses rule-based languages of the kind used for expert systems.

(2) There are two ways to 'execute' the specification of gcd: by means of a standard theorem-prover for first-order logic or by using negation by failure. Because negation by failure is incomplete in the general case, it may be incomplete in a particular case such as the specification of gcd, especially if, as D. Sannella points out, the definition of divides(x y) does not have some explicit or implicit constraint that $x < y$.

However, if we use any complete theorem-prover for first-order logic and the definition of gcd implies the existence of a gcd, for particular numbers x and y, then, by the completeness theorem for first-order logic, the theorem-prover is guaranteed to terminate successfully with an existence proof. Most theorem-provers, including all theorem-provers based on the resolution principle, will construct the gcd as a by-product of the proof. Thus, except for the inefficiency involved in using a general-purpose theorem-prover for computation, there is no difference in principle between a program and a complete specification, except for efficiency.

M. M. LEHMAN (*Department of Computing, Imperial College, London, U.K.*). Professor Kowalski said 'you cannot get a specification right the first time'. May I suggest that he should have said 'you cannot get a specification right', period.

A specification can be wrong in one of two ways (or both). It may, for example, be internally inconsistent, in that it includes (at least) two inconsistent statements, a situation that could be detected (for example by a verification procedure) calculable for a formal specification. But for a specification defining a program that is to be used to find a solution to a real problem currently of interest, the issue is one of satisfaction, not correctness. A specification may be *effectively* incorrect in that, as formulated, even though totally self consistent, the problem whose solution is specified is not that to which a solution is required.

In practice, this always happens. The very development of a specification changes one's viewpoint of the problem and of means for its solution. The very execution of a program changes one's view and definition of the problem one wishes to solve. Hence computer applications and the specifications that define programs that implement them are, by their very nature, evolutionary. A specification must be viewed as a dynamic object that always needs to be adapted. A specification is never absolutely right.

R. KOWALSKI. I very much agree with the spirit of Professor Lehman's remark: it is very difficult to get a specification absolutely right. However, the ability to execute a specification would help a great deal to test its assumptions and to identify where they might be changed to avoid unacceptable consequences. The conventional software life cycle that waits to test a specification until it is implemented as a program is a very inefficient way of improving specifications.

Whether it is ever possible to get a specification absolutely right is not the main issue. What matters is that we should be easily able to change a specification when it is necessary or desirable to do so. The use of logic to formalize specifications provides a proof theoretic framework which facilitates the alteration of specifications to more adequately meet user requirements as well as to meet changing requirements.

D. Park (*Computer Science Department, Warwick University, Coventry, U.K.*). Many people are reluctant to discard *procedural* programming concepts; perhaps this is because they see the execution of a program as primarily a *simulation* of a succession of events in the world, rather than as a process of *deduction* about what holds in one particular state of the world. Does the ideal programming language perhaps need concepts of both sorts? Is there some compromise position?

R. Kowalski. You have identified what is probably the most important, unresolved problem in logic programming. It is an instance of a more general problem, known as the 'frame problem', in artificial intelligence. There are various proposals and outlined solutions for this problem. I have discussed one of these proposals in Kowalski (1983). Although I am not certain what the right solution is, I hope that it will not involve procedural programming with explicit destructive assignment as we know it today.

Functional programs as executable specifications

By D. A. Turner

Computing Laboratory, University of Kent, Canterbury, Kent CT2 7NF, U.K.

To write specifications we need to be able to define the data domains in which we are interested, such as numbers, lists, trees and graphs. We also need to be able to define functions over these domains. It is desirable that the notation should be higher order, so that function spaces can themselves be treated as data domains. Finally, given the potential for confusion in specifications involving a large number of data types, it is a practical necessity that there should be a simple syntactic discipline that ensures that only well typed applications of functions can occur.

A functional programming language with these properties is presented and its use as a specification tool is demonstrated on a series of examples. Although such a notation lacks the power of some imaginable specification languages (for example, in not allowing existential quantifiers), it has the advantage that specifications written in it are always executable. The strengths and weaknesses of this approach are discussed, and also the prospects for the use of purely functional languages in production programming.

1. Introduction

Computers are a species of the genus 'symbol-processing machine'. By a symbol-processing machine we mean one that receives symbols at one or more input channels, and in response, possibly after an elapse of time during which the machine may undergo many changes of internal state, the machine transmits symbols along one or more output channels. We ignore the physical representation of the symbols and the nature of the processes whereby they are delivered to the machine or received from it, since by definition a symbol-processing machine is one built to transmit or transmute *information*, not energy or power or some other physical quantity.

From this point of view a symbol-processing machine may be regarded as the physical realization of a mathematical function. The idea of a function will be familiar: a function is a relation between two previously given sets (or 'types') called the *domain* and the *codomain*. To each element of the domain the function assigns a unique element of the codomain. Here the domain is the set of allowed input symbols (or vectors of input symbols if the machine has several input channels) and the codomain is a set that includes all possible output symbols (or vectors of symbols). The relation between the two is the function that the machine implements.

A convenient way to define a function is by giving a series of equations. For example, if the domain of possible input values is {A, B, C} and the codomain is {X, Y, Z}, a function f might be defined by the equations

$$\mathrm{f\,A = X, \quad f\,B = Y, \quad f\,C = Z.}$$

Equivalently, we can give a set of input–output pairs describing the behaviour of the function, in this case {(A, X), (B, Y), (C, Z)}; this set is called the *graph* of the function. It is clear that if the function has an infinite graph it will in general require an infinite number of equations to describe it. Sometimes, however, it will still be possible to describe the function in a finite number of equations, for example by introducing a variable. Thus if the domain and codomain are integers, we might define a function g, by

$$g\ n = n+n,$$

where n stands for an arbitrary integer; such an equation is really a schema, standing for an infinite number of equations of the earlier sort.

An important property of functions is *extensionality*: this is the principle that if two functions have the same graph they must be regarded as the same function. So if we were to define the function h (also on integers) by

$$h\ n = 2 \times n,$$

then g and h would be the *same* function, and we shall write g = h. So the mathematical idea of a function corresponds rather closely to the engineering notion of a *black box*: what matters is the input–output behaviour, not the internal mechanism by which it is achieved.

Returning now to the computer as a species of symbol-processing machine, if we leave aside purely physical differences (such as the fact that computers are built out of micro-electronic circuits, which enables them to operate much more rapidly than earlier devices), what are the differences between the computer and all the other kinds of symbol-processing machine, some of which have existed since much earlier periods? There is one essential difference: the computer is a *universal* symbol-processing machine, which can simulate the logical behaviour of any symbol-processing machine that it is possible to construct. Thus arises the problem of programming. Programming the computer consists of instructing it which, out of the infinity of possible symbol-processing machines, is the one we wish it to simulate on any particular occasion.

Note then that all computers are equivalent in this sense, that each is a universal machine that can simulate the behaviour of any other machine, and therefore among the machines that they can simulate are each other. Computers differ from one another (apart from physical differences such as speed, or number of input–output channels) solely in the language in which they require to be instructed as to the machine they are to simulate.

If we accept that a symbol-processing machine is an implementation of a mathematical function, then the problem of programming a computer can be restated as that of instructing it as to which function we require it to implement, with the function being given as a series of equations or something similar. This is the point of view of functional programming.

Before proceeding further with the ideas of functional programming, there are two issues that warrant further discussion. The first is whether we have glossed over certain difficulties in treating symbol-processing machines as implementations of functions; the second is that the notion of a universal machine is itself rather remarkable and merits some further comment.

There are three apparent objections to the claim that the behaviour of an arbitrary symbol-processing machine can be captured by the mathematical notion of function. The first is that the machine might behave unreliably, so that, for example, if there are two legal outputs X and Y, represented say by 1 V (volt) and 2 V respectively, the machine might sometimes get into a funny state that gave a reading 1.5 V, or break altogether and give a reading of 0 V. We can dismiss this problem as not our concern: machines that are unreliable in this sense are of no interest to computing science (except as objects that we return to the manufacturer with a note asking that they be replaced).

There is, however, one way in which the machine can fail to produce a meaningful answer that we cannot dismiss as being outside the concern of computing science. Anyone who has had even the most casual exposure to programming will have observed that it is possible to write programs corresponding to machines that fail to produce any output by getting into an endless cycle of state changes. This is an inescapable problem because it can be shown that any programming language that is universal (in the sense that every computable function can be defined in it) will contain programs with endless loops. It is not theoretically possible to have a universal language from which all such programs have been filtered out (for example, by a test in the compiler). The class of functions implemented by symbol-processing machines must therefore be understood to include *partial functions*, which fail to assign a value to some of the points in their domain. Partial functions are a nuisance mathematically, because with them functional composition is not always defined, so we adopt the convention, due to Scott (1970), that computations that fail to terminate are considered to yield a special value, $\perp$ (pronounced 'bottom'). Throughout what follows we assume that a bottom element has been adjoined to each type and that the term 'function' therefore includes partial function.

A second objection to the 'machines-as-functions' hypothesis is that the machine may be *non-deterministic*, in the sense that for a given input the machine may be capable of returning one of several outputs, all of which we regard as legitimate, and that we either cannot, or do not wish to, predict which one we will obtain on any particular occasion. A number of computing scientists, most notably E. W. Dijkstra (1976), have argued that non-deterministic machines should be considered the normal case. We can remark here that a non-deterministic machine may be represented by a function that returns a set, and thus does not fall outside the functional point of view. Nevertheless it is only fair to say that the programming of non-deterministic systems within a purely functional style poses certain logical problems that at the time of writing do not have any generally agreed solution; we shall return to this point in the closing section of the paper. Most work on functional programming has been concerned with the description of deterministic systems and this is the point of view we shall adopt in the bulk of the remainder of this paper.

The third possible objection to the characterization of machines as functions is that this appears not to cover machines whose behaviour is history sensitive. Consider, for example, a machine whose input symbols are drawn from the set {0, 1} and whose output is the same as its input if the number of '1' symbols previously received is even, but the complement of its input if the number of previous '1' symbols is odd. (Such a machine would be said to have two internal states and to flip state every time it received a '1'.) Although the behaviour of this machine cannot be characterized by a function from input events to output events, it is still the case that the output history, taken as a whole, is a function of the input history, taken as a whole. To write down some equations describing this function we need some notation for infinite sequences. We shall adopt the convention (common to several programming languages, including the one used for all the examples in this paper) that a:x denotes a sequence whose first member is 'a' and whose remainder is the sequence 'x'. With this convention the function f, which characterizes the behaviour of our parity flipping machine, can be described as

```
f(0:x) = 0:f x,
f(1:x) = 1:g x,
g(0:x) = 1:g x,
g(1:x) = 0:f x.
```

Here f is a function whose input and output are both infinite sequences of 0s and 1s, and g is an auxiliary function of the same type. Note that f describes the behaviour of a machine that starts life in the 'even' state, while g describes a machine that starts life in the 'odd' state. In fact these equations do not give an explicit definition of f and g, but only set up a relation of mutual recurrence between them; it is easy to see, however, that the equations are sufficient to determine both functions uniquely.

The class of machines whose behaviour can be described by functions from input history to output history is quite general and comprises all (deterministic) machines with internal state. Functional programming in its modern form may be said to date from the development of programming systems that made it easy to write down definitions of functions whose domain and codomain consist of infinite sequences (Friedman & Wise 1976; Henderson & Morris 1976; Turner 1976).

The remaining task of this introduction is to elucidate the claim that the digital computer is a universal machine. The claim is that a computer can (given a suitable program) simulate the behaviour of any symbol-processing machine that it is possible to construct; or equivalently, compute any function that it is possible to compute by mechanical means. It might be though that there is no limit to the ingenuity that can be employed in calculating the value of a function mechanically, and that therefore the class of functions computable by mechanical means is not a definite class at all.

It turns out, however, that there is a definite class of functions whose value at any point in their domain can be computed mechanically (see, for example, Davis 1958). A fairly small amount of apparatus is sufficient to compute all of these functions, and adding more apparatus (so long as it is mechanically realizable) makes no difference at all to the class of functions that can be computed. This class of functions is called the *recursive functions* (because the functions that can be computed by mechanical means are the same as the functions that can be characterized by recursion equations).

There are many interesting functions that are not recursive. Consider, for example, the function that when applied to a formula of first-order logic, returns 1 if it is a theorem and 0 if it is not. It can be shown that if we suppose a machine can be constructed to compute this function, paradoxes ensue, and that therefore such a machine cannot be built (Turing 1936). This is not because there is something ill-defined about the notion of truth in first-order logic; on the contrary, we can build a machine, M, which will, one after another, generate all the theorems of first-order logic (for example, by constructing in order of increasing length, all valid proof sequences). Moreover, it is known that first-order logic is *complete*, in the sense that every formula that logically follows from the axioms can be proved as a theorem and will therefore eventually show up on the output list of machine M. A formula that does not eventually appear on the output list is not a theorem and does not follow from the axioms.

The function that maps formulae of first-order logic onto $\{0, 1\}$ as they are or are not theorems is therefore perfectly well specified mathematically, it just happens not to be computable. Note, however, that a partial function that maps formulae onto $\{\perp, 1\}$, returning 1 for theorems and failing to terminate on non-theorems *is* computable, it can obviously be computed by a minor variant of machine M. Another well known example of a function known not to be computable is one that takes a computer program (complete with any data it may require) and returns 0 or 1 as the program terminates or fails to terminate. Fortunately almost all of the functions in which we are interested for practical reasons do turn out to be computable.

The distinction between functions that are in principle computable by mechanical means and those that are not so computable, even in principle, is a fundamental discovery of mathematical logic. A consequence of this distinction is that when we consider possible notations for defining functions, these notations fall into two classes: first, those notations that have the property that any function that can be defined by using them is known to be mechanically executable; second, those more powerful notations that also enable us to write down definitions of functions, such as the decision function for first-order logic or the halting function for computer programs, which are not even in principle computable. Examples of notations of the first kind include recursion equations, lambda-calculus and FORTRAN. An example of a notation of the latter kind would be standard (i.e. Z.F.) set theory (see, for example, Drake 1974). Only notations of the first kind can be considered for use as programming languages; but for the purposes of general mathematical discourse, notations of the second kind are definitely required. (At least, this seems to be the view of the overwhelming majority of mathematicians at the time of writing.) Moreover in the process of reasoning about programs, which are written in notations of the first kind, we shall sometimes need to write down ideas that can only be expressed in notations of the second kind.

In what follows we present (by means of a series of examples) a style of functional programming that makes use of recursion equations together with some notation from set theory. Such a language may be regarded as lying somewhere on the boundary between programming languages and specification languages. Compared with a conventional programming language it is often rather concise, and shares with ordinary mathematics the property, which programming languages do not usually possess, of being *static* (i.e. equations do not change their truth value over time). Considered as a specification language it suffers from the restrictions inherent in being recursive: only computable functions can be denoted, so there are some useful and interesting specifications that cannot be expressed within it. It does, however, have the compensating advantage that specifications written in it are always executable. It can also be regarded, whenever we wish to do so, as being embedded in a richer mathematical language including notations for non-computable functions (we shall give one example of this).

In the closing sections of the paper we discuss briefly the current state of knowledge as regards the efficiency of functional programs (both in space and in time) when compared with conventional ones, the relation between functional programming and logic programming in the style of PROLOG, and the prospects for the adoption of purely functional languages in production use.

2. A FUNCTIONAL PROGRAMMING LANGUAGE

The functional programming language used in this paper is called MIRANDA and is based on the author's earlier languages SASL (Turner 1976) and KRC (Turner 1982*b*) with the addition of a type discipline essentially the same as that of ML (Gordon *et al.* 1979). There are a number of quite similar languages in use, of which perhaps the best known is HOPE (Burstall *et al.* 1980). What is presented here may therefore be regarded as representative of the modern style of functional programming, and should be contrasted with the more traditional style of functional

When used as the name of a programming language, MIRANDA is a trade mark of Research Software Ltd.

programming based on LISP (McCarthy *et al.* 1962). We shall begin with a simple example, which brings out the basic idea of using recursion equations both to define data types and to define functions over those data types. We shall then elaborate on the basic theme by introducing other necessary features of the notation before proceeding to some more substantial examples.

An example

Suppose that we are interested in binary trees, of the following rather simple kind. There are two atomic trees, called ALPHA and BETA, of which we suppose no properties other than that they are equal to themselves and unequal to each other. If a tree is not atomic, then it is an ordered pair, with two components, both of which are trees. Suppose also that we are interested in making on trees the operation of *reflection*, by which we mean recursively reversing the order of the components at every node in the tree. Figure 1 illustrates this with a diagram of a typical tree together with the result of reflecting it.

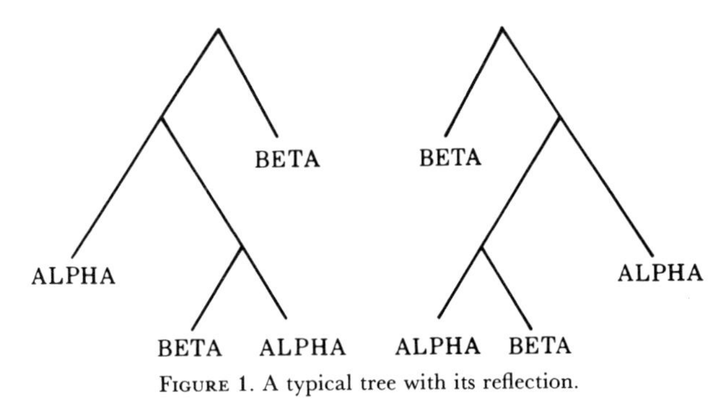

FIGURE 1. A typical tree with its reflection.

If we are to express this problem in a programming language, the first thing that we require is that it should allow us to introduce the data type *tree* in a suitably abstract way. No doubt we could find some scheme for encoding trees in terms of an already existing data type, say lists of integers, but it is clearly very undesirable that we should be forced to do so. There is now general agreement that any reasonable programming language should permit the user to introduce new data types with just the properties he required, and no irrelevant ones. Secondly we want to define the function *reflect*, which is a mapping from trees onto trees. Recursion equations can be used to accomplish both tasks, as follows (this is our first complete example of a functional program):

```
tree ::= ALPHA|BETA|pair tree tree
reflect ALPHA = ALPHA                                  (1)
reflect BETA = BETA                                    (2)
reflect (pair x y) = pair (reflect y) (reflect x).     (3)
```

The first line of the program defines the data type *tree* (the '::=' sign should be pronounced 'comprises'). Note that it introduces four new identifiers: 'tree', which is the name of a type; 'ALPHA' and 'BETA', which are the names of atomic trees; and 'pair', which is a function that generates a new tree from two existing trees. It says that the data type 'tree' is the free algebra generated by the two 0-ary operators 'ALPHA' and 'BETA' and the 2-ary operator 'pair'. The remaining three lines of the program define the behaviour of the reflect function on the three kinds of tree (the numbering of the equations is for our convenience here and is not part of the program). Note that the use of pattern matching in equation (3) avoids the need to invent names (such as 'left' and 'right') for the selector functions on a non-atomic tree.

It should be clear that the three equations given are sufficient to deduce the result of reflecting any finite tree. For example, the result of reflecting the tree in figure 1 may be inferred as

```
reflect (pair (pair A (pair B A) B)
= pair (reflect B) (reflect (pair A (pair B A))                (by (3))
= pair B (pair (reflect (pair B A)) (reflect A))           (by (2), (3))
= pair B (pair (pair (reflect A) (reflect B)) A)           (by (3), (1))
= pair B (pair (pair A B) A)                               (by (1), (2))
```

where for brevity we have written A and B for ALPHA and BETA. This demonstrates that for computational purposes the equations of the program can be used as left-to-right replacement rules. Note that it is in general possible to make two or more replacements simultaneously in different parts of the expression under evaluation.

From the three equations of the program other properties of reflect can be inferred by using standard mathematical proof techniques. For example, the fact that reflect is its own inverse is shown by the following little proof (which works by induction over the structure of trees)

THEOREM reflect (reflect x) = x for all x :: tree

Proof by induction on x

Case ALPHA

```
reflect (reflect ALPHA) = reflect ALPHA                    (by (1))
                        = ALPHA                            (by (1))
```

Case BETA

```
similarly...                                               (by (2), (2))
```

Case pair x y

```
reflect (reflect (pair x y))
= reflect (pair (reflect y) (reflect x))                   (by (3))
= pair (reflect (reflect x)) (reflect (reflect y))         (by (3))
= pair x y                                       (ex hyp, ex hyp)
```

The sign :: means 'is of type'. This style of proof, based on the substitutivity of equality and structural induction (see Burstall 1969) is really very straightforward. Nevertheless it can get one quite a long way: for example, using essentially this method, the author has proved the correctness of a compiler for an applicative language (Turner 1981).

This example of a program to reflect binary trees has brought out several central points about the type of programming language here under discussion:

(i) that recursion equations are a convenient notation to define both data types and functions over those data types;

(ii) that the equations of the program can be read mathematically as premises from which to deduce other properties of the functions involved;

(iii) that they can be used to compute values of the functions by treating them as left-to-right replacement rules (so that computation is here a special case of deduction.)

In connection with (iii), it should be noted that in general more than one replacement can be made at a time, so there is significant opportunity to exploit concurrency in the implementation of a functional programming language.

A basic result of mathematical logic, Kleene's (1952) first recursion theorem tells us that whenever a system of recursion equations has a unique function for its solution, the function computed by treating the equations as left-to-right replacement rules is the *same* one. This result should be considered as the logical foundation of functional programming.

This basic theme will now be elaborated by the introduction of a number of necessary additional notions and notations.

Infinite and partial data structures

Continuing for a moment with the tree example, there is no reason why we should be forced to confine our attention to finite trees. We might be interested, for example, in the infinite tree shown in figure 2. This tree can be defined uniquely by the equation

inftree = pair ALPHA inftree.

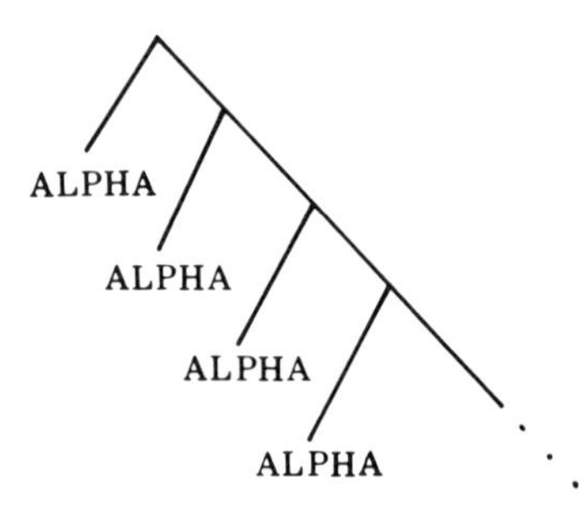

FIGURE 2. An infinite tree.

Moreover its reflection can be defined as

inftree2 = reflect inftree,

from which we may deduce

inftree2 = reflect (pair ALPHA inftree)
= pair (reflect inftree) (reflect ALPHA)
= pair (reflect (pair ALPHA inftree) ALPHA
= pair (pair (reflect inftree) ALPHA) ALPHA
and so on....

It is clear that we can compute with infinite trees in the sense that as much of their structure as may be required in any particular computation can be inferred in a finite number of steps. This will work on condition that the constructor function 'pair' is *lazy*, i.e. does not force premature evaluation of its arguments. The use of the term 'lazy evaluation' in this context was initiated by Henderson & Morris (1976). Of course the programmer must take care not to force complete evaluation of an infinite object; for example by trying to count the number of ALPHAs in inftree.

Having a lazy constructor function will also permit us to build *partial* trees. If we let ⊥ denote the completely undefined tree (the result of a non-terminating computation of type tree), then the partial trees

pair ALPHA ⊥
pair ALPHA (pair ALPHA ⊥)
pair ALPHA (pair ALPHA (pair ALPHA ⊥))...

exist and are all different from each other and from ⊥, and it is clear that their *limit*, in a sense that can be made precise, is the infinite tree 'inftree'. Every infinite tree that can be defined by recursion equations is the limit of such a series of partial trees. The richer data type including partial and infinite trees can be derived from the finite type by including ⊥ as an extra generator and closing the resulting data type under limits. The extension of recursion theory to deal with recursion over infinite objects is essentially due to Scott (1976).

Obviously an important question when we define a new data type is whether we intend it to be an ordinary finite algebra or whether we wish to include partial and infinite objects. We will assume that our programming language gives us some simple syntactic means (not discussed here) for discriminating between the various different possibilities that arise along these lines.

It is possible to make inductive proofs of the properties of programs that operate on infinite data objects by using a modified version of structural induction (Turner 1982*a*). Alternatively, one can use the fixpoint induction rule of Scott (1970).

Generic types

It is a highly desirable feature of a programming language that there should be some simple syntactic discipline that ensures that only well typed applications of functions to arguments can occur. For example, our function reflect is a mapping from trees to trees, for which we write

reflect :: tree → tree

and we expect to get an error message (at compile time) if reflect is applied to an object of another type, say an integer. That is to say, our programming language is *strongly typed*. We do not require the user to declare the type of reflect in the program, however, It is deduced from the equations of the program by using the algorithm of Milner (1978). The Milner type-discipline also permits generic (or 'polymorphic') functions; for example, if we define the identity function by

I x = x

then the type attributed to I is

I :: * → *,

where '*' is a type variable, standing for an arbitrary or generic type. The identifier I should be thought of as ambiguously denoting any one of a whole family of functions, one for each data type.

We can extend this idea to user-defined type constructors in the following way. Suppose we wish to modify the type 'tree' so that an atomic tree, instead of being just ALPHA or BETA, is a leaf of some arbitrary type; say, integer or boolean or string; the only constraint being that in any one given tree, all the leaves must be of the same type. This new type, or rather *family* of types, is defined by

tree * :: = leaf * | pair (tree *) (tree *).

The name 'tree' is now that of a *type-constructor*, '*' stands for an arbitrary type, and 'tree int', 'tree bool' are examples of types that can be constructed by using the type constructor. So we have

pair (leaf true) (leaf false) :: tree bool
pair (leaf 1) (leaf 3) :: tree int
leaf (pair (leaf 1) (leaf 2)) :: tree (tree int),

whereas, say, pair (leaf 1) (leaf true) is *not* a legal tree and will evoke a compile-time error message. In connection with the new generalized trees the reflect function may be defined

reflect (leaf x) = leaf x
reflect (pair x y) = pair (reflect y) (reflect x).

The type of this new reflect function is (tree * → tree *), meaning that it may be applied to any object in the tree family, returning in each case a tree of the same type as its argument.

The Milner type-system embodies a major step forward in programming language design by making it possible to have polymorphic functions without compromising the ability to detect type errors at compile time. Previously it was possible to support polymorphism only by delaying type checking until run time. The Milner type scheme has been successfully used in ML, the metalanguage of the LCF proof system (Gordon *et al.* 1979), (Milner, this symposium). For a fuller discussion of the type structure of MIRANDA, which differs in some respects from that of ML, the reader is referred elsewhere (Turner 1984).

Built-in types

It should be clear that the type-definition apparatus is sufficiently powerful that the language does not need to have any built-in type notions at all, apart from the notion of *function*. All the standard types can be defined from first principles, by using the type definition mechanism. For example, the boolean type, the list type-family (for each type T there is the type of lists whose elements are in T), and the type of natural numbers, may each be introduced as

bool :: = true | false
list * :: = nil | cons * (list *)
nat :: = zero | suc nat.

By using the notation introduced by the last equation above, the number seven would be written

suc (suc (suc (suc (suc (suc (suc zero)))))).

Being forced to represent numbers in this way would actually be rather inconvenient, as well as inefficient in both time and space. This seems sufficient reason to allow numbers, and certain other data types, to be provided built-in to the language, even though it is not logically necessary to do so. The built-in type notions of MIRANDA are Booleans, numbers (both integer and floating point), characters (the usual ASCII character set), lists, tuples and, of course, functions. This choice is obviously to some extent arbitrary, and either a greater or a smaller selection of built-in data types could be provided.

To help the reader follow the examples in the next section we here introduce the notation used with lists. Lists are written by using square brackets and commas; so, for example, if we write

```
x = [2, 3, 4, 5]
```

then x is of type [int], that is 'list of int'. The main operations on lists are '#' (length), '!' subscripting, ':' (prefix), '++' (concatenation) and '--' (list or set difference). So, for example, #x is 4, x!2 is 3, (note that subscripting starts at 1) 1:x is the list [1, 2, 3, 4, 5], x++x is the list [2, 3, 4, 5, 2, 3, 4, 5] and x--[2, 5] is the list [3, 4]. On lists containing repeated elements the -- operator behaves as "bag difference", see (Turner 1982*b*) for its definition.

All the elements of a list must of course be of the same type. For sequences of mixed type we use tuples, which are denoted by round brackets and commas; for example (1, true, "red") is a tuple, of type (int, bool, [char]). Tuples and lists are quite different: so for example, tuples cannot be subscripted. Note that the string constant "red" is just shorthand for the list of characters ['r', 'e', 'd'].

Some shorthand notation is also provided for lists whose elements form an arithmetic series. For example [1..10] denotes the list of the numbers 1 through 10, and [0..] is the list of all the natural numbers in ascending order (lists can be infinite). Finally, note that the ':' operator can be used on the left, inside a formal parameter, in the equations defining a function. So, for example, the function for reversing a list is defined

```
reverse [ ] = [ ]
reverse (a:x) = reverse x++[a].
```

Higher order functions and currying

MIRANDA is fully higher order. One can define functions that are second-order, third-order, and so on without limitation. In fact any function of two or more arguments is really a higher order function, in the following way. Suppose we define the function 'plus' by

```
plus a b = a+b,
```

then plus is of type **int**→(**int**→**int**) and (plus 3) say, has a meaning in its own right: it is the function that adds 3 to integers. This device is known as 'currying', after the logician H. B. Curry (Curry & Feys 1956). As is normal when working with curried functions, we adopt the convention that functional application is left-associative.

An interesting example of a higher order function is the famous fixpoint operator of Curry, which we can define by

```
fix h = f
        where f = h f.
```

Note that the type of fix is given by

```
fix :: (*→*)→* .
```

Another useful higher order function, which is defined in the library of standard functions, is assoc, which has the type

```
assoc :: [(*, **)]→(*→**) .
```

This is an example of a generic type that requires more than one type variable to write it down; following ML, we use '*', '**', '***', etc. for successive type variables. The action of assoc is to take a list of pairs that represent the graph of a function, and to return the function itself. For instance

assoc [(1, red), (2, blue), (3, green)]

would be a function that maps integers to colours; we assume a type colour has been appropriately declared with constituents red, blue, etc.

Set abstraction

The last example just given introduces the idea that a list without repetitions may be used to represent a set. A powerful feature of ordinary mathematical notation is the ability to define a set by some property that all its members hold in common. This is a feature also of our functional programming language, by using a notation very similar to that of Z.F. set theory. We can write

{f x | x ← A},

which we pronounce 'set of all f x such that x in A'. The sign '←' denotes set membership, and the variable introduced on its left is a local variable of the set expression, whose scope is delimited by the curly brackets. The general form of these set expressions is

{EXP | CONDITION; . . . ; CONDITION},

where each CONDITION is either a GENERATOR or a FILTER. A GENERATOR is of the form

VARS ← EXP

and states that one or more variables (local to the set expression) are drawn from some previously existing set. A FILTER is just a boolean expression, further restricting the range of the variables introduced by the generators.

As already implied, the set is not a separate data type in this programming language; a set here is just a list from which repetitions have been removed. In addition to set abstraction we also permit list abstraction, which has the same syntax except that we use square brackets instead of braces around the expression, thus [. . . | . . .]. With list abstraction, repetitions are not removed from the result. We give three examples of the use of set abstraction:

squares = {n × n | n ← [0 . .]}

is the set of all the squares of natural numbers. The Cartesian product of two lists x and y (set of all pairs with one member from each) can be defined

cp x y = {(a, b) | a ← x; b ← y}.

Finally, the list of all Pythagorean triangles, that is right-angled triangles with integer sides, such as [3, 4, 5], can be written

pyths = {[a, b, c]) | a, b, c ← [1 . .]; a × a + b × b = c × c}.

We do also permit set abstraction in the form

{GENERATOR | FILTER},

which is a case that occurs commonly enough to be worth having a special form for it. For instance, if we have a set of pairs, R, representing the graph of a relation, and we wanted to derive from R a relation made irreflexive by removing all pairs of the form (a, a) we could write

$\{(a, b) \leftarrow R \mid a \neq b\}$.

In one sense set abstraction adds no power to the language, because no data structure can be built with its aid that could not also be constructed by some kind of explicit recursion over the lists involved. In practice, however, the presence of set expressions can lead to a considerable improvement in the conciseness and clarity of programs and may be said to permit the expressions of ideas at a higher level of abstraction, by removing the necessity to deal with a layer of housekeeping details.

As an example of this we give a functional presentation of quicksort, due to Silvio Meira, a graduate student at the University of Kent (Meira 1983), Quicksort is the method of sorting, originally devised by Hoare (1962), in which the elements to be sorted are first partitioned into all those less than some arbitrary element (say the first), and all those greater than the chosen element. The two parts are then each sorted, recursively, by using the same method. Meira's definition of quicksort is

```
sort [ ] = [ ]
sort (a:x) = sort [b<-x|b ≤ a]++[a]++sort [b<-x|b > a].
```

To appreciate the conciseness of this definition the reader should compare it with the definition of quicksort in a conventional programming language; see, for example, Graham (1983).

3. Some examples of program development

As illustration of the thesis embodied in the title of this paper, 'functional programs as executable specifications', we here take a small number of problems and for each one show how, working within the functional language framework sketched above, we can arrive at an executable solution expressed at a high level of abstraction. In each case except the first we will exhibit a series of solutions of increasing efficiency. In fact example (*c*) is a counter-example to the thesis in that the first solution we arrive at is not executable, but we show how an executable solution may be derived from it.

(*a*) *Permutations*

We seek to define a function that will take a finite list of distinct objects, and return a set (list) of all possible permutations of the original list. So we wish to define a function 'perms' with the type

```
perms :: [*]->[[*]].
```

Clearly the set of all permutations of the empty list is a singleton, containing just the empty list. For a non-empty list we can generate a permutation by choosing any member of the list for the first member of the permutation, and then follow this by any permutation of the remaining elements; if we do this in each possible way we shall generate all the permutations. This reasoning leads directly to the recursive definition

```
perms [ ] = [[ ]]
perms x = {a:p | a←x; p←perms (x -- [a])}.
```

(b) Topological sort

Given a *partial ordering* relation, we have to derive any total ordering that is compatible with the given information. An example of a partial ordering is shown in figure 3.

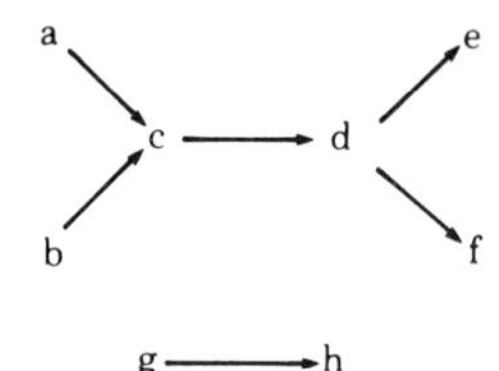

FIGURE 3. A partial ordering.

In this case there are many total orderings acceptable as output, two of which are

a b c d e f g h,
b a c g h d f e.

Given the information about the initial partial ordering, we have to produce any one of the compatible total orderings as output. In various guises, this is a problem that repeatedly turns up in computing science. For example, the type-checking phase of the compiler for MIRANDA involves an application of topological sort.

The first thing we have to decide is how the information about the partial ordering relation will be presented. We shall suppose that we are given (i) the set of all the elements involved in the ordering (this is called the 'carrier' of the relation) and (ii) a list of pairs such that if (p, q) is in the list, then p immediately precedes q in the ordering. For the partial ordering shown, this second item of information could be given as the list

[(a, c), (b, c), (c, d), (d, e), (d, f), (g, h)].

At first sight one might think that the carrier could be deduced from the list of pairs. The partial ordering might contain isolated elements (elements that do not precede nor are preceded by, anything else), however, and these would not be present in the list of pairs, since our notion of 'immediately precedes' is irreflexive.

We give first a very naïve definition of topological sort, which arises from a more or less literal formalization of the natural language definition of topological sort:

```
tsort :: [*]→([(*,*)]→[*])
tsort carrier R = any {x←perms carrier | respects R x}
respects R x = and {posn a x < posn b x | (a, b)←R}
posn a x = hd [i←[1 . . #x] | x!i = a].
```

This uses four library functions: 'perms', of which we have seen a definition earlier; 'any', which picks a member of a list (and we do not care which); 'and', which takes a list of truth values and returns their conjunction; and 'hd', which takes the first member of a list. The method used by the above definition of tsort is to look at all permutations of the carrier, and pick any one that respects the given precedence relation R. A list x is said to 'respect' a relation R if whenever (**a, b**) is in R, **a** comes before **b** in the list x. The function 'posn' finds the index number of the first occurrence of an item in a list.

It is easy to convince oneself that the above solution is correct, and it is clearly executable, but at a cost in time that is completely unacceptable for any but very small carriers. This is a 'British Museum' algorithm. It proceeds by searching the space of all permutations of the carrier, completely blindly, until it finds one that is compatible with the partial ordering. Given a partial ordering involving, say, a few hundred elements, which would be typical of a practical application, the number of permutations of the elements is extremely large. To search them all, or even a significant fraction of them, is out of the question.

To find a solution in a reasonable time it is obvious that we must construct it piecewise, and using some intelligence. We begin by observing that for a first member of the output list we may choose any member of the carrier that is not preceded by anything in the relation. We can then remove this element from the carrier, and all pairs involving it from the relation, and topologically sort the remainder. This gives us the makings of an efficient solution.

```
tsort [ ] [ ] = [ ]
tsort carrier R = a: tsort (carrier--[a]) {(m, n)<-R|m ≠ a}
                  where
                  a = any (carrier--range R)
range R = {b|(a, b)<-R}.
```

Note that we generate the set of elements with no predecessor by taking the set difference between the carrier and the range of the relation. The program runs in polynomial time and is usable in practice. The most efficient known solutions may be derived from the above by building ancillary data structures that speed up the detection of elements with no predecessor (see, for example, Tarjan 1972).

(*c*) *The Hamming numbers*

The following problem is found in Dijkstra (1976) and is attributed by him to R. W. Hamming. We have to print in ascending order the series

1, 2, 3, 4, 5, 6, 8, 9, 10, 12...

of those numbers whose prime factors are 2, 3, 5 only.

The solution can be written down directly as

```
ham = SORT{2↑a×3↑b×5↑c|a, b, c<-[0..]},
```

where SORT is a sorting function on infinite lists. This is not an executable program, even in principle, however, because there cannot exist a recursive definition of a function SORT that works on infinite lists. (We leave it as an exercise for the reader to prove that SORT is not computable (hint: assume SORT is computable and derive a decision procedure for a problem known to be undecidable). For example by applying SORT to the output of a program that generates all the theorems of first-order logic we would obtain a decision procedure for first-order logic.) We can *derive* a recursive definition of ham from the above, however, as follows:

$$\begin{aligned}
\text{ham} &= \text{SORT}\ \{2\uparrow a \times 3\uparrow b \times 5\uparrow c \mid a, b, c \leftarrow [0\,..]\} \\
&= \text{SORT}\ (\{1\} \cup \{2\times h \mid h \leftarrow H\} \cup \{3\times h \mid h \leftarrow H\} \cup \{5\times h \mid h \leftarrow H\}) \\
&\quad \textbf{where } H = \{2\uparrow a \times 3\uparrow b \times 5\uparrow c \mid a, b, c \leftarrow [0\,..]\} \\
&= 1{:}\text{SORT}\ (\{2\times h \mid h \leftarrow H\} \cup \{3\times h \mid h \leftarrow H\} \cup \{5\times h \mid h \leftarrow H\}) \\
&= 1{:}\text{MERGE}[\text{SORT}\ \{2\times h \mid h \leftarrow H\}, \text{SORT}\ \{3\times h \mid h \leftarrow H\}, \text{SORT}\ \{5\times h \mid h \leftarrow H\}) \\
&\quad \textbf{where } \text{MERGE}[\text{SORT X1}, \ldots, \text{SORT Xn}] = \text{SORT}\ \{\text{X1} \cup \ldots \cup \text{Xn}\} \\
&= 1{:}\text{MERGE}[[2\times h \mid h \leftarrow \text{SORT H}], [3\times h \mid h \leftarrow \text{SORT H}], [5\times h \mid h \leftarrow \text{SORT H}]].
\end{aligned}$$

But SORT H is ham, so we have

$$\text{ham} = 1{:}\text{MERGE}[[2\times h \mid h \leftarrow \text{ham}], [3\times h \mid h \leftarrow \text{ham}], [5\times h \mid h \leftarrow \text{ham}]].$$

This is a recursive definition of ham, the list of all hamming numbers, in terms of MERGE, a function that takes a list of sorted lists, and interleaves them to produce a sorted result. Unlike SORT, the function MERGE is computable, and from the last line, after a little rearranging, we arrive at the program

```
ham = 1:MERGE[mult 2 ham, mult 3 ham, mult 5 ham]
mult n x = [n × a|a←x]
MERGE[X, Y, Z] = merge X(merge Y Z)
merge (a:x) (b:y) = a:merge x (b:y), a < b
                  = b:merge (a:x) y, a > b
                  = a:merge x y, a = b:
```

Here we have defined the three-way infinite merging function 'MERGE' in terms of two calls to a two-way infinite merging function 'merge'. In the definition of 'merge' we have written three right-hand sides, distinguished by *guards* (these are boolean expressions written to the right of a comma). This program is both time and space efficient, and the reader may recognize it as the 'stream-processing' solution of Kahn & McQueen (1977). If we think of a function from infinite lists to infinite lists as being a *process* then the above program can be thought of as describing a system of five communicating processes, namely 'mult 2', 'mult 3', 'mult 5' and two instances of a 'merge' process (see figure 4).

It is instructive to compare the functional solution given here with the corresponding solution written in a language based on communicating processes, such as OCCAM (Inmos 1982). In fact the program is very much harder to write in OCCAM, partly because of the need to make explicit the existence of buffers in the input channels to the merge processes.

This example is interesting for two reasons. First, because it shows how systems of communicating processes can be described in a purely functional language by recursion over infinite lists; this is important because it open up the way for problems involving input–output and communication to be dealt with cleanly within the functional style, as in Henderson (1982). The second point of interest brought out by this example is that an equational language of

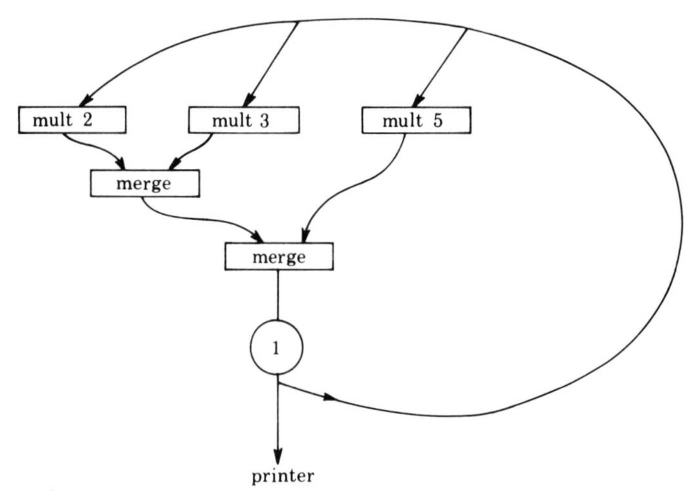

FIGURE 4. The process struture of the Hamming problem.

the kind being used here can be regarded when convenient as being embedded in a richer mathematical language including notations for non-recursive functions, and that it is often possible to derive an executable program, by a process of successive transformations, from an initial specification written in the richer, non-executable language. The problem of formal program derivation by the method of successive transformation and the related problem of formally transforming an inefficient program into a more efficient one have been widely studied within the functional language framework (see Darlington 1982; Bird 1983).

(*d*) *The knight's tour*

As our final example we consider the well known problem of the knight's tour. We have to find a sequence of positions on a chess board such that each position after the first is a knight's move from the previous one, and every square on the board is visited exactly once. We here exhibit four solutions of progressively increasing efficiency. Our first program is a more or less literal transcription of the problem statement:

```
tour = any {t←perms squares | istour t}
istour t = and [knights_move (t!i) (t!(i+1)) | i←[1 . . #t−1]]
knights_move (a, b) (c, d) = ((a−c)↑2+(b−d)↑2 = 5)
squares = {(a, b) | a, b←[1 . . 8]}.
```

This is a 'British Museum' algorithm, which proceeds by searching blindly among all factorial (64) candidate tours, looking for ones that consist only of knight's moves. Our first refinement is to replace this program by a solution that builds the tours one move at a time, considering *only* knight's moves. We introduce a function 'gentours', such that if t is a partial tour (i.e. a list of zero or more squares separated by knight's moves, and with no square represented more than once) then 'gentours t' is the set of all maximal tours that can be obtained by extending t. A tour is maximal if there is no unvisited square within a knight's move of the last square added to the tour. We introduce also a function 'nextmoves', which when applied to a tour returns the set of all unvisited squares within a knight's move of the last square added. By convention, if 'nextmoves' is applied to the empty tour it returns the set of all squares on the board:

```
tour = any {t←gentour [ ]| #t = 64}
gentours t = [t], nextmoves t = [ ]
           = union {gentours (x:t) | x←nextmoves t}
nextmoves [ ] = squares
nextmoves (x:t) = {x1←moves x | legal x1 & ~ member t x1}
moves (a, b) = {(a+i, b+j) | i, j←[−2..2]; i↑2+j↑2 = 5}
legal (a, b) = 1 ⩽ a ⩽ 8 & 1 ⩽ b ⩽ 8.
```

The definition of 'squares' is the same as in the earlier solution and 'member' is a library function of type [*]→(*→bool). This second solution has brought about a huge reduction in the size of the space to be searched, and is much closer to being practical. It still proceeds by trial and error, however, in that it considers at each stage all possible ways of extending the given tour by a knight's move in any direction. In our next refinement we replace this by a deterministic procedure in which at each stage we choose, out of the set of possible next squares, one particular square, by using a heuristic rule.

The heuristic we use can be explained as follows. Let us define the 'freedom' of an unvisited square in a partly toured board, as the number of unvisited squares a knight's move away from it. A square with a low freedom is in danger of being 'boxed-in' (i.e. becoming surrounded by visited squares, so that it can no longer be reached, making a successful completion of the tour impossible) and such a square should therefore be visited early, in preference to a square with a higher freedom. The heuristic rule then is that at each stage, out of the set of possible next squares for the knight to visit, we choose one for which the 'freedom' takes a minimum value.

So in our next solution the function 'gentours t', which returns the set of all maximal extensions of t, is replaced by a function 'gentour t', which returns just one extension of t, namely that obtained by applying the heuristic repeatedly until the tour can be extended no further. We are now relying on a specialised piece of knowledge about the problem, which is that the heuristic rule just given always succeeds in generating a complete tour, regardless of the starting square. This is by no means an obvious fact, but it is a fairly well-known piece of folklore about this problem, and it therefore seem legitimate to use it. Thus we obtain for our next refinement of the program:

```
tour = gentour [ ]
gentour t = t, nextmoves t = [ ]
          = gentour (x:t)
            where
            x = minimise freedom (nextmoves t)
            freedom x = # nextmoves (x:t).
```

We have omitted the definition of the function 'nextmoves', since it is exactly as in the previous version of the program. The function 'minimise' takes a function and a set (list) and returns a member of the list for which the function assumes a minimum value; it is in fact a MIRANDA library function and we omit its definition. Notice that in the above we have allowed the heuristic to determine our starting square also. This will have the effect of causing us to start in one of the corners of the board, because in a completely unvisited board the freedom takes its lowest value at the corner squares.

The program given has the makings of an efficient solution. It is, however, suboptimally coded, because for each partial tour t on the path to the complete tour, 'nextmoves t' is calculated three times. Our last step is to eliminate this repeated calculation of 'nextmoves'. We modify 'gentour' so that it takes a pair, consisting of a tour together with the set of next moves available from it. Making this last refinement we arrive at our final and efficient program:

```
tour = gentour (squares, [ ])
gentour (m, t) = t, m = [ ]
               = gentour (m1, t1)
                 where
                 (m1, t1) = minimise freedom {(nextmoves(x: t), x: t) | x ← m}
                 freedom (m, t) = # m.
```

In this program the definition of 'squares' and 'nextmoves' are as in previous refinements.

4. Observations and concluding remarks

We have outlined a style of functional programming based on recursion equations and demonstrated its use in constructing executable solutions to several small but non-trivial programming problems. Compared with the more traditional style of functional programming, as represented by LISP, we can see the strengths of our notation as being that it permits the introduction of user-defined types by what are in effect recursion equations over data domains; that it is higher order and supports functions as data objects in a fully extensional way; that it has a polymorphic type-discipline whereby type errors can be detected at compile time while still permitting generic functions and generic data types; that it permits the definition of infinite data objects of many different kinds; and that it has a facility for set-abstraction.

We have seen that by using the set notation it is often possible to write down, in a more or less direct transcription of the problem statement, a solution that is executable in principle although perhaps extremely inefficient. From this we can then develop more efficient solutions, either by a process of formal transformation, or by a series of refinements based on informal reasoning. The solutions we arrive at in this way are usually very much more concise than would be the expression of the corresponding solution in a conventional imperative programming language.

If we draw a distinction between the basic idea of an algorithm, and the housekeeping details needed for its efficient implementation on a Von-Neumann computer, we can say that a language of the kind used in this paper gives us a way to capture the former without getting entangled in the latter. The other important advantage that we have over an imperative language is that the static, equational, style in which our programs are written makes very much more straightforward the task of inferring program properties from the program text.

The efficiency of functional programs compared with imperative ones is still to some extent an open question (on which we shall comment briefly), but even if we make pessimistic assumptions about this, a functional programming language can still be a useful tool in software production. By using such a language it is often possible to construct a working piece of software, and indeed to experiment with a series of different designs for it, at a small fraction of the cost in programmer time that would be required in a language like PASCAL. That is to say, even without an efficient implementation, a functional programming system could earn its keep in an industrial environment as a rather high-level tool for software prototyping.

In the remaining sections of this conclusion we discuss briefly some of the outstanding research topics in functional programming.

(*a*) *Non-determinism*

There is of course a gap between the tidy and rather mathematically motivated problems of the kind for which we have exhibited solutions in § 3 of this paper, and the larger and somewhat messier problems that characterize production programming. It is legitimate to wonder whether it continues to be possible to program in a purely functional style when the size of the problem is scaled up. (In this regard we must discount previous experience with LISP, because it is in no sense a purely functional language.) In recent years a number of groups have shown that it is possible to write larger programs, such as editors, compilers and so on, within a purely functional language, and the author is currently engaged in a S.E.R.C. funded project at the University of Kent, to construct a complete operating system in a functional language essentially the same as the one used in this paper.

There is, however, one extension to the language that seems to be necessary to write an operating system (in particular, to program the scheduling of concurrent tasks), and this is a certain kind of non-determinism. In some of the programming examples given, we made use of a selection function 'any' to express indifference as to which element of a set was chosen. For the purposes for which we have used it up to now, 'any' does not need to be non-deterministic other than in a very weak sense; it is in fact just the name of a particular selection function, which in the definition of the language we do not choose to specify (but which in the current implementation happens to be 'hd'). To solve certain kinds of systems programming problems, however, we need a version of 'any' with the stronger property that when applied to a list not all of whose element are $\perp$, it will return one of the non-bottom elements.

It is fairly easy to see that a version of 'any' with this bottom avoiding behaviour, if it is to be computable, cannot be a function at all, but must instead be a non-deterministic operator. Although there is no particular difficulty in implementing an operator with the required properties, its presence means that we have a language in which expressions are no longer single-valued, a circumstance that greatly complicates both the semantics and the proof theory (see, for example, Broy 1981). At the time of writing there is no consensus as to what is the best way to handle these problems. It is to be hoped that further research will bring about some simplifications in this area.

(*b*) *Efficiency*

The other issue that arises if we consider the prospects for functional programming 'in the large' is that of efficiency. There are some quite encouraging results in this issue. A recent study of sorting algorithms by Meira (1983) shows that for each known imperative sorting algorithm, there exists a functional sorting program of the same fundamental (time) complexity. By the same fundamental complexity we mean that if the original algorithm was say, quadratic in the length of the input, it remains quadratic; it it was $n \log n$ it remains $n \log n$, and so on. For example, the average case behaviour of the functional version of quicksort, which we gave at the end of §2, is, like its imperative counterpart, of $n \log n$ complexity.

On the basis of this and related work, the author is strongly tempted to conjecture that for time complexity, there is no *fundamental* difference between imperative and applicative programming, i.e. that for each imperative algorithm of a given complexity there exists an applicative algorithm that has the same complexity (to within a multiplicative constant). We can here give only the briefest sketch of the argument in favour of this conjecture.

So far as the author is aware, all of the alleged counterexamples to this proposition depend on the presence, in imperative programming languages, of constant-time access data structures, such as the PASCAL *array* type. The absence of a constant-time access data structure from functional languages is, however, a matter of tradition and not of logical necessity. Furthermore there are ways to achieve, within the functional framework, the same effect as the imperative notion of 'update-in-place' on such data structures (see Meira 1984). This would appear to give us the basis for a general method of transcribing an imperative algorithm into a functional one while preserving its complexity (within a multiplicative constant).

The above remarks concern time complexity. For the space complexity of functional programs the situation is much less clear. In a language with lazy evaluation it is in general rather difficult either to predict or to control the space behaviour of programs. In fact Hughes (1984) has shown that there are some very simple problems for which it is surprisingly difficult to construct functional solutions with a reasonable space behaviour. This is an area where further research is needed.

Notwithstanding these difficulties there is much promising work now in progress on the design of machine architectures and instruction sets for the efficient support of functional languages and it seems probable that in the future we shall have implementations of purely functional languages efficient enough to allow their use in production programming.

(c) *Relation to logic programming*

Functional programming, as presented here, and logic programming in the style of PROLOG, as presented by Professor Kowalski and others (Kowalski this symposium), are obviously closely related, and both may be regarded as species of declarative programming. In both cases the program consists of *assertions*, and the computation proceeds by a process of deduction from those assertions. For functional programming the assertions consist of *equations*, for logic programming they consist of *material implications*. For the former the subject of discourse is *functions*, for the latter it is *relations*.

Each of these two styles of programming has advantages not possessed by the other. An important advantage of logic programming is that because it is based on relations, it can accommodate non-determinism in a straightforward way. Functional programming, however, has the important advantage of being *higher order*, i.e. it permits the manipulation of functions as data objects, in a way that respects the principle of extensionality, whereas nothing quite equivalent to this exists in logic programming.

At the present stage of our knowledge of logic programming and functional programming, it seems that neither can be regarded as a subject of the other, and that further research is required into both, and into the relation between them. It would be very desirable if we could find some more general system of assertional programming, of which both functional and logic programming in their present forms could be exhibited as special cases.

References

Bird 1983 Some notational suggestions for transformational programming. *Tech. Rep.* no. 153. University of Reading.

Broy, M. 1981 A fixed point approach to applicative multiprogramming. In *Proceedings of Nato summer school on theoretical foundations of programming methodology, Munich*, pp. 565–624. Dordrecht: Reidel.

Burstall, R. M. 1969 Proving properties of programs by structural induction. *Computer J.* **12**, 41–48.

Burstall, R. M., MacQueen, D. B. & Sannella D. T. 1980 HOPE, an experimental applicative language. *Univ. Edinburgh tech. rep.* no. CSR-62-80.

Curry, H. B. & Feys, R. 1958 *Combinatory logic*, vol. 1. Amsterdam: North-Holland.

Darlington, J. 1982 Program transformation. In *Functional programming and its applications* (ed. J. Darlington, P. Henderson & D. A. Turner), pp. 193–215. Cambridge University Press.

Davis, M. 1958 *Computability and unsolvability*. New York: McGraw-Hill.

Dijkstra, E. W. 1976 *A discipline of programming*. Englewood Cliffs, N.J.: Prentice-Hall.

Drake, F. R. 1974 *Set theory*. Amsterdam: North-Holland.

Friedman, D. P. & Wise, D. S. 1976 CONS should not evaulate its arguments. In *Proceedings 3rd International Colloquium on Automata Languages and Programming*, pp. 257–284. Edinburgh University Press.

Gordon, M. J., Milner, R. & Wadsworth, C. P. 1979 Edinburgh LCF. *Lecture notes in computer science*, vol. 78, Berlin: Springer-Verlag.

Graham, N. 1983 *Introduction to PASCAL*, p. 202. Minnesota: West.

Henderson, P. 1982 Purely functional operating systems. In *Functional programming and its applications* (ed. J. Darlington, P. Henderson & D. A. Turner), pp. 177–192. Cambridge University Press.

Henderson, P. & Morris, J. M. 1976 A lazy evaluator. In *Proceedings 3rd Symposium on principles of programming languages, Atlanta Georgia*, pp. 95–103.

Hoare, C. A. R. 1962 Quicksort. *Computer J.* **5**, 10–15.

Hughes, J. M. 1984 The design and implementation of programming languages. D.Phil. thesis. Oxford University.

Inmos Ltd 1982 *OCCAM programming manual*. Bristol: Inmos Ltd.

Kahn, G. & McQueen, D. 1977 Coroutines and networks of parallel processes. In *Proceedings IFIP 77*, pp. 993–998. Amsterdam: North-Holland.

Kleene, S. C. 1952 *Introduction to metamathematics*. Amsterdam: North-Holland.

McCarthy, J., Abrahams, P. W., Edwards, D. J., Hart, T. P. & Levin, M. I. 1962 *The LISP 1.5 programmer's manual*. M.I.T. Press.

Meira, S. R. L. 1983 Sorting algorithms in KRC: implementation, proof and performance. *Computing Laboratory rep.* no. 14. University of Kent at Canterbury.

Meira, S. R. L. 1984 A linear applicative solution to the set union problem. *Computing Laboratory tech. rep.* no. 23. University of Kent at Canterbury.

Milner, R. 1978 A theory of type polymorphism in programming. *J. computer system Sci.* **17**, 348–375.

Scott, D. S. 1970 Outline of mathematical theory of computation. Oxford University Programming Research Group, *tech. monogr.* no. 2.

Scott, D. S. 1976 Data types as lattices. *SIAM Jl Computing* **5**, 522–587.

Tarjan, R. E. 1972 Depth first search and linear graph algorithms. *SIAM Jl Computing* **1**, 146–160.

Turing, A. M. 1936 On computable numbers, with an application to the Entscheidungs problem. *Proc. Lond. math. Soc.* **42** (ser. 2), 230–265.

Turner, D. A. 1976 SASL language manual. *St Andrew's University tech. rep.* no. CS/75/1.

Turner, D. A. 1981 Aspects of the implementation of programming languages. D. Phil thesis, Oxford University.

Turner, D. A. 1982*a* Functional programming and proofs of program correctness. In *Tools and notions for program construction* (ed. D. Néel) pp. 187–209. Cambridge University Press.

Turner, D. A. 1982*b* Recursion equations as a programming language. In *Functional programming and its applications* (eds. J. Darlington, P. Henderson & D. A. Turner), pp. 1–28. Cambridge University Press.

Turner, D. A. 1984 The type structure of MIRANDA. (In the press.)

Discussion

J. FAIRBAIRN (*Cambridge University Computer Laboratory, U.K.*). I am unhappy with the way that in MIRANDA the existence of an equality function is assumed. We all know that equality is not computable for several types of object; infinite trees and arbitrary functions being examples. Hence the function 'assoc' of type $(* \times ** \text{ list}) \rightarrow * \rightarrow **$ cannot work unless the type substituted for '$*$' is a finite list or product of zero-order (non-function) types. This restriction is rather subversive, since the type of 'assoc' suggests that it should work for any kind of argument.

Instead, 'assoc' could be parameterized on the equality function, and would have type $(* \to * \to \text{bool}) \to (* \times ** \text{ list}) \to * \to **$. Similarly, functions for sorting may be parameterized on the order relation chosen, and so the same function could be used to sort into ascending or descending order. Surely this constitutes a more general approach, and does not subvert the type structure?

D. A. TURNER. MIRANDA, like the earlier languages SASL and KRC, provides a built in equality test. This is a three valued function, yielding *true*, *false* or $\perp$. On discrete data objects it is always defined, and has an obvious and natural meaning. When applied to, say, a pair of functions it must yield $\perp$, because, as Dr Fairbairn points out, there is no reliable way of testing for equality on objects like that. I do not feel that there is anything illogical or subversive about this. A built-in equality test is a very useful thing to have, and the fact that it cannot be total (i.e. everywhere defined) does not seem to me to be a reason for not having it at all.

One might have wanted to have a type discipline that prevented people from applying the equality test to, say, functions. This is a perfectly reasonable thing to want. It is not possible within the Milner type-discipline, however, because there is only one kind of type variable and it ranges over all types. One cannot have a kind of type variable that ranges over, say, only discrete types. I decided to use the Milner type-system for MIRANDA because it is relatively simple and well understood, and does more or less exactly what I want. I have no objection, however, to other people experimenting with more complex and subtle type systems, however, such as I believe Dr Fairbairn is doing with his language PONDER.

With regard to Dr Fairbairn's proposal that the user should pass in the comparison function as a parameter, this is of course equally possible in MIRANDA and I do not see any conflict here. One could have a version of 'assoc' that works in the way Dr Fairbairn suggests. For example there is a built-in ordering relation (tested by '>' '<', etc.) on all finite data objects; it does the obvious thing on numbers and strings, and imposes some arbitrary but reproducible order on other types. The library function 'sort' sorts with respect to this built-in ordering. There is also a function 'sortwith', which takes a comparison function provided by the user as a parameter and sorts with respect to that. Having built-in comparison operators in no way prevents one from using the more general approach when it is appropriate.

D. PARK (*Computer Science Department, Warwick University, U.K.*). I would like to draw attention to what appears to be an essential difficulty in the choice of primitives for programming with infinite sets in languages like MIRANDA.

(1) If the empty set $\varnothing$ is uniquely representable in MIRANDA, then the Scott approximation

$$\varnothing \sqsubseteq X$$

should hold between it and all other 'sets' X. Otherwise (assuming the usual relations between computability and lattice structure) the question

$$\varnothing = Y$$

would be decidable for MIRANDA expressions Y, which include arbitrary effective enumerations of sets. This would contradict well known computability results. (A typical expression that seems to demand such a 'non-terminating' empty set might be as intersect (X, {x}), with X an infinite set not containing x.)

(2) Using the monotonicity of (1) in the usual way, we should have

$$0 = \text{any}(\{0\}) = \text{any}(\text{union}(\{0\}, \varnothing) \sqsubseteq \text{any}(\text{union}(\{0\}, \{1\})$$

and similarly

$$1 \sqsubseteq \text{any}(\text{union}(\{0\}, \{1\}).$$

The only interpretation of these two inequalities appears to be that the expression any (union ({0}, {1}) is in some sense essentially non-deterministic. Whether 0 or 1 is produced depends on unspecified detail as to the timing of the processes that supply them.

Apparently, therefore, a system of primitives that allows both the 'choice' function any (X) and the conventional union (X, Y) must include a 'non-deterministic' notion, which violates the constraints needed for the usual reasoning with equations.

The reasoning involved appears to be very general. By taking 'sets' to be sequences of their elements, the non-deterministic notion is union (X, Y), which merges sequences 'angelically'. By factoring out sequencing, the non-determinism moves to the choice function any (X).

D. A. Turner. The logic of Professor Park's argument seems inescapable: any programming language with a proper implementation of infinite sets in it and a choice function must involve non-determinism. I was in fact aware of this, but I am very grateful to Professor Park for providing us with an argument that exposes the problem in a very clear way.

In the design of MIRANDA I tried to postpone dealing with this problem by a decision *not* to introduce sets as a separate data type. Sets are just lists, from which repetitions have been removed. This enables the choice operator 'any' to be implemented in a deterministic way (in fact 'any' is just 'hd'). By the logic of Professor Park's argument, the problem must therefore shift to 'union'. Let us look at union then to see what difficulty arises.

The MIRANDA library function 'union' is defined (for simplicity I show it as the union of two sets, rather than of a list of sets, which is now it is actually defined) as

```
union x y = mkset (interleave x y)
interleave x [ ] = x
interleave [ ] y = y
interleave (a:x) (b:y) = a:b:interleave x y.
```

The function 'mkset' removes repetitions from a list; there is no problem about this (provided the list elements are finite objects) and its definition need not detain us here. The problem is with 'interleave'. There are three kinds of list that could occur as arguments to interleave: infinite lists like [1 . .]; ordinary finite lists like [1, 2]; and finite *partial* lists like $1:2:\bot$. (Note then that in a lazy functional language, finite sets have two distinct kinds of representations over the last few years I have fallen into the habit of calling these 'strong' and 'weak' sets respectively.) Unfortunately one cannot always arrange that a finite set will be represented by a list of the second kind, representations in terms of lists of the third kind are sometimes inevitable.

The definition of union given works correctly both on infinite sets and on 'strong' finite sets, but does not in general give correct answers on 'weak' sets. This is less than fully satisfactory, but it seems to be the best one can do without introducing non-determinism. To get a definition of union that also works correctly on weak sets we would need a version of interleave that is bottom-avoiding (symmetrically in its two arguments). This would obviously involve non-determinism (of precisely the kind that we probably need anyway to write operating systems).

So MIRANDA in its present form does provide a representation of infinite sets with a deterministic choice function, but at the cost of having an incomplete version of set union. Curiously, however, the difficulty with set union does not concern infinite sets but finite ones (of a certain kind). To overcome this problem would require the introduction of non-determinism.

The reason that non-determinism seems undesirable, and the reason that I am trying to avoid introducing it until I am forced to do so (by some application that cannot be done without it), is that, as Professor Park says, it violates 'the constraints needed for the usual reasoning with equations'.

P. WADLER (*Programming Research Group, Oxford, U.K.*). First, an important language that Professor Turner ignores is LISP. I have written a moderate-sized program in both LISP and KRC (the predecessor to the language used in the talk). The program was about 40 pages in LISP and about 4 pages in KRC, which speaks well for KRC. The main reasons for brevity were the syntax of KRC and the use of lazy evaluation. Set expressions did not contribute much to brevity; I tended to avoid them in favour of the standard MAP function.

Second, Professor Turner mentioned 'serious' uses of functional languages. Some very efficient implementations of LISP have been developed. One version, for the S-1 computer used at the Lawrence Livermore Laboratories, may be more efficient than the FORTRAN provided on the same machine. This makes it quite possible that LISP will be used for designing nuclear weapons, which is a very serious use indeed.

D. A. TURNER. I am certainly aware that there has been a great deal of experience built up, over the last twenty years or so, of programming in LISP and that there exist by now some quite efficient implementations of it. Unfortunately, however, this experience has very little bearing on the issues of functional programming. It needs to be said very firmly that LISP, at least as represented by the dialects in common use, is not a functional language at all. LISP does have a functional subset, but that is a rather inconvenient programming language and there exists no significant body of programs written in it. Almost all serious programming in LISP makes heavy use of side effects and other referentially opaque language features.

I think that the historical importance of LISP is that it was the first language to provide 'garbage-collected' heap storage. This was a very important step forward. For the development of functional programming, however, I feel that the contribution of LISP has been a negative one. My suspicion is that the success of LISP set back the development of a properly functional style of programming by at least ten years.

B. A. WICHMANN (*National Physical Laboratory, Teddington, U.K.*). Has Professor Turner any results on the space efficiency of his techniques?

D. A. TURNER. There has been rather little work done in this area, so far as I am aware. We have some quite encouraging results on the time complexity of functional programs, as I mentioned, but for space complexity the picture is much murkier. It is in general rather hard to analyse the space behaviour of 'lazy' languages, but one can give some simple examples where the space behaviour of a lazy functional program is much worse than that of the corresponding imperative program. There are several possible lines of attack on this problem, but much more work needs to be done. It may be that we shall discover that there are classes of problem for which functional languages have fundamentally worse space behaviour than imperative ones. I very much hope that this is not so, but in our present state of knowledge we cannot discount it. Of course memory is getting cheaper very rapidly, so such a discovery would not necessarily be disastrous, although it would be bound to limit the applicability of functional techniques to applications that are not space-critical.

M. H. Rogers (*School of Mathematics, University of Bristol, U.K.*). How do functional programming languages compare with procedural and logical languages in (i) ease of programming, (ii) proving correctness of some specification expressed in ordinary mathematical language?

D. A. Turner. What one means by 'ease of programming' is rather hard to define, so it is difficult to make precise statements about this. However, I observe from my own behaviour and that of others, that the time required to produce an executable solution to a given problem (assuming for the moment that the level of performance of the solution is not an issue) is in general very much less when working in a functional language than in a conventional imperative one. I observe from the behaviour of others that logic programs have the same property. This presumably is one measure of 'ease of programming'.

On the other hand one can ask about the prerequisites on the programmer, in terms of length of training, level of previous knowledge required and so on. It seems to me that to learn to program well in a functional language requires a rather longer period of training and a more mathematical knowledge than is commonly expected of programmers today. The advantage is that programmers become more productive.

With regard to a comparison between functional programming and logic programming I am probably the wrong person to ask, since I have much more experience of the former than the latter and any answer I could give might only reflect this bias.

Of the three types of programming Professor Rogers mentioned, functional programming is much the closest to ordinary mathematics, because it is based on equations. This allows a rather nice style of proof, by use of the substitutivity of equality, which has been explored by myself and others, and which I have written about elsewhere.

Mechanical proofs about computer programs

By D. I. Good

2100 *Main Building, Institute for Computing Science, The University of Texas at Austin, Austin, Texas* 78712, *U.S.A.*

The Gypsy verification environment is a large computer program that supports the development of software systems and formal, mathematical proofs about their behaviour. The environment provides conventional development tools, such as a parser for the Gypsy language, an editor and a compiler. These are used to evolve a library of components that define both the software and precise specifications about its desired behaviour. The environment also has a verification condition generator that automatically transforms a software component and its specification into logical formulas that are sufficient to prove that the component always runs according to specification. Facilities for constructing formal, mechanical proofs of these formulas also are provided. Many of these proofs are completed automatically without human intervention. The capabilities of the Gypsy system and the results of its application are discussed.

1. Introduction

One of the major problems with the current practice of software engineering is an absence of predictability. There is no sound, scientific way of predicting accurately how a software system will behave when it runs. There are many compelling examples of important software systems that have behaved in unpredictable ways: a Space Shuttle fails to launch; an entire line of automobiles is recalled because of problems with the software that controls the braking system; unauthorized users get access to computer systems; sensitive information passes into the wrong hands, etc. (Neumann 1983*a*, *b*). Considering the wide variety of tasks that now are entrusted to computer systems, it is truly remarkable that it is not possible to predict accurately what they are going to do!

Within current software engineering practice, the only sound way to make a precise, accurate prediction about how a software system will behave is to build it and run it. There is no way to predict accurately how a system will behave before it can be run. So design flaws often are detected only after a large investment has been made to develop the system to a point where it can be run. The rebuilding that is caused by the late detection of these flaws contributes significantly to the high cost of software construction and maintenance. Even after the system can be run, the situation is only slightly better. A system that can be run can be tested on a set of trial cases. If the system is deterministic, a trial run on a specific test case provides a precise, accurate prediction about how the system will behave in *that one case*. If the system is re-run on exactly the same case, it will behave in exactly the same way. However, there is no way to predict, from the observed behaviour of a finite number of test cases, how the system will behave in any other case. If the system is non-deterministic (as many systems are), the system will not even necessarily repeat its observed behaviour on a test case. So in current software engineering practice, predicting that a software system will run according to specification is based almost entirely on subjective, human judgment rather than on objective, scientific fact.

In contrast to software engineering, mathematical logic provides a sound, objective way to make accurate, precise predictions about the behaviour of mathematical operations. For example, if x and y are natural numbers, who among us would doubt the prediction that $x+y$ always gives exactly the same result as $y+x$? This prediction is accurate not just for *some* cases or even just for *most* cases; it is accurate for *every* pair of natural numbers, no matter what they are. The prediction is accurate because there is a *proof* that $x+y = y+x$ logically follows from accepted definitions of 'natural number', '=' and '+'.

The Gypsy verification environment is a large, interactive computer program that supports the construction of formal, mathematical proofs about the behaviour of software systems. These proofs make it possible to predict the behaviour of a software system with the same degree of precision and accuracy that is possible for mathematical operations. These proofs can be constructed *before* a software system can be run and, therefore, they can provide an objective, scientific basis for making predictions about system behaviour throughout the software life cycle. This makes it possible for the proofs actually to guide the construction of the system. In theory these proof methods make possible a new approach to software engineering that can produce systems whose predictability far exceeds that which can be attained with conventional methods.

In practice the use of this mathematical approach to software engineering requires very careful management of large amounts of detailed information. The Gypsy environment is an experimental system that has been developed to explore the viability of applying these methods in actual practice. The purposes of the environment are to amplify the ability of the human software engineer to manage these details and to reduce the probability of human error. The environment, therefore, contains tools for supporting the normal software development process as well as tools for constructing formal proofs.

2. A MATHEMATICAL APPROACH

The Gypsy verification environment is based on the Gypsy language (Good *et al.* 1978). Rather than being based on an extension of the hardware architecture of some particular computer, the Gypsy language is based on rigorous, mathematical foundations for specifying and implementing computer programs. The specification describes *what* effect is desired when the program runs, and the implementation defines *how* the effect is caused. The mathematical foundation provided by the Gypsy language makes it possible to construct rigorous proofs about both the specifications and the implementations of software systems. The language, which is modelled on Pascal (Jensen & Wirth 1974), also is designed so that the implementations of programs can be compiled and executed on a computer with a conventional von Neumann architecture.

The basic structure of a Gypsy software system is shown in figure 1. The purpose of a software system is to cause some effect on its external environment. The external environment of a Gypsy software system consists of data objects (and exception conditions). Every Gypsy data object has a name and a value. The implementation of a program causes an effect by changing the values of the data objects in its external environment (or by signalling a condition). To accomplish its effect, an implementation may create and use internal (local) data objects (and conditions). In figure 1, X and Y represent external objects, and U represents an internal object.

The specifications of a program define constraints on its implementation. In parallel with the structure of implementations, Gypsy provides a means of stating both internal and external specifications. The external specifications constrain the externally visible effects of an implementation. Internal specifications constrain its internal behaviour.

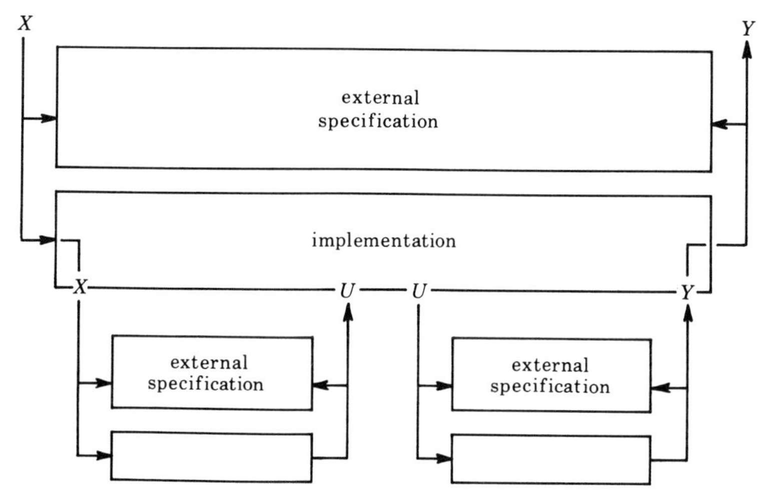

FIGURE 1. Gypsy software system structure.

The external specifications of a program consist of two parts: a (mandatory) environment specification and an (optional) operational specification. The environment specification describes *all* of the external data objects that are accessible to the procedure. The specification also states the type of each of these objects and whether it is a variable or a constant object. A program may change the value of a data object *only* if it is a variable object.

The type of an object specifies the kind of values it may have. The mathematical foundations of Gypsy begin with its types. The Gypsy types are all well known mathematical objects (integers, rational numbers, the Boolean values *true* and *false*, sets, sequences, mappings) or they can be easily derived from such objects (types character, record, array, buffer). For example, in Gypsy, type *integer* represents the full, unbounded set of mathematical objects. It is not restricted only to the integers that can be represented on a particular machine. For each of these pre-defined types, the Gypsy language also provides a set of primitive, pre-defined functions with known mathematical properties.

The operational specification for an implementation is a relation (a Boolean-valued function) that describes what effect is to be caused on the objects of the external environment. These relations are defined by ordinary functional composition from the Gypsy pre-defined functions.

The implementation of a Gypsy program is defined by a procedure. Running a Gypsy procedure is what actually causes an effect to be produced in its external environment. For implementation, the Gypsy language provides a set of pre-defined procedures (assign a value to an object, send a value to a buffer, remove an object from a sequence, etc.) that have precisely defined effects. It also provides a set of composition rules (*if*...*then*...*else*...*end*, *loop*...*end*, *cobegin*...*end*, etc.) for composing these pre-defined procedures into more complex ones. So the implementation of every Gypsy software system is some composition of the pre-defined procedures.

These composition rules are designed so that the effect that is caused by the composition can be deduced from the effects caused by its components. In particular, it is always possible to construct a set of formulas in the first-order predicate calculus that are sufficient (but not always necessary) to show that the effect caused by a procedure satisfies its specifications. These formulas are called *verification conditions*. They are the logical conditions that are sufficient to verify that the implementation meets its specifications. By constructing them, the task of proving that an implementation always causes an effect that satisfies its specifications is reduced to a task of proving a set of formulas in the first-order predicate calculus. The methods for constructing the verification conditions are based on the pioneering work of Naur (1966), Floyd (1967), Dijkstra (1968), Hoare (1969), King (1969), Good (1970). Dijkstra (1976), Jones (1980), Gries (1981), Hoare (1982) provide more recent discussions of these basic ideas and their relation to software development.

One of the most important aspects of the Gypsy composition rules is illustrated in figure 1. Only the external specifications of the components are required to construct the verification conditions for the composition. Neither the internal specifications nor the implementation of the components are required. The proof of the composition is completely independent of the internal operation of the components. Therefore, the proof of the composition can be done *before* the components are proved or even implemented; all that is required is that the components have external specifications. Because of this characteristic of the proof methods, a software system can be specified, implemented and proved by starting at the top and working downward rather than by building upward from the Gypsy pre-defined functions and procedures. Thus, when working from the top down, the proofs provide a sound, scientific basis for predicting how the system will behave long before it can be run. It is in these high levels of system design that proofs often can be most effective.

3. The Gypsy environment

The Gypsy verification environment is an interactive program that supports a software engineer in specifying, implementing and proving Gypsy software systems. The specific goals of the environment are to increase the productivity of the software engineer and to reduce the probability of human error. To meet these goals, the Gypsy environment provides an integrated collection of conventional software development tools along with special tools for constructing formal, mathematical proofs. Figure 2 shows the logical structure of the environment.

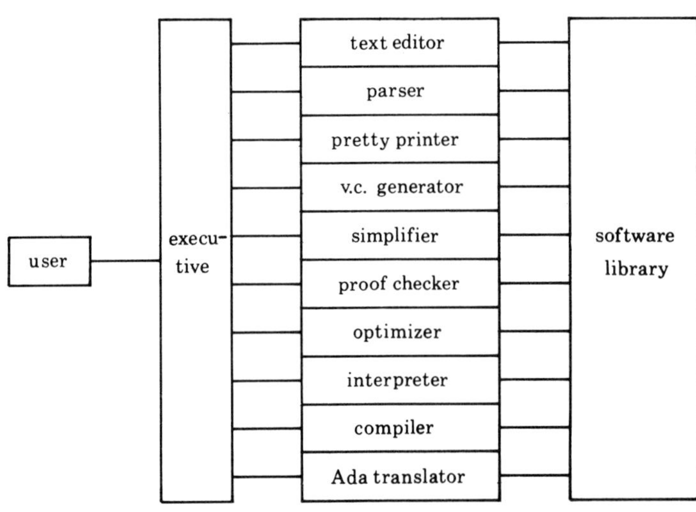

Figure 2. Gypsy environment components.

A single user interacts with the executive component of the environment to use a number of different software tools to build and evolve a software library. This library contains the various Gypsy components of the specification and implementation of a software system, as well as other supporting information such as verification conditions and proofs. The executive notes the changes that are made as the library evolves and marks components that need to be reconsidered to preserve the validity of the proofs (Moriconi 1977).

The Emacs text editor (Stallman 1980), parser and pretty printer are conventional tools for creating and modifying Gypsy text. The parser transforms Gypsy text into an internal form for storage in the library. The pretty printer transforms the internal form back into parsable Gypsy text. The interpreter, compiler (Smith 1980) and Ada translator (Akers 1983) also are fairly conventional tools for running Gypsy programs. Although the interpreter would be a very useful debugging tool, it is not well developed and it is not presently available.

The tools that are involved in constructing proofs are the verification condition generator, the algebraic simplifier, the interactive proof checker and the optimizer. The verification condition generator automatically constructs verification conditions from the Gypsy text of a program. The algebraic simplifier automatically applies an *ad hoc* set of rewrite rules that reduce the complexity of the verification conditions and other logical formulas produced within the Gypsy environment. These rewrite rules are based on equality (and other) relations that are applied by the definitions of the Gypsy pre-defined functions. The interactive proof checker has evolved from one described by Bledsoe & Bruell (1974). It provides a set of truth preserving transformations that can be performed on first-order predicate calculus formulas. These transformations are selected interactively.

The optimizer (McHugh 1983) is unique to the Gypsy environment. It produces logical formulas whose truth is sufficient to show that certain program optimizations are valid. The optimizer works in a manner similar to the verification condition generator. From the implementation of a program *and* its specifications, logical formulas called *optimization conditions* are constructed automatically. These conditions are proved, and then the compiler uses this knowledge to make various optimizations.

4. An example

To illustrate the capabilities of the Gypsy language and environment, consider the design of a simple software system that filters a stream of messages. Two computers, A and B, are to be coupled by a transmission line so that A can send messages to B. These messages are strings of ASCII characters arranged in a certain format. However, certain kinds of these messages, even when properly formatted, cause machine B to crash. To solve this problem a separate microcomputer is to be installed between A and B as shown in figure 3. The microcomputer is to monitor the flow of messages from A to B, remove the undesirable messages and log them on an audit trail.

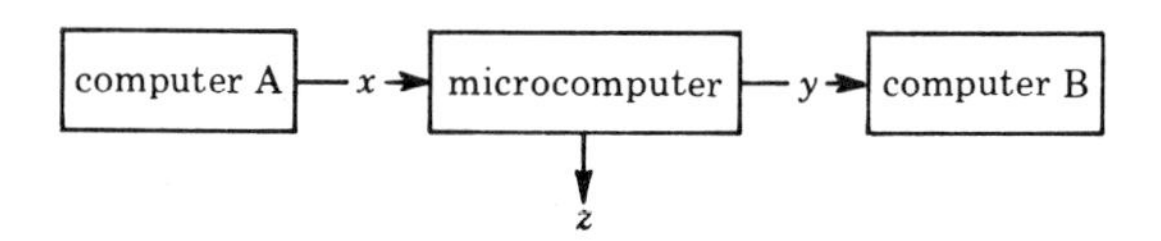

Figure 3. Microcomputer filter.

(a) *Top level specification*

The microcomputer filter will be developed from the top downwards. The process begins by defining an abstract specification of its desired behaviour. The Gypsy text for this top level specification is shown in figure 4. When using the Gypsy environment, the first step would be to create this text and store it in the software library.

```
scope message_stream_separator =
begin

  procedure separator(x:a_char_seq; var y, z:a_char_seq) =
  begin
  exit separated(msg_stream(x), y, z);
    pending;
  end;

  function msg_stream(x:a_char_seq):a_msg_seq = pending;

  function separated(s:a_msg_seq; y, z:a_char_seq):boolean =
  pending;

  type a_char_seq = sequence of character;
  type a_msg = a_char_seq;
  type a_msg_seq = sequence of a_msg;

end;
```

FIGURE 4. Microcomputer filter top level specification.

The Gypsy text defines a scope called *message_stream_separator* that contains six Gypsy units, procedure *separator*, functions *msg_stream* and *separated* and types *a_char_seq*, *a_msg* and *a_msg_seq*. (A Gypsy scope is just a name that identifies a particular collection of Gypsy units. The Gypsy units are procedures, functions, constants, lemmas and types. All Gypsy programs are implemented and specified in terms of these five kinds of units.)

Procedure *separator* is the program that will filter the messages going from computer A to B. The external environment specification of *separator* is (*x*:*a_char_seq*; *var y*, *z*:*a_char_seq*). It states that *separator* has access to exactly three external data objects, x, y and z, as illustrated in figure 3. The object x is a constant, and y and z are variables. Each of the objects has a value that is a sequence of ASCII characters.

The operational specification is *exit separated*(*msg_stream*(x), y, z). This defines a relation among x, y and z that must be satisfied whenever *separator* halts (exits). The messages that arrive from computer A are supposed to be in a given format. However, there is no way to force A to deliver them properly, and even if it does there is the possibility of noise on the transmission line. Therefore, *separator* must be designed to extract properly formatted messages from an arbitrary sequence of characters. *Msg_stream*(x) is the function that applies the formatting rules and determines the sequence of properly formatted messages that are contained in an arbitrary sequence of characters. *Separated*(s, y, z) defines what it means for a sequence of messages s to be separated into two character strings y and z.

This top level specification does not give precise definitions for *msg_stream* and *separated*; only environment specifications for them are given. (The environment specifications for functions are interpreted in the same way as for procedures, except that the additional type name immediately preceding the '=' identifies the type of value produced by the function.) The precise definitions of *msg_stream* and *separated*, as well as the implementation of *separator*, are left *pending* at this stage of development. At this stage, the interface between *separator* and its external environment has been defined, and it has been acknowledged that *separator* must be prepared to deal with an input sequence that may contain improperly formed messages. Formulation of precise definitions for the pending items will be deferred to a later stage.

(*b*) *Specification refinement*

The next stage is to refine the operational specifications of *separator*. Figure 5 shows the actual Gypsy text that would be entered into the software library. This text extends scope *message_stream_separator* by replacing the old version of *separated* by the new one and by defining some new functions, types and lemmas.

In this refinement, the *separated* specification is given a precise definition in terms of two new functions *passed* and *rejected*. The definition is given by the operational specification of *separated*.

```
$extending
scope message_stream_separator =
begin

  function separated(s:a_msg_seq; y, z:a_char_seq):boolean =
  begin
  exit [assume result iff y = passed(s) & z = rejected(s)];
  end;

  function passed(s:a_msg_seq):a_char_seq =
  begin
  exit [assume result =
        if s = null(a_msg_seq) then null(a_char_seq)
        else passed(nonlast(s)) @ image(last(s)).pass fi];
  end;

  function rejected(s:a_msg_seq):a_char_seq =
  begin
  exit [assume result =
        if s = null(a_msg_seq) then null(a_char_seq)
        else rejected(nonlast(s)) @ image(last(s)).reject fi];
  end;

  function image(m:a_msg):an_image = pending;

  type an_image = record(pass, reject:a_char_seq);

  lemma null_separation =
  separated(null(a_msg_seq), null(a_char_seq),
                             null(a_char_seq));

  lemma extend_separation(s:a_msg_seq; m:a_msg;
                          y, z:a_char_seq) =
  separated(s, y, z)
  -> separated(s @ [seq: m], y @ image(m).pass,
                             z @ image(m).reject);

  lemma null_stream =
  msg_stream(null(a_char_seq)) = null(a_msg_seq);

end;
```

FIGURE 5. Microcomputer filter specification refinement.

Result is the Gypsy convention for the name of the value returned by a function, and the specification states that *result* is to be true iff $y = passed(s)$ and $z = rejected(s)$. The keyword *assume* indicates that this specification is to be assumed without proof. This is the normal Gypsy style for defining a function that is to be used just for specification.

Functions *passed* and *rejected* are defined in terms of pre-defined Gypsy functions and the function *image*. *Last* is a pre-defined function that gives the last element of a non-empty sequence, and *nonlast* gives all the other elements. The operator '@' denotes a pre-defined function that appends two sequences.

Image is a function that takes a message and produces a record of two parts, *pass* and *reject*. At a subsequent development stage, the definition of *image* will be refined to include the criterion for identifying a message that causes computer B to crash. *Image* also will define the actual output that is sent to computer B *and* to the audit trail for *each* message. If the message is of the form that will cause B to crash, the *pass* part of the record will contain a null sequence of characters and the *reject* part will contain the offending message and any other appropriate information. This record form for the result of *image* was chosen so that messages that are forwarded to B also can be audited if desired. This can be done by sending characters to both the *pass* and *reject* parts of the record. This design choice retains a large amount of flexibility for the subsequent design of the audit trail. The function *passed* applies the *image* function to each successive message *m* and appends the *pass* part of *image*(m) to y. Similarly, *rejected* applies *image* to each *m* and appends the *reject* part to z.

(c) *Specification proof*

The Gypsy text for the specification refinement also contains three lemmas. These are properties that can be proved to follow from the preceding definitions. These lemmas are the beginning of a simple problem domain theory of separating messages. The lemmas (theorems) of this theory serve several important purposes. First, to the extent that they are properties that the software designer intuitively believes *should* follow from the assumed definitions, proving that they *do* follow provides confidence in these assumptions. Secondly, these properties are the basis for the implementation in the next stage. They are used in the proof of the implementation to decompose the proof into manageable parts. Thirdly, to the extent that the lemmas in this theory are reusable, they can significantly reduce the cost of other proofs that are based on the same theory (Good 1982*a*).

The *null_separation* lemma is a rather trivial one that states that if a sequence of messages s is empty, then $separated(s, y, z)$ is satisfied if y and z also are empty. Lemma *extend_separation* describes how to extend the *separated* relation to cover one more message m. If $separated(s, y, z)$ is satisfied, then so is $separated(s@[seq{:}m], y@image(m).pass, z@image(m).reject)$.

A formal proof of both of these lemmas can be constructed with the assistance of the interactive proof checker in the Gypsy verification environment. The proof checker provides a fixed set of truth-preserving transformations that can be performed on a logical formula. Although the proof checker has some very limited capability to make transformations without user direction, the primary means of constructing a proof is for the user to select each transformation. Expansion of the definition of a function is one kind of transformation that can be made. The user directs the proof checker to expand the definition of a particular function, and then the expansion is done automatically. Other examples of transformations provided by the proof checker are instantiation of a quantified variable, substitution of equals for equals, and use of a particular lemma. A formula is proved to be a theorem by finding a sequence of transformations that transform the formula into *true*. This sequence constitutes a formal, mathematical proof.

A complete transcript of the interactive proof of *extend_separation* is given in Appendix A. The key steps in the proof are to expand the definition of the *separated* relation and the *passed* and *rejected* functions with the expand command. The theorem command shows the state of the formula at various intermediate stages of transformation. The *null_separation* lemma is proved in a similar way.

Notice that both of these lemmas about message separation can be proved at this rather high level of abstraction without detailed knowledge of the specific format for incoming messages and without knowing the specific formatting details for the outputs y and z. These details are encapsulated in the functions *msg_stream* and *image* respectively. These definitions (which would need to be provided in subsequent refinement stages) might be quite simple or very complex. In either case, however, detailed definitions of these functions are *not* required at this stage. The use of abstraction in this way is what makes it possible to construct concise, intellectually manageable, formal proofs about large complex specifications. The next §4 (*d*) illustrates how similar techniques can be used in proofs about an implementation.

Finally, it is noted that the *null_stream* lemma cannot be proved at this stage of refinement. However, it is required in the subsequent implementation proof, and therefore, it serves as a constraint on the refinement of the definition of *msg_stream*.

(*d*) *Implementation refinement*

An implementation of procedure *separator* that satisfies the preceding specifications is shown in figure 6. The implementation contains two internal variable objects m and p of types *a_msg* and *integer* respectively. *Separator* causes its effect on its external variable objects, y and z, first by assigning each of them the value of the empty sequence of characters; then it enters a loop that separates the messages in x one by one, and for each message the appropriate output is appended to y and z.

The desired effect of the loop is described by the *assert* statement. It states that on each iteration of the loop, messages in the subsequence $x[1..p]$ have been separated. (The Gypsy notation for element i of sequence x is $x[i]$, and $x[1..p]$ is the notation for the subsequence $x[1], \ldots, x[p]$.) This assertion is an *internal* specification about the operation of the procedure.

The loop operates by successively calling the procedures *get_msg* and *put_msg*. *Get_msg* assigns to m the next properly formatted message in x and increases p to be the number of the last character in x that has been examined. *Put_msg* appends to y and z the appropriate output for the new message m. The properties of *get_msg* and *put_msg* are stated precisely in the specifications that are given for them in figure 6. (For the variable p, p' refers to its value at the time *get_msg* is started running, and p refers to its value when the procedure halts. The operator <: appends a single element to the end of a sequence.)

(*e*) *Implementation proof*

The remaining task for this level of the design of the microcomputer filter is to prove that this abstract implementation of *separator* satisfies its specifications (both internal and external). This proof is possible without any further refinement of the specifications or the implementation. The current form is an instance of the one shown in figure 1. Specifications and an

```
$extending
scope message_stream_separator =
begin

procedure separator(x:a_char_seq; var y, z:a_char_seq) =
begin
exit separated(msg_stream(x), y, z);
  var m:a_msg;
  var p:integer := 0;
  y := null(a_char_seq);
  z := null(a_char_seq);
  loop assert separated(msg_stream(x[1..p]), y, z)
        & p le size(x);
    if p = size(x) then leave;
    else get_msg(x, m, p);
         put_msg(m, y, z);
    end;
  end;
end;

procedure get_msg(x:a_char_seq; var m:a_msg; var p:integer) =
begin
exit msg_stream(x[1..p]) = msg_stream(x[1..p']) <: m
     & p > p' & p le size(x);
  pending
end;

procedure put_msg(m:a_msg; var y, z:a_char_seq) =
begin
exit y = y' @ image(m).pass & z = z' @ image(m).reject;
  pending
 end;

end;
```

FIGURE 6. Microcomputer filter implementation refinement.

implementation for *separator* have been constructed, but there is no implementation of either *get_msg* or *put_msg*. This level of proof simply assumes that these procedures eventually will be implemented and proved to satisfy their specifications. However, at this level, only their external specifications are required.

It is easy to see that the *exit* specification of *separator* logically follows from the assert statement in the loop whenever the procedure leaves the loop. This follows simply from the facts that, when the loop halts, $p = size(x)$ and that for every Gypsy sequence $x[1\,..\,size(x)] = x$. It is also easy to see that the assert statement is true the first time the loop is entered. This is because the local variable p is zero, and y and z are both equal to the empty sequence. The assertion then follows from the *null_stream* and *null_separation* lemmas because in Gypsy, $x[1\,..\,0]$ is the empty sequence and the size of a sequence is always non-negative. Finally, the *extend_separation* lemma can be used to prove that if the loop assertion is true on one iteration of the loop, then it also is true on the next. These steps form an inductive proof that the loop assertion is true on every iteration of the loop (even if it never halts). The loop, however, does halt because, according to the specifications of *get_msg*, p is an integer that increases on each iteration and yet never increases beyond the number of characters in the constant x. Therefore, the loop must halt; and when it does, the *exit* specification follows from the loop assertion.

The Gypsy verification environment automates all of this argument (except the argument about the loop halting). From the Gypsy text shown in figure 6, the verification conditions generator automatically constructs the formulas shown in figure 7.

```
Verification condition separator#2
separated (msg_stream (null (#seqtype#)),
           null (a_char_seq), null (a_char_seq))

Verification condition separator#3
  H1: msg_stream (x[1..p]) @ [seq: m#1] = msg_stream (x[1..p#1])
  H2: y @ image (m#1).pass = y#1
  H3: z @ image (m#1).reject = z#1
  H4: separated (msg_stream (x[1..p]), y, z)
  H5: p le size (x)
  H6: p + 1 le p#1
  H7: p#1 le size (x)
  H8: size (x) ne p
 -->
  C1: separated (msg_stream (x[1..p#1]), y#1, z#1)
```

FIGURE 7. Separator verification conditions.

Verification condition *separator#2* is the formula that states that the loop assertion is true the first time the loop is entered. *Separator#3* is the one that states that if the assertion is true on one iteration of the loop, it also is true on the next. Lines labelled *Hi* are the hypotheses of an implication, and lines labelled *Ci* are conclusions. Both the hypotheses and the conclusions are connected implicitly by logical conjunction. The notation *m#1* denotes a value of *m* upon completing the next cycle of the loop, and similarly for *p*, *y* and *z*. The notation [*seq*: *m#1*] means the sequence consisting of the single element *m#1*. The verification condition generator also has constructed a *separator#4* for the case when the loop terminates. The generator, however, does not present this one because the formula has been proved automatically by the algebraic simplifier. The best way to see the effect of the simplifier is to see what the verification conditions look like without it. The unsimplified formulas are shown in figure 8. (There also is a *separator#1*, which is so trivial that the generator does not even bother to use the algebraic simplifier.)

A complete transcript of the interactive proof of *separator#3* is given in Appendix B. The key steps are to do equality substitutions based on hypotheses H1, H2 and H3 with the <u>eqsub</u> command and then <u>use</u> the *extend_separation* lemma. *Separator#2* is proved by <u>use</u> of the lemmas *null_stream* and *null_separation*.

Once *separator* has been proved, the process of refinement can be resumed. In general, the refinement of both specifications and implementations is repeated until all specifications and procedures are implemented in terms of Gypsy primitives.

It is important to observe that the proof of *separator* has identified formal specifications for *get_msg* and *put_msg* that are adequate for the subsequent refinements of these procedures. It has been proved that *separator* will run according to its specification if *get_msg* and *put_msg* run according to theirs. Therefore, these specifications are completely adequate constraints for the subsequent refinements. Some of the specifications may not be necessary, But they are sufficient to ensure that *separator* will satisfy its specification.

```
Verification condition separator#2
  H1: true
 -->
  C1: separated (msg_stream (x[1..0]), null (a_char_seq),
                 null (a_char_seq))
  C2: 0 le size (x)

Verification condition separator#3
  H1: separated (msg_stream (x[1..p]), y, z)
      & p le size (x)
  H2: not p = size (x)
  H3: msg_stream (x[1..p#1]) = msg_stream (x[1..p]) <: m#1
      & p#1 > p
      & p#1 le size (x)
  H4: y#1 = y @ image (m#1).pass
      & z#1 = z @ image (m#1).reject
 -->
  C1: separated (msg_stream (x[1..p#1]), y#1, z#1)
  C2: p#1 le size (x)

Verification condition separator#4
  H1: separated (msg_stream (x[1..p]), y, z)
      & p le size (x)
  H2: p = size (x)
 -->
  C1: true
  C2: separated (msg_stream (x), y, z)
```

FIGURE 8. Unsimplified verification conditions.

5. TRIAL APPLICATIONS

The Gypsy environment has been developed to explore the practicality of constructing formal proofs about software systems that are intended to be used in actual operation. Throughout its development, the environment has been tested on a number of trial applications. The two major ones are summarized in §5(*a*), (*b*).

(*a*) *Message flow modulator*

The most recent application of Gypsy is the message flow modulator (Good *et al.* 1982*b*). The microcomputer filter that has been specified, designed and proved in §4 is a good approximation of the modulator. The microcomputer filter example was chosen deliberately to show how it is possible to construct concise, formal proofs about much larger software systems. The modulator consists of 556 lines of implementation, and the proofs in the preceding sections apply, with only very minor alteration, to the design of the modulator. The lower level details that are unique to the modulator are encapsulated in the *msg_stream* and *image* functions.

The message flow modulator is a filter that is applied continuously to a stream of messages flowing from one computer system to another. As in the microcomputer filter, messages that pass the filter are passed on to their destination with a very minor modification. Messages that do not are rejected and logged on an audit trail. A properly formatted message consists of a sequence of at most 7200 ASCII characters that are opened and closed by a specific sequence.

The filter consists of a list of patterns. Each pattern defines a sequence of letters and digits that may be interspersed with various arrangements of delimiters (a delimiter is any character other than a letter or digit). If a message contains any phrase that matches any pattern, it is rejected to the audit trail along with a description of the offending pattern. Messages that do not contain any occurrence of any pattern are forwarded on to their destination.

In essence, the formal specifications of the modulator have the form $y = f(x, r)$ & $z = g(x, r)$, where r is the list of rejection patterns. The specification describes the exact sequences of characters that must flow out of the modulator for every possible input sequence. This includes handling both properly and improperly formatted messages in the input stream, detecting phrases that match the rejection patterns, and formatting both output sequences. The Gypsy formulation of these specifications is described in further detail in Good *et al.* (1982*b*).

The modulator was developed within the Gypsy environment as a converging sequence of prototypes. First, Gypsy specifications and proofs were constructed for the top levels of the modulator design. This design covered the basic separation of messages into the two output streams. Then, a sequence of running prototypes was implemented. The purpose of these prototypes was to help decide what some of the detailed behaviour of the modulator *should* be. These prototypes were used to investigate various approaches to handling improperly formed messages and to formatting the audit trail. Specifications for these aspects of the modulator were decided upon only after considerable experimentation with the prototypes. Next, another sequence of performance prototypes was built to evaluate the performance of various pattern matching implementations. Once adequate performance was attained, the Gypsy specifications and proofs were completed for the entire modulator.

As the final step, the proved modulator was tested in a live, operational environment on test scenarios developed by an independent, external group. Without any modification, the proved modulator passed all of these tests on the first attempt.

(*b*) *Network interface*

The first major application of Gypsy, and the most complex one to date, was a special interface for the ARPANET. Each ARPANET host has message traffic that needs to be transported over the network according to the standard Transmission Control Protocol (Version 4.0). The ARPANET, however, is assumed to be an untrustworthy courier. The special interfaces are to ensure proper message delivery across this potentially unreliable network.

Normally, each host is connected directly to the network by a bi-directional cable. Each cable is cut and an interface unit is installed at the cut (figure 9). This turns the 'dumb' cable into

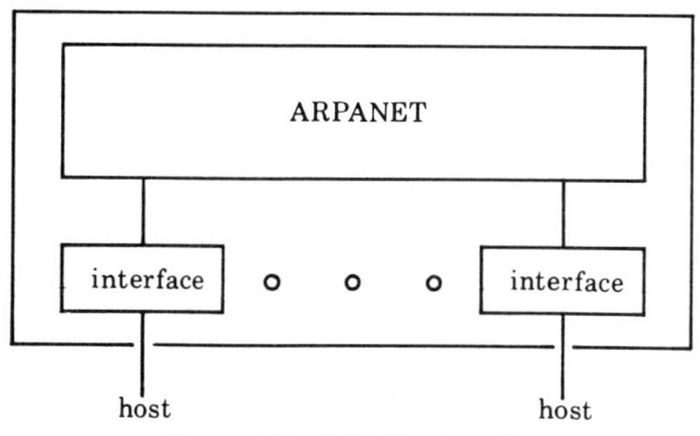

FIGURE 9. ARPANET interface.

a 'smart' one. When the smart cable receives a message from the host, the message is checked to see that it is return-addressed to the sending host. If it is not, the message is dropped. If it is properly return-addressed, then, in effect, the smart cable seals the message in a plain brown envelope that cannot be opened by the network, addresses and return-addresses the envelope and sends it to the ARPANET for delivery. In the other direction, when the cable receives an envelope from the network, it is opened and its message is examined. If the message shows no sign of damage and it is addressed to the receiving host, the message is forwarded on to the host; otherwise it is dropped. So if the network behaves in some unpredictable way and delivers an envelope to the wrong smart cable, the smart cable detects this and refuses to deliver the message to its host.

The specification for the interface unit is relatively straightforward. It states that all messages that are sent into the network must be properly return addressed and packaged and that all messages that are sent out to the host must be properly unpackaged and addressed. The implementation of the interface, however, is rather involved because of a variety of fixed, external constraints. One of the major constraints was that the interface was required to use standard ARPANET link and transport protocols; another was the hardware that was to run the interface. The interface hardware consisted of two PDP-11 minicomputers packaged into a single box. One PDP-11 was connected to the host, and the other was connected to the network. The two PDP-11s could communicate only in an extremely restricted way, and no other communication between the host and the network was allowed.

The proved network interface also was developed as a converging sequence of prototypes. First, the formal specification and proof methods were applied at the highest levels of system design. This involved a specification and proof about the concurrent host-to-host communication across the entire set of interfaces (including the ARPANET). Then, the formal specification and proof methods were applied to obtain the distribution of the interface software onto the two PDP-11 processors of the actual hardware. At this point, a sequence of running prototypes was implemented to evaluate the performance that could be attained with this design. The resources required by the initial design were much greater than those that were available, so a new design was developed and proved, and new performance prototypes were built. When adequate performance was attained, the formal specification and proof methods were applied through all the remaining levels of the interface design and implementation. The general approach that was used on the network interface is illustrated in Good (1982*c*).

The final result was a formally specified and proved interface, implemented in Gypsy, that operated successfully across the ARPANET with a companion interface that was implemented independently, in conventional assembly code, by Bolt, Beranek and Newman, Inc. As in the flow modulator, without any modification, the proved interface worked properly in every trial run. (A small number of inadequacies in the statement of the constraints for the message formats and protocols were detected and fixed during the prototype stage.)

(*c*) *Economics*

These trial applications indicate the kinds of specifications and proofs that are within the capability of the Gypsy environment. However, if formal specifications and proof are to be used as the basis for a new approach to software engineering, there also is the matter of economics. Table 1 shows various measures of the scale of the trial applications and estimates of the amounts of resources used.

Table 1. Resources used

	flow modulator	network interface
lines of Gypsy specifications	1283	3135
lines of executable Gypsy	556	4211
words of compiled PDP-11 code	3849	42271
verification conditions	304	2600
lemmas used	44	90
automatic proofs	146	2287
interactive proofs mechanically checked	198	313
lemmas assumed without proof	4	2
work-months	13	52
DEC 2060 c.p.u.-hours	220	444
page-months of file storage	45000	84465
proved, total Gypsy lines per work-day	6.43	6.42
proved, total Gypsy lines per c.p.u.-hour	8.36	16.54
proved executable Gypsy lines per work-day	1.94	3.68
proved, executable Gypsy lines per c.p.u.-hour	2.53	9.48

The 'lines of Gypsy specifications' and 'lines of executable Gypsy' must be interpreted with caution. These count actual lines of Gypsy text (excluding comments). A line count, however, obviously depends on the style in which the Gypsy text is written, and therefore these counts are quite subjective. Also, a line count is not necessarily a good measure of complexity. In spite of these obvious weaknesses, line counts are one of the most frequently quoted measures of program size.

'Lines of Gypsy specifications' refers to those lines that are used to express formal specifications. One of the important differences between the flow modulator and the network interface was the strength of their specifications. The specifications for the flow modulator were very strong; they completely defined the two output sequences as functions of the input sequence. The specifications for the network interface, however, were much weaker; they were stated as relations rather than as functions, and there are some important aspects of the behaviour of the interface that are not covered by these relations. The difference between these two specification forms is like the difference between $y = f(x)$ and $y < x$. The first defines exactly what y must be for every x and the second states only a relatively weak relation between x and y. This is an important difference to consider in interpreting the numbers in table 1.

'Lines of executable Gypsy' refers to lines of Gypsy that actually cause run-time code to be compiled. These line counts do not, for example, include type declarations. 'Words of compiled PDP-11 code' refer to the number of (16 bit) words of PDP-11 machine code that were produced by the Gypsy compiler. In both applications, the target machine was a PDP-11/03 with no operating system other than the Gypsy run-time support package. This package is not included in the word count. The two applications were compiled with different Gypsy compilers. The flow modulator was compiled through the Gypsy-to-Bliss translator (Smith 1980). The network interface was compiled with the original Gypsy compiler (Hunter 1981).

'Verification conditions' refers to the number of verification conditions constructed by the Gypsy environment. 'Lemmas used' refers to the number of these stated in the Gypsy text. 'Automatic proofs' refers to the number of verification conditions proved fully automatically by the algebraic simplifier. 'Interactive proofs mechanically checked' refers to the number of verification conditions and lemmas that required the use of the proof checker. In both applications, a small number of lemmas were assumed without proof. The four lemmas that were not proved at the time the flow modulator was completed have since been proved. The two lemmas that were not proved for the network interface were key assumptions about the problem domain.

'Work-months' refers to the total number of (22 day) working months required to complete the application. These months include the full development of the application, from initial conception through the final testing of the proved software. This includes all iterations of all levels of specifications, prototypes and proofs. Similarly, 'c.p.u.-hours' and 'page-months' also cover the full development cycle. 'Proved, total Gypsy lines' is computed from 'lines of Gypsy specifications' plus 'lines of executable Gypsy'. This gives a measure of the total number of Gypsy lines produced per working day. 'Proved, executable Gypsy lines' considers just 'lines of executable Gypsy'.

6. Conclusion

The Gypsy verification environment is an experimental system that has been developed to explore the practicality of a new approach to software engineering that is based on rigorous, mathematical foundations. These foundations, together with the tools provided in the Gypsy environment, make it possible for a software engineer to construct formal, mathematical proofs about a software system. By appropriate use of abstraction, the formal proofs can be kept concise and intellectually manageable even though they cover large, complex systems. These proofs provide an objective, scientific basis for predicting, accurately and precisely, how a software system will behave when it runs. These proofs can be constructed at all stages of the software life cycle, from the earliest design stages through to system maintenance. Therefore, they also provide the software engineer a basis for evaluating the effects of early design decisions at the time they are made rather than having first to build a system that runs. The proofs also provide a basis for predicting the effects of maintenace modifications.

The results of the first trial applications of the Gypsy environment have been very encouraging. The flow modulator and the network interface are non-trivial software systems. They are intended to be used in actual operation, and their predictability is a genuine, major concern. Although these applications do not approach the scale and complexity of what normally are regarded as 'large' systems, they do support the claim that a formal, mathematical approach to software engineering is technically viable. The next major research goal seems to be making this approach economically viable. Although the cost of applying this new technology in the two applications was much less than what might have been expected (and one always must weigh the cost of applying this mathematical approach against the cost of an unpredictable software system), there seem to be many ways in which the amount of resources used to apply the technology can be reduced. If this can be done, this new technology can become the basis for a new practice of software engineering that can provide dramatic improvements in the predictability and quality of software systems.

On this euphoric note, it is all too easy to be lulled into a false sense of security because it is tempting to believe that a formally specified and proved program should be absolutely correct. It should always behave perfectly and never malfunction. However, there are several reasons why a program that has been proved within the Gypsy environment may not behave exactly as expected. First, the formal specifications may not describe exactly the expected behaviour of the program. Secondly, the formal specifications may not describe all of the aspects of program behaviour. Thirdly, invalid lemmas may have been assumed without proof. Finally, either the verification environment, the compiler, the Gypsy run-time support or the hardware might malfunction.

The last of these potential sources of error, in principle, can be minimized by specifying and proving the verification environment, the compiler, the run-time support and to some degree, the hardware. These would be large complex proofs that are well beyond present capabilities; but, given sufficient cost reductions, these proofs eventually may well be possible. The first three, however, are subjective and involve some element of human judgment. Therefore, these potential sources of error cannot be eliminated. These sources of error are cited not to belittle the potential of a scientific basis for software engineering but to make clear that the formal, mathematical approach offers no absolutes. As with any other science, it must be applied in the context of human judgment.

The development and initial experimental applications of Gypsy have been sponsored in part by the U.S. Department of Defense Computer Security Center (contracts MDA904-80-C-0481, MDA904-82-C-0445), by the U.S. Naval Electronic Systems Command (contract N00039-81-C-0074), by Digital Equipment Corporation, by Digicomp Research Corporation and by the National Science Foundation (grant MCS-8122039).

Appendix A. Formal proof of lemma *extend_separation*

The following is the complete transcript of the interactive proof of the lemma *extend_separation*. The input supplied by the human user is underlined.

```
Entering Prover with lemma extend_separation

   H1: separated (s, y, z)
->
   C1: separated (s @ [seq: m],
                  y @ image (m).pass,
                  z @ image (m).reject)

Prvr -> expand
        Unit name -> separated
Which ones?
   1. in H1:  separated (s, y, z)
   2. in C1:  separated (s @ [seq: m],
                         y @ image (m).pass,
                         z @ image (m).reject)

          <number-list>, ALL, NONE, PRINT, ^E: all
```

```
Prvr -> theorem
   H1: passed (s) = y
   H2: rejected (s) = z
->
   C1: y @ image (m).pass = passed (s @ [seq: m])
   C2: z @ image (m).reject = rejected (s @ [seq: m])

Prvr -> expand
       Unit name -> passed
Which ones?
   1. in H1:  passed (s)
   2. in C1:  passed (s @ [seq: m])

        <number-list>, ALL, NONE, PRINT, ^E: 2

Prvr -> expand
       Unit name -> rejected
Which ones?
   1. in H2:  rejected (s)
   2. in C2:  rejected (s @ [seq: m])

        <number-list>, ALL, NONE, PRINT, ^E: 2

Prvr -> theorem
   H1: passed (s) = y
   H2: rejected (s) = z
->
   C1: y @ image (m).pass = passed (s) @ image (m).pass
   C2: z @ image (m).reject = rejected (s) @ image (m).reject

Prvr -> qed

9.  ANDSPLIT
   11.  SIMPLIFYC
      14.  UNIFY
   12.  SIMPLIFYC
      18.  UNIFY
Theorem proved!.
```

Appendix B. Formal proof of verification condition *separator#3*

The following is the complete transcript of the interactive proof of the verification condition *separator#3*. The input supplied by the human user is underlined.

```
Entering Prover with verification condition separator#3

    H1: msg_stream (x[1..p]) @ [seq: m#1] = msg_stream (x[1..p#1])
    H2: y @ image (m#1).pass = y#1
    H3: z @ image (m#1).reject = z#1
    H4: separated (msg_stream (x[1..p]), y, z)
    H5: p le size (x)
    H6: p + 1 le p#1
    H7: p#1 le size (x)
    H8: size (x) ne p
->
    C1: separated (msg_stream (x[1..p#1]), y#1, z#1)

Prvr -> retain
        hypothesis labels, ALL, NONE -> h1 h2 h3 h4

Prvr -> theorem
    H1: msg_stream (x[1..p]) @ [seq: m#1] = msg_stream (x[1..p#1])
    H2: y @ image (m#1).pass = y#1
    H3: z @ image (m#1).reject = z#1
    H4: separated (msg_stream (x[1..p]), y, z)
->
    C1: separated (msg_stream (x[1..p#1]), y#1, z#1)

Prvr -> eqsub
         Hypothesis label -> h1
  msg_stream (x[1..p#1]) := msg_stream (x[1..p]) @ [seq: m#1]

Prvr -> theorem
    H1: y @ image (m#1).pass = y#1
    H2: z @ image (m#1).reject = z#1
    H3: separated (msg_stream (x[1..p]), y, z)
->
    C1: separated (msg_stream (x[1..p]) @ [seq: m#1], y#1, z#1)

Prvr -> eqsub
         Hypothesis label -> h1
  y#1 := y @ image (m#1).pass

Prvr -> theorem
    H1: z @ image (m#1).reject = z#1
    H2: separated (msg_stream (x[1..p]), y, z)
->
    C1: separated (msg_stream (x[1..p]) @ [seq: m#1],
                   y @ image (m#1).pass, z#1)
```

```
Prvr -> eqsub
       Hypothesis label -> h1
  z#1 := z @ image (m#1).reject

Prvr -> theorem
   H1: separated (msg_stream (x[1..p]), y, z)
->
   C1: separated (msg_stream (x[1..p]) @ [seq: m#1],
                  y @ image (m#1).pass,
                  z @ image (m#1).reject)

Prvr -> use
      Unit name -> extend separation

Prvr -> theorem
   H1:    separated (s$#2, y$#2, z$#2)
      -> separated (s$#2 @ [seq: m$#2],
                    y$#2 @ image (m$#2).pass,
                    z$#2 @ image (m$#2).reject)
   H2: separated (msg_stream (x[1..p]), y, z)
->
   C1: separated (msg_stream (x[1..p]) @ [seq: m#1],
                  y @ image (m#1).pass,
                  z @ image (m#1).reject)

Prvr -> proceed

11. BACKCHAIN
   12. UNIFY
      13. ANDSPLIT
   13. UNIFY
Theorem proved!.
```

References

Akers, R. L. 1983 A Gypsy-to-Ada program compiler. Master's thesis, University of Texas at Austin. Also *Tech. Rep.* no. 39, Institute for Computing Science, The University of Texas at Austin.

Bledsoe, W. W. & Bruell, P. 1974 A man–machine theorem-proving system. In *Advance Papers of Third International Joint Conference on Artificial Intelligence* (ed. W. W. Bledsoe), **5–1** (Spring), pp. 51–72.

Dijkstra, E. W. 1968 A constructive approach to the problem of program correctness. *BIT* **8**, 174–186.

Dijkstra, E. W. 1976 *A discipline of programming*. Englewood Cliffs, N.J.: Prentice-Hall.

Floyd, R. W. 1967 Assigning meanings to programs. In *Proceedings of a Symposium in Applied Mathematics* (ed. J. T. Schwartz), vol. 19, pp. 19–32. Providence, Rhode Island: American Mathematical Society.

Good, D. I. 1970 Toward a man–machine system for proving program correctness. Ph.D. thesis, University of Wisconsin.

Good, D. I., Cohen, R. M., Hoch, C. G., Hunter, L. W. & Hare, D. F. 1978 Report on the language Gypsy, Version 2.0. *Tech. Rep.* ICSCA-CMP-10, Certifiable Minicomputer, Project, ICSCA, The University of Texas at Austin.

Good, D. I. 1982*a* Reusable problem domain theories. In *Formal Specification – Proceedings of the Joint IBM/University of Newcastle-upon-Tyne Seminar* (ed. M. J. Elphick), pp. 92–115. Also *Tech. Rep.* no. 31, Institute for Computing Science, The University of Texas at Austin.

Good, D. I., Siebert, Ann E. & Smith, L. M. 1982*b* Message Flow Modulator – Final Report. *Tech. Rep.* no. 34, Institute for Computing Science, The University of Texas at Austin.

Good, D. I. 1982*c* The proof of a distributed system in Gypsy. In *Formal Specification – Proceedings of the Joint IBM/University of Newcastle-upon-Tyne Seminar* (ed. M. J. Elphick), pp. 443–489. Also *Tech. Rep.* no. 30, Institute for Computing Science, The University of Texas at Austin.
Gries, D. 1981 *The science of computer programming.* New York: Springer-Verlag.
Hoare, C. A. R. 1969 An axiomatic basis for computer programming. *Commun. Ass. comput. Mach.* **12–10**, 576–580.
Hoare, C. A. R. 1982 Programming is an engineering profession. *Tech. Rep.* no. PRG-27, Programming Research Group, Oxford University Computing Laboratory.
Hunter, L. W. 1981 *The first generation Gypsy compiler. Tech. Rep.* no. 23, Institute for Computing Science, The University of Texas at Austin.
Jensen, K. & Wirth, N. 1974 *Pascal user manual and report.* New York: Springer-Verlag.
Jones, C. B. 1980 *Software development: a rigorous approach.* Englewood Cliffs, N.J.: Prentice-Hall.
King, J. C. 1969 A program verifier. Ph.D. thesis. Carnegie–Mellon University.
McHugh, J. 1983 Toward the generation of efficient code from verified programs. Ph.D. thesis, University of Texas at Austin.
Moriconi, M. S. 1977 A system for incrementally designing and verifying programs. Also Ph.D. thesis, *Tech. Rep.* ICSCA-CMP-9. The University of Texas at Austin.
Naur, P. 1966 Proof of algorithms by general snapshots. *BIT* **6**, 310–316.
Neumann, P. G. 1983*a* Letters from the Editor. *Software engineering Notes* **8** (3), 2–6.
Neumann, P. G. 1983*b* Letters from the Editor. *Software engineering Notes* **8** (5), 1–9.
Smith, L. M. 1980 Compiling from the Gypsy verification environment. Master's thesis, The University of Texas at Austin. Also *Tech. Rep.* no. 20. Institute for Computing Science, The University of Texas at Austin.
Stallman, R. M. 1980 *EMACS Manual for Twenex Users*, M.I.T. Artificial Intelligence Laboratory.

Discussion

B. A. Wichmann (*National Physical Laboratory, Teddington, Middlesex, U.K.*). Could Dr Good comment upon the dependence of his work on the correctness of the compilers and hardware?

D. I. Good. Certainly, the claim that a proved program actually will run correctly is based on the assumption that it is compiled correctly and that the hardware runs correctly and on a number of other things. These are discussed briefly in the conclusion of the paper. This question, however, also raises two other important issues.

The first is program 'correctness'. This term is widely used, but I believe it is highly ill-chosen because it conveys a misleading connotation of absolute perfection. For example, when someone says they have proved that a program is 'totally correct', who would believe that it would ever do anything but always run absolutely perfectly? Yet, it is quite possible for such a program to malfunction. This is because when a program is proved, it is proved against a particular specification. The proof provides assurance that the program will run according to its specification; but, the proved program very well might do other things that are not covered by the specification, and it might do them wrong! Whenever someone claims to have proved a program, the first question should be 'what did you prove?'

The second question should be 'what did you assume?'. Every proof, whether it is about a program or anything else, is based upon certain assumptions. These may be very simple, or they may be arbitrarily complex. All that is produced in any proof is a chain of deductive steps that imply that a conclusion follows from a set of assumptions. If the assumptions are not true, then the conclusion need not be either. Thus, in the end, all that *any* proof does is to make explicit the assumptions upon which the conclusion is based. A proof provides us confidence in its conclusion to the extent that the conclusion is deduced from believable assumptions. For software systems, the simple accomplishment of identifying a precise set of assumptions that imply that a software system runs according to a particular specification is a dramatic improvement over conventional methods. There always remains, however, the question of the validity of the assumptions. For a proof to provide confidence that a system runs according to specification, its assumptions must be simple, concise, and believable.

The use of machines to assist in rigorous proof

By R. Milner

Computer Science Department, University of Edinburgh, James Clerk Maxwell Building, The King's Buildings, Mayfield Road, Edinburgh EH9 3JZ, U.K.

A methodology for computer assisted proof is presented with an example. A central ingredient in the method is the presentation of tactics (or strategies) in an algorithmic metalanguage. Further, the same language is also used to express combinators, by which simple elementary tactics – which often correspond to the inference rules of the logic employed – are combined into more complex tactics, which may even be strategies complete for a class of problems. However, the emphasis is not upon completeness but upon providing a metalogical framework within which a user may express his insight into proof methods and may delegate routine (but error-prone) work to the computer. This method of tactic composition is presented at the start of the paper in the form of an elementary theory of goal-seeking. A second ingredient of the methodology is the stratification of machine-assisted proof by an ancestry graph of applied theories, and the example illustrates this stratification. In the final section, some recent developments and applications of the method are cited.

1. A theory of goal-seeking

The search for a proof of a conjecture expressed as a formula in some formal language is strikingly similar to many goal-seeking activities. These activitives are as widely different as seeking to win at chess and seeking to meet a friend before noon on Saturday. But the similarity can be articulated in terms of a little theory of goal-seeking; a theory that has nothing to do with finding the best strategy, or with minimizing the prospect of failure (important though these things are), but which tries to make precise how concepts like goal, strategy, achievement, failure, etc. relate logically to each other. Before applying this theory to the business of machine-assisted proof, we shall exhibit some of its generality by means of an every-day example.

We may discern two prime entity classes in any sphere of goal-seeking activity: the goals and the events. A *goal* may sometimes be thought of as a description that may be satisfied by one or more (or no) occurrences, and an *event* is simply a particular occurrence. For example:

a goal, G_1: A and B to meet before noon on Saturday;
an event, E_1: A meets B under the clock at Waterloo Station at 11h53 on Saturday.

It is clear that event E_1 satisfies the description that has been designated as goal G_1, i.e. it achieves goal G_1. In general, whatever the sphere of activity, we must postulate or define a relation of *achievement* between events and goals:

$$\text{achieves} \subseteq \text{event} \times \text{goal}$$

(where we use the nouns event, goal in the singular as type symbols, standing for the classes of all possible events and all possible goals).

Now, in planning how to achieve G_1, we might justifiably replace it by two rather more specific subgoals:

G_{11}: A to arrive under the clock at Waterloo Station before noon on Saturday;
G_{12}: B to arrive under the clock at Waterloo Station before noon on Saturday.

In fact we can isolate the method by which G_{11} and G_{12} are gained from G_1, and call it a *tactic*. In this case we might call it the clock-at-Waterloo-Station tactic, and it could be applied to many different goals (differing from G_1 in time, date and persons, for example) to yield in each case a different pair of subgoals. In general then, we may express tactics as partial functions from goals to lists of goals:

$$\text{tactic} = \text{goal} \rightharpoonup \text{goal list}$$

and we say that a tactic *fails* upon, or is inapplicable to, a goal outside its domain. In our example, the clock-at-Waterloo-Station tactic would fail on the goal 'A must never meet B again', but may not fail on 'Ronald Reagan to meet Napoleon Bonaparte before noon on Saturday' (though some later tactic, applied to a refined subgoal, will fail in the attempt to get a dead man to move).

It is important to note that a tactic may be invalid. In our example, a variant of the chosen tactic would be invalid which, when applied to G_1, yielded variants of G_{11} and G_{12} in which 'noon' was replaced by '13h00'. We now make precise the property of *validity* of tactics; to do so we need a new entity class. For each sphere of activity, we postulate a collection of *procedures*; each procedure represents how, given a list of events, some new event may be realized; that is:

$$\text{procedure} \subseteq \text{event list} \rightharpoonup \text{event}$$

(procedures are partial functions; they too may fail). Now we can see the clock-at-Waterloo-Station tactic is justified just because we are assuming the existence of a waiting procedure,

W: A and B each waits until he sees the other.

For W, when applied to the following pair of events that achieve G_{11} and G_{12} respectively,

E_{11}: A arrives under the clock at Waterloo Station at 11h47 on Saturday;
E_{12}: B arrives under the clock at Waterloo Station at 11h53 on Saturday;

will yield an event that achieves G_1, namely the event E_1 given above.

In fact, we can see that the procedure W is stronger still; it has the property that it will, from *any* pair of events that achieve G_{11} and G_{12} (differing perhaps in time from E_{11}, E_{12}), produce an event that achieves G_1. This is what truly justifies the clock-at-Waterloo-Station tactic when applied to G_1.

But we can conceive a tactic whose application to one goal G_1 may be justifiable, but whose application to another goal G'_1 (even though it succeeds in producing some subgoals, G'_{11} and G'_{12} say) is unjustifiable because there is no justifying procedure that, given achievements (achieving events) of G'_{11} and G'_{12}, will always produce an achievement of G'_1. Such dishonest tactics – ones that promise more than can be performed – are to be avoided; an honest tactic will be called *valid*, and to define validity we first wish to refine the notion of tactic.

A sensible tactic, when it resolves a goal G into subgoals, should make explicit a procedure (which may depend upon G) that it claims will always lead from achievements of the respective subgoals to an achievement of G. We therefore redefine

$$\text{tactic} = \text{goal} \rightharpoonup \text{goal list} \times \text{procedure}$$

and now we may define a tactic to be valid just when its claim, in the present sense, is always justified.

Definition. A tactic T is *valid* if, whenever

$$T(G) = [G_1; \ldots; G_n],P$$

is defined for a goal G, and whenever events $[E_1; \ldots; E_n]$ respectively achieve the goals $[G_1; \ldots; G_n]$, then the event $P[E_1; \ldots; E_n]$ in turn achieves G.

Now it is essential for the achievement of distant or difficult goals that simple tactics be composed into more complex ones, which are objects of the same type but may be called *strategies*. Even in our example, if A starts from Andover and B from Birmingham then the complete strategy will involve many component tactics. (The procedures that validate these will be, for example, 'B walks from the Underground station to the clock at Waterloo'.) We shall illustrate below, in the context of machine-assisted proof, how tactics can be composed in distinct ways, each represented by a certain combinator; we call such combinators *tacticals*, and we say that a tactical is valid just when it preserves validity of tactics. Of course, where possible only valid tacticals should be used.

Let us suppose that a strategy S for our toy problem has been composed in this way from valid tactics, and is therefore itself valid. In the best case, we have

$$S(G_0) = [\ ],P_0,$$

which is to say that no subgoals remain to be achieved (we used [ ] to mean the empty list). P_0 is then a plan for achieving G_0, and need only be executed, i.e. it is applied to the empty list of events, giving the event

$$P_0[\ ],$$

which will achieve G_0. In the toy problem, this execution consists of real travel (and other action) by A and B; in the context of machine-assisted proof, it consists of the performance of a formal proof. Here, it is a matter of taste whether the human prover wishes to see this performance done by the machine, in all its frequently repulsive detail, or wishes only to see the highlights, or is merely content to let the machine announce the result (a theorem!). We indicate in the sequel that the last alternative is often appropriate, since the human user has often exercised (or gained) his insight into the problem in the process of composing his strategy. During this composition he may well have interacted with the machine, in applying partial strategies and then deciding whether or not he can make progress from the subgoals generated at each stage.

2. The use of a computer to make proofs

The formal logic of LCF (Gordon *et al.* 1979) is a blend of the predicate calculus (with equality) and the lambda calculus. It was based upon Dana Scott's theory of domains of continuous functions, and is particularly suited to the formulation and proof of properties of algorithms and algorithmic languages. We need not be more precise here about its formulae, since we are mainly concerned with aspects of proof methodology that apply to arbitrary logics. For the present it is enough to state that its sentences are sequents (Γ,F), where F is a formula and Γ a finite set (or list) of formulae, and its theorems (proved sequents) are written $\Gamma \vdash F$.

Within the goal-seeking jargon of the previous section we have the following interpretations

(1) A *goal* is a sequent (Γ,F). (Prove F from assumptions Γ.)

(2) An *event* is a theorem $\Delta \vdash G$.

(3) An event $\Delta \vdash G$ *achieves* a goal (Γ,F) if for some subset Γ' of Γ the sequents (Δ,G) and (Γ',F) are identical, up to renaming of bound variables.

(4) A *procedure* is therefore a partial function that takes a list of theorems and yields a theorem. The primitive (given) procedures are just the inference rules of the logic; further, derived procedures (derived inference rules, or proof procedures) are derivable naturally by composition, controlled algorithmically.

To manipulate these entities, and others relating to them, an algorithmic metalanguage called ML is used. It is a general purpose functional programming language, whose power of handling higher-order functions is particularly important; this is because tactics (as explained earlier) yield proof procedures, which are functions, as results, and even more so because tacticals are functions over tactics.

Basically, the elementary tactics are just 'inverses' of the given inference rules. The rule of universal generalization provides a good example. The rule

$$\text{GEN} \quad \frac{\Gamma \vdash F}{\Delta \vdash \forall x\,.\,F} \quad (\text{x not free in } \Gamma)$$

is provided in ML by the function GEN, such that

$$\text{GEN ``x''}: (\Gamma \vdash F) \mapsto (\Gamma \vdash \forall x\,.\,F).$$

Note that GEN takes an extra parameter, which is a variable of the object language. Object language constructions are quoted within the metalanguage, and we shall here use lower case letters for object language variables, and upper case for metavariables over object language constructs. The use of antiquotation $\uparrow$ allows metavariables to occur within quotation, so that if X = "x" and F = "x = y", then we may write "$\forall\uparrow$X.$\uparrow$F" in the metalanguage to mean "$\forall$x.x = y". Now the tactic GENTAC, which inverts GEN, must take any goal (Γ,"$\forall\uparrow$X.$\uparrow$F") and return the subgoal (Γ,F), together with the procedure GEN X, which justifies the application of the tactic. In fact more care is needed, since the rule GEN fails when X is free in Γ; the following declaration of the tactic takes care of this, and is almost exactly as written in ML:

```
val GENTAC (Γ,"∀↑X.↑F") =
  let val X′ = variant X Γ      {X′ is a variable not free in Γ}
      val F′ = subst [X′,X]F    {replace X by X′ in F}
  in [(Γ,F′)], GEN X′     {subgoal list and justification)
  end
```

(the exact ML definition takes care to require the input formula to be of the form "$\forall$x. ..." and to fail appropriately otherwise).

At a slightly higher level, we already need tacticals to build simple composite tactics that a mathematician would apply without thinking. A good example is a tactic that repeatedly strips off leading universal quantifiers, and 'assumes' the antecedent of any implication in the goal formula, so that a goal like

$$(\Gamma, \text{“}\forall x . \uparrow F_1 \supset \forall y . \forall z . \uparrow F_2 \supset \uparrow F_3\text{”})$$

is transformed (assuming that x, y and z only occur bound) to the goal

$$(\Gamma \cup \{F_1, F_2\}, F_3).$$

If, besides GENTAC, we have a primitive tactic DISCHTAC, which assumes a single antecedent if there is one (i.e. it inverts the rule of assumption-discharge), then with two tacticals, ORELSE and REPEAT, our composite tactic is just

REPEAT (GENTAC ORELSE DISCHTAC).

The tactic T_1 ORELSE T_2, when applied to G, acts like $T_1(G)$ unless this fails, in which case it acts like $T_2(G)$; the tactic REPEAT T, when applied to G, applies T to G, then to all the subgoals of T(G) and so on, until failure occurs or no subgoals remain. These tacticals have one line definitions in ML, and are easily seen to preserve validity.

At a higher level still, we may express full automatic proof methods as tactics. One such method is the resolution method due to Robinson. This is a complete proof method, at least for the pure first-order predicate calculus, but in the context of interactive proof it is wise to apply it in a controlled manner, just at those points in a strategy at which progress may be expected by routine logical methods such as instantiation of assumptions, modus ponens and the like. We shall not describe the tactic in detail, but we shall call it RESTAC when we later employ it in an example.

At a similar level is a simplification tactic, called SIMPTAC, based upon a collection of equational theorems of form

$$\Gamma \vdash t_1 = t_2,$$

where t_1 and t_2 are terms, possibly containing variables that may be instantiated to match t_1 to some subterm of a goal, which may then be simplified by substituting the corresponding instance of t_2.

All of these tactics, together with others based upon appropriate forms of induction and case analysis, are indubitably part of the standard repertoire of a mathematician. But towards the end of our list (certainly with simplification, induction and case analysis) we begin to meet tactics that take a different specialized form in each problem domain. To take an introverted example, proofs *about* a formal language typically employ a case analysis upon the leading connective of a formula, and the number and nature of the cases is clearly domain-dependent. Again, in some problem domains it is almost routine to use a combination of induction and case analysis, while in others (consider elementary topology) induction is of no use; a relevant induction rule may even not exist.

These observations suggest that in any realistic work with the machine as a proof assistant we expect to be working in a particular problem domain, or *theory* as we shall call it, and that when we specify the theory that concerns us the machine makes available to us all the data types, non-logical constants and axioms of that theory, together with theorems that have already been proved in that theory; it should also allow us access to those tactics that we have previously defined either of general use or pertaining to the theory in question. Futhermore, almost every interesting applied theory is founded upon more primitive theories (called its ancestor theories), and while working in any theory we expect to have access to all material pertaining to its ancestors.

An important function of the proof assistant is therefore to keep our tower of theories properly organized, allowing us both to introduce new theories – by specifying their parents and their own new types, constants and axioms – and to work in any existing theory (not only those at the top of the tower) by proving new theorems in them.

In this work, *polymorphic* theories play a vital role. An example of such a theory is a theory of trees whose nodes are labelled by objects of arbitrary type, where theorems (which are also polymorphic) are proved without any assumption of the nature, i.e. the type, of the node-labelling objects. Such theorems may be instantiated (by an inference rule called *type instantiation*) later, during work on a daughter theory that involves trees with node labels of some particular type; for example, this type may be *integer* in a theory of tree-sorting.

In the next section we illustrate several of these points by giving an outline of an approach to a particular problem. Before we do so, we have to admit that the preceding exposition has oversimplified one detail of our methodology (this was deliberate, since the methodology is not clearly the best, and others are possible). In place of sequents (Γ,F) as goals, we adopt the slightly more complex form (Γ,F,S) for goals; here, S is a set of assumptions that are equational, and suitable for use as simplification rules by the tactic SIMPTAC. Other tactics are embellished by letting them add suitable equations to S; for example, the tactic DISCHTAC, which assumes an antecedent, is understood to add this antecedent to S as well as to Γ, in cases where it is equational (and satisfies other criteria).

Finally, we draw attention to a point of great pragmatic significance. Our metalanguage allows a user to write tactics – even invalid ones – with great freedom. But with this freedom he can by no means generate an event that which is not a theorem. This follows from the fact that events are objects of type *theorem*, and that the only operations for generating them are the basic inference rules (like GEN) and rules derived from them. This is a fine illustration of the security provided by a type discipline; indeed, without it we could not claim to present a viable methodology.

3. An example: a theorem about parsing

We suppose that we wish to investigate the performance of a particular parsing algorithm, which operates upon a list of symbols and produces a particular kind of tree known as a parse tree.

Since there are two polymorphic theories – the theory of lists and the theory of trees – relevant to our problem, we first discuss the creation of these theories, each as a daughter theory of the NULL or *pure* theory, which contains no non-logical types, constants or axioms. We suppose that the theory NULL possesses a type ONE, whose only proper member object is denoted by the constant symbol ( ) (which may be pronounced 'nothing').

To construct the theory called LIST, we first create a unary *type constructor*, also called LIST. This will allow us to discuss objects of type α LIST; greek letters are used for type variables, and type constructors are postfixed to their argument(s). We then introduce two *constants*, with their polymorphic types:

$$\begin{aligned}&\text{NIL} && :\alpha\ \text{LIST}\\ &\text{CONS} && :\alpha\to\alpha\ \text{LIST}\to\alpha\ \text{LIST}\\ &\text{APPEND} && :\alpha\ \text{LIST}\to\alpha\ \text{LIST}\to\alpha\ \text{LIST}\end{aligned}$$

(more constants may be useful, but we only need these for now). Finally, to establish the basis of the theory, we introduce axioms that characterize the LIST constructor by establishing the isomorphism

$$\alpha\ \text{LIST} \simeq \text{ONE}+\alpha\times\alpha\ \text{LIST}$$

and which characterize the constants, by stating (or entailing as simple corollaries) such equations as

$$\text{APPEND (CONS a x) y} = \text{CONS a (APPEND x y)}.$$

From this slender basis, many polymorphic theorems will follow while working in the theory LIST; other list-processing functions may be introduced as constants to enrich the theory.

Entirely analogously, the theory TREE can be created. We first introduce a binary type constructor TREE, characterized by the isomorphism

$$(\alpha,\beta)\text{TREE} \simeq \alpha+\beta\times(\alpha,\beta)\text{TREE}+\beta\times(\alpha,\beta)\text{TREE}\times(\alpha,\beta)\text{TREE},$$

which states, in effect, that a tree is either an α object (a TIP labelled with an object of type α) or a node labelled with an object of type β and possessing either one or two son-trees. Then we naturally introduce as constants the three tree constructors

$$\begin{aligned}&\text{TIP} && :\alpha\to(\alpha,\beta)\text{TREE}\\ &\text{NODE1} && :\beta\to(\alpha,\beta)\text{TREE}\to(\alpha,\beta)\text{TREE}\\ &\text{NODE2} && :\beta\to(\alpha,\beta)\text{TREE}\to(\alpha,\beta)\text{TREE}\to(\alpha,\beta)\ \text{TREE},\end{aligned}$$

which construct, from appropriate arguments, trees of the three respective kinds (just as NIL and CONS are the list constructors).

It is a particular strength of the underlying logic of LCF, which is due to pioneering work by Dana Scott, that from its induction rule (called computation induction) can be derived the rules of structural induction for both lists and trees. Each of these may then be inverted in the standard manner, described in the previous section, to form (for trees) the induction tactic TREEINDUCTAC, which we shall have occasion to use in our example.

With the theories LIST and TREE as parents, we are now ready to introduce the lexical theory, which we shall call LEX, in which we can state and prove our theorem about parsing. The ancestry graph of theories is shown here.

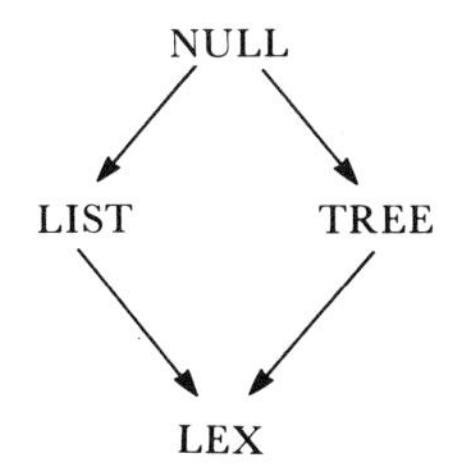

For LEX, we first postulate two arbitrary types ID and OP, for the variables and operators that occur in the symbol strings to be parsed. Since brackets '('and ')' also occur as symbols, we then define the type isomorphism

$$\text{SYMB} \simeq \text{ONE}+\text{ONE}+\text{ID}+\text{OP}+\text{OP}.$$

The first two summands represent the left and right brackets, respectively, and the last two represent the distinguished occurrences of an operator as a unary and a binary function symbol respectively. We therefore introduce and axiomatize the five constructors

```
LB     :SYMB
RB     :SYMB
VAR    :ID→SYMB
UNARY  :OP→SYMB
BINARY :OP→SYMB.
```

We are now ready to give the parsing algorithm, expressed as a set of axioms about a function PARSE, whose type is

$$\text{PARSE:SYMB LIST} \rightarrow \text{(ID,OP)TREE} \times \text{SYMB LIST}.$$

Thus, PARSE takes an arbitrary symbol list, which begins with a well formed formula, and produces from it a parse tree, representing the shortest initial segment of the argument that is parsable, together with the remainder of the argument string. Notice that our theory will instantiate polymorphic theorems about lists and trees, since, for example, a parse tree is a tree whose tips are labelled with identifiers in ID, and whose nodes are labelled with operators in OP.

Now the axioms for PARSE can be written (with a little syntactic sugar) as follows, where we use logical variables $x \in$ ID, $f \in$ OP, $s \in$ SYMB LIST and $t \in$ (ID,OP)TREE:

```
PARSE (CONS(VAR x)s) = (TIP x,s)
PARSE (CONS(UNARY f)s) = (NODE1 f t', s')
                         where (t',s') = PARSE s
PARSE (CONS LB s) = PARSETWO t' s'
                         where (t',s') = PARSE s
PARSETWO t (CONS(BINARY f)s) = (NODE2 f t t',CHECKRB s')
                         where (t',s') = PARSE s
CHECKRB (CONS RB s) = s.
```

The sugaring here is the use of **where**, which is expressible by a simple logical combinator. Note that the action of PARSE depends upon the nature of the leading symbol of its argument. The detailed working of the parser need only concern the most assiduous reader; we intend mainly to illustrate the style in which an algorithm may be presented as a set of equational axioms.

To express the property that we wish to prove, we also need a simpler function

$$\text{UNPARSE:(ID,OP)TREE} \rightarrow \text{SYMB LIST},$$

which linearizes any parse tree into the symbol string that it represents. UNPARSE is axiomatized thus:

UNPARSE(TIP x) = CONS(VAR x)NIL
UNPARSE(NODE1 f t) = CONS(UNARY f) (UNPARSE t)
UNPARSE(NODE2 f t t′) =
  APPEND(CONS LB(UNPARSE t))
    (APPEND(CONS(BINARY f) (UNPARSE t′))
      (CONS RB NIL))).

The correspondence that we intend, between strings and parse trees, can be illustrated by a little example, in which $+, \times$ appear as binary operators and $\surd$ as a unary operator:

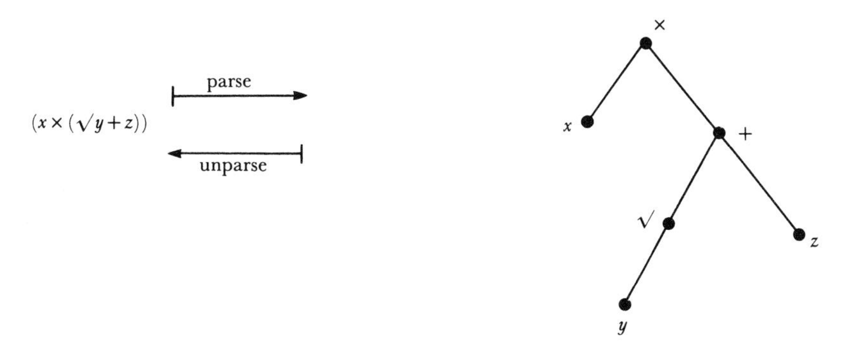

where we have ignored the 'tail' string also produced by PARSE.

Indeed, this correspondence is precisely the goal that we wish to prove; it may be expressed more exactly, and in general, as

$$\forall t.\forall s.\ \mathrm{WD}[t] \supset \mathrm{PARSE}(\mathrm{APPEND}(\mathrm{UNPARSE}\ t)s) = (t,s).$$

Here, the antecedent WD[t] is a formula (which we do not detail) with a free variable t, and expresses that the tree t is appropriately well defined. Let us call this formula F. Then the first step of tactical proof is to set up a goal

$$G = (\Gamma, F, S),$$

where Γ is empty and S is a set of simplification rules that includes simple properties of the basic functions over lists and trees, and all the axioms of PARSE and UNPARSE.

The intuition that the user must provide, for this problem, is that it is natural to attack it by structural induction upon trees, and that thereafter it should yield to a mixture of simplification (SIMPTAC) and routine logical manipulation (RESTAC). But other ingredients are needed in the complete strategy. First, because quantification and implication both occur in the goal formula, it is reasonable to expect some use of GENTAC and DISCHTAC. Second, the formula WD[t] (which we did not detail) is the subject of some simple lemmas, which would be applicable in many problems about trees and may reasonably be expected to have been proved in advance. It is worth noting that these lemmas, and many of the simplification rules in S, are theorems not of the theory LEX but of its parent theories LIST and TREE. This illustrates how a proof in an interesting applied theory will often be stratified; it will rarely be conducted entirely within the theory in which it is stated.

In view of the above remarks, a reasonable interactive approach to the goal G would be to attack it with TREEINDUCTAC, followed perhaps by SIMPTAC, and then to inspect the resulting goals to see what further tactics are appropriate. This was the approach adopted when we first tackled the problem with LCF. When the theorem was successfully achieved by such means, it was observed that the combination of tactics used was remarkably similar to that which succeeded on other problems, in totally different problem domains. The difference was mainly in the particular induction rule used, in the particular auxiliary lemmas employed, and in the particular simplification rules embodied in the main goal G. This suggested that a widely applicable strategy could be expressed parametrically (the above particulars being supplied as parameters in each different problem). While we have not yet fully separated the general from the parametric ingredients in this strategy, it is informative to present the instance of it that works with no interaction whatever for our present problem, and exactly as it is written in ML. In doing so, we employ one further tactical THEN, which is of general use; the tactic T1 THEN T2 first applies T1 to a goal, then T2 to all subgoals produced. Note that THEN is clearly associative.

If we represent by L the set of auxiliary lemmas (pertaining to our antecedent formula WD[t]), then the complete strategy is expressed in ML as

```
USELEMMASTAC (L) THEN
TREEINDUCTAC THEN SIMPTAC THEN
REPEAT (GENTAC ORELSE DISCHTAC) THEN
RESTAC THEN SIMPTAC.
```

All ingredients of this strategy have been discussed previously, except the first line, which merely has the effect of introducing the lemmas, so that when (eventually) RESTAC is applied to descendent goals it may employ these lemmas.

This discussion cannot, for lack of space, explore many finer points of strategy construction (for example, why has SIMPTAC been used here in exactly two places?), but it has illustrated that powerful strategies can find a pleasantly simple and legible form of expression. For a more detailed exposition of the parsing problem, see Cohn & Milner (1982). A point that deserves the strongest emphasis is that this proof methodology does not pursue the 'will-o-the-wisp' of magically all-powerful strategies; it merely represents a step towards the ability to capture whatever expertise we develop in particular problem domains, by providing a suitably expressive metalogical framework.

4. Some recent developments

The nature of the metalanguage ML is independent of the logic that is to be used. The richness of (meta)types in ML is such that any logic can be presented within it. Since it is proposed to use ML with a variety of logics, and since the language has evolved somewhat since its inception, it has become important to establish a standard design for it. A step towards this standard is presented in Milner 1983; though written by the present author, it represents the work of many interested researchers.

Concerning application, several studies have been made. We cite two recent examples of proofs made in LCF with its original logic, which was also used for the example in the present paper. Michael Gordon has shown how to validate computer hardware design; he verifies that a simple but non-trivial complete computer meets its behavioural specification (Gordon 1983*a*, *b*). Stefan Sokolowski has formally demonstrated the soundness of a Hoare logic for reasoning about imperative programs (Sokolowski 1983). These two very different applications show that the original logic is quite appropriate for problems in computer science itself. Larry Paulson has enriched the logic in his work with Gordon at Cambridge; in particular, he has shown how the simplification mechanism can be rendered much more flexible and powerful by the use of tactical methods to compose simplification primitives in a variety of ways (Paulson 1983).

The ML framework, with its method of tactical engineering, has also been applied to other logics. At Göteborg, Sweden, a group have adapted LCF to implement the logic of intuitionistic type theory (Peterssen 1983). At Cornell University, Robert Constable and his colleagues are building PRL, an environment for computer assisted proof particularly in constructive mathematics; they employ tactics and tactic combination in an adventurous way, in particular to combine large tactics – such as a partial decision procedure for arithmetic – into still larger ones (Constable & Bates 1983).

Recently David Schmidt, at Edinburgh, has been studying the fundamental relation between inference rules and tactics (Schmidt 1984). Specifically, he addresses the question whether an inference rule may be represented directly by a tactic, rather than, as here, by a function (from theorems to theorems) from which in turn a tactic is derived.

It emerges from these various studies that the method of composing proof tactics, which is illustrated in this paper on a rather simple example, not only provides a means of communicating proof methods to a machine, and of tuning them to particular needs, but also presents to mathematicians and engineers a lucid way of communicating such methods among themselves.

References

Cohn, A. & Milner, R. 1982 On using Edinburgh LCF to prove the correctness of a parsing algorithm. *Internal rep.* no. CSR-113-82, Computer Science Dept, Edinburgh University.

Constable, R. L. & Bates, J. L. 1983 The nearly ultimate pearl. *Tech. rep.* no. TR 83–551, Computer Science Dept, Cornell University.

Gordon, M. 1983*a* LCF–LSM: a system for specifying and verifying hardward. *Tech. rep.* no. 41, The Computer Laboratory, Cambridge University.

Gordon, M. 1983*b* Proving a computer correct with the LCF–LSM hardware verification system. *Tech. rep.* no. 42, The Computer Laboratory, Cambridge University.

Gordon, M., Milner, R. & Wadsworth, C. 1979 Edinburgh LCF. *Lecture Notes in Computer Science*, vol. 78. Berlin: Springer-Verlag.

Milner, R. 1983 A proposal for standard ML. *Internal Rep.* no. CSR-157-83, Computer Science Dept, Edinburgh University.

Paulson, L. 1983 Higher order implementation of rewriting. *Sci. computer Programming* **3**, 119–149.

Peterssen, K. 1983 A programming system for type theory. *LPM Memo.* no. 21, Dept of Computer Science, Chalmers University of Technology, Göteborg, Sweden.

Schmidt, D. 1984 A programming notation for tactical reasoning. In *Proceedings of Seventh International Conference on Automated Deduction, Lecture Notes in Computer Science*, vol. 170, pp. 445–459.

Sokolowski, S. 1983 An LCF proof of soundness of Hoare's logic. *Internal rep.* no. CSR-146-83, Computer Science Dept, Edinburgh University.

Discussion

R. S. BIRD (*Programming Research Group, Oxford University, U.K.*). I have a question about induction. The major problem about inductive proofs is surely that of finding the right generalization of the induction hypothesis to enable the proof to go through. I have a suspicion that the parse–unparse problem Dr Milner presented was formulated in such a way as to incorporate the necessary generalization from the start. Is this suspicion correct and, if so, what can be done to systematize the search for generalizations of hypotheses?

R. MILNER. I agree that a major problem in inductive proof is to find a sufficiently general induction hypothesis, and confirm that the induction formula for the parse–unparse formula was found by us and not by the machine.

LCF was not designed to incorporate the kind of intelligence needed to find such induction formulae, which is an arbitrarily hard task. But it *was* designed to allow a user to communicate strategies for such tasks to the machine. Indeed, the pioneering work by Boyer and Moore, on finding induction formulae, consists of a composite strategy that can be written in ML quite conveniently.

The characterization problem for Hoare logics

By E. M. Clarke, Jr

Department of Computer Science, Carnegie – Mellon University, Schenley Park, Pittsburgh, Pennsylvania 15213, *U.S.A.*

Research by myself and by others has shown that there are natural programming language control structures that are impossible to describe adequately by means of Hoare axioms. Specifically, we have shown that there are control structures for which it is impossible to obtain axiom systems that are sound and relatively complete in the sense of Cook. These constructs include procedures with procedure parameters under standard ALGOL 60 scope rules and coroutines in a language with parameterless recursive procedures.

A natural question to ask is whether it is possible to characterize those programming languages for which sound and complete proof systems can be obtained. For a wide class of programming languages and interpretations, it can be shown that P has a sound and relatively complete proof system for every expressive interpretation iff the halting problem for language P is decidable for all finite interpretations.

Nevertheless, we are still far from a completely satisfactory characterization of the programming languages that can be axiomatized in this manner. The proof system that is generated in proving the above result does not have the property of being 'syntax-directed', which is distinctive of the Hoare axioms. Moreoever, theoretical considerations suggest that good axioms for total correctness may exist for a wider spectrum of languages than for partial correctness. In this paper we discuss these questions and others that still need to be addressed before the characterization problem can be considered solved.

1. Introduction

A key trend in program verification has been the use of axioms and rules of inference to specify the meanings of programming language constructs. This approach was first suggested by C. A. R. Hoare (Hoare 1969). Although the most complicated control structure in Hoare's original paper was the **while** statement, there has been considerable success in extending his method to other language features. Axioms have been proposed for the **go to** statement, functions, recursive procedures with value and reference parameter passing, simple coroutines, and concurrent programs. Research by Clarke (1979*a*) has shown, however, that there are natural programming language control structures that are impossible to describe adequately by means of Hoare axioms. Specifically, Clarke has shown that there are control structures for which it is impossible to obtain axiom systems that are sound and complete in the sense of Cook (1978). These constructs include procedures with procedure parameters under standard ALGOL 60 scope rules and coroutines in a language with parameterless recursive procedures.

A natural question to ask is whether it is possible to characterize those programming languages for which sound and complete proof systems can be obtained. The incompleteness results are established by observing that if a programming language P has a sound and relatively complete proof system for all expressive interpretations, then the halting problem for P must be decidable for finite interpretations. This condition also appears to be sufficient: for a wide class of programming languages and interpretations, it can be shown that if the halting problem for language P is decidable for all finite interpretations, then P has a proof system that will be sound and relatively complete for any expressive interpretation. Nevertheless, we are still far from a completely satisfactory characterization of the programming languages that can be axiomatized in this manner. In this paper we identify and discuss four specific issues that we believe still need to be addressed before the characterization problem can be considered solved.

(1) The present version of the characterization theorem predicts that certain programming languages should have good Hoare proof systems, even though no natural systems have been found.

(2) The characterization theorem should result in a usable proof system, not just an enumeration procedure. Also, the proof system should follow the syntax of the programming language (i.e. be syntax-directed) in the same way that Hoare's original system does.

(3) It appears from the proof of the characterization theorem that certain programming languages may have good total correctness proof systems even though they do not have good partial correctness proof systems.

(4) Lastly, the hypothesis of expressiveness for interpretations deserves more thought. This hypothesis is important because it determines the degree of encoding that is permitted in reasoning about programs. Is it too strong or, perhaps, not strong enough?

The organization of the paper is now described. Section 2 contains a short discussion of the basic ideas of Hoare logic and gives definitions for partial and total correctness. Soundness and relative completeness are introduced and motivated in §3. Expressibility and the implications of this concept are discussed in some detail in §4. Section 5 briefly outlines how incompleteness results are obtained for various combinations of programming language features. In §6 the proof of the characterization theorem is sketched and the limitations of this theorem are discussed. Section 7 contains a discussion of the research problems mentioned above and is the heart of the paper. Finally, §8 discusses the relevance of the characterization problem to programming language design.

2. Hoare logics

The formulas in a *Hoare axiom system* are triples $\{P\}\,S\,\{Q\}$, where S is a statement of the programming language and P and Q are formulas describing the initial and final states of the program S. The logical system in which the predicates P and Q are expressed is called the *assertion language* (AL) and in this paper will always be a first-order language with *type* or *signature* Σ. Intuitively, the partial correctness formula $\{P\}\,S\,\{Q\}$ is true iff whenever *pre-condition* P holds for the initial program state and S terminates, then *post-condition* Q will be satisfied by the final program state.

Although this paper is primarily concerned with partial correctness, we will occasionally need to discuss *total correctness* as well. Total correctness formulas will be triples with the syntax $\langle P\rangle\,S\,\langle Q\rangle$. Such a formula is true iff whenever the precondition P holds for some initial program state, then program S will terminate when started in this state and Q will be satisfied by the final program state.

The control structures of a programming language are specified by axioms and rules of inference for the partial correctness formulas. A typical rule of inference is

$$\frac{\{P \wedge b\}\,S\,\{P\}}{\{P\}\ \mathbf{while}\ b\ \mathbf{do}\ S\,\{P \wedge \neg b\}}.$$

The predicate P is the *invariant* of the **while** loop. Proofs of correctness for programs are constructed by using the axioms together with the proof system T for the assertion language. We write $\vdash_{H,T}\{P\}\, S\, \{Q\}$ if the partial correctness formula $\{P\}\, S\, \{Q\}$ is provable by using the Hoare axiom system H and the proof system T for the assertion language AL.

To discuss whether a particular Hoare axiom system adequately describes the programming language PL, it is necessary to have a definition of *truth* for partial correctness formulas that is independent of the axiom system H. The definition of truth requires two steps. First, we give an interpretation I for the assertion language AL. The interpretation I (over type Σ) specifies the primitive data objects of our programming language; its consists of a set Dom (I) (the domain of the interpretation) and an assignment of a function (respectively, predicate) over Dom(I) of the appropriate arity to each function (respectively, predicate) symbol of Σ. Typical interpretations might be the integers with the standard functions and predicates of arithmetic, or linear lists with the list processing functions car, cdr, etc. Th(I) is the set of all first-order sentences (over Σ) true in I.

Second, we provide an interpreter for the statements of the programming langage. There are many ways such an interpreter may be specified: in terms of computation sequences or as the least fixed point of a continuous functional (denotational semantics). The result is a relation $M[S] \subseteq \text{STATES} \times \text{STATES}$, which associates with each statement S the input–output relation on $\text{STATES} \equiv [\text{VAR} \rightarrow \text{Dom(I)}]$ determined by that statement. Once the relation M has been specified, a formal definition may be given for partial correctness. The partial correctness formula $\{P\}\, S\, \{Q\}$ is *true with respect to interpretation* I ($\models_I \{P\}\, S\, \{Q\}$) iff for all states σ and σ' under I, if predicate P holds for state σ under interpretation I and $(\sigma, \sigma') \in M[S]$, then Q must hold for σ' under I also. Note that by this definition the partial correctness formula $\{\mathit{true}\}\, S\, \{\mathit{false}\}$ will hold in interpretation I iff S diverges regardless of what state it is started in.

A similar definition can also be given for total correctness. The formula $\langle P \rangle\, S\, \langle Q \rangle$ is *true with respect to interpretation* I ($\models_I \{P\}\, S\, \{Q\}$) iff for every state σ, if predicate P holds for σ under interpretation I, there exists a state σ' such that $(\sigma, \sigma') \in M[S]$ and Q must hold for σ' under I also.

3. Soundness and completeness

When can we be satisfied that a Hoare axiom system H adequately describes the programming language PL? There are two possible ways a Hoare axiom system may be inadequate. First, some theorem $\{P\}\, S\, \{Q\}$, which can be proven in the axiom system may fail to hold for actual executions of the program S; in other words, there is a terminating computation of S such that the initial state satisfies P but the final state fails to satisfy Q. One way of preventing this source of error is to adopt operational or denotational semantics for the programming language, which is close to the way statements are actually executed. We then show that every theorem that can be proven by using the axiom system will be true in the model of program execution that we have adopted. In the notation defined above we prove that for all P, Q, S, if $\vdash_{H,T}\{P\}\, S\, \{Q\}$ then $\models_I \{P\}\, S\, \{Q\}$. In general, this type of *soundness* property is fairly easy to establish.

A second source of inadequacy is that the axioms for the programming language may not be sufficiently powerful to handle all combinations of the control structures of the language. However, the question of when it is safe to stop looking for new axioms is much more difficult to answer than the question of soundness. One solution is to prove a completeness theorem for the Hoare axiom system. We can attempt to prove that every partial correctness formula that is true of the execution model of the programming language is provable in the axiom system. In general, it is impossible to prove such completeness theorems; the proof system for the assertion language may itself fail to be complete. For example, when dealing with the integers for any consistent axiomatizable proof system, there will be formulas that are true of the integers but not provable within the system. Also, the assertion language may not be powerful enough to express the invariants of loops. This difficulty occurs if the assertion language is Presburger arithmetic (i.e. integer arithmetic without multiplication). Note that both the difficulties above are faults of the underlying assertion language and interpretation; not of the Hoare axiom system.

How can we talk about the completeness of a Hoare axiom system independently of its assertion language? Cook (1978) gives a Hoare axiom system for a subset of ALGOL including the while statement and non-recursive procedures. He then proves that if there is a complete proof system for the assertion language (for example, all true statements of the assertion language) and if the assertion language satisfies a certain natural expressibility condition, which will be discussed in detail in the next section, then every true partial correctness assertion will be provable.

Definition 1. A Hoare axiom system H for a programming language PL is *sound* and *complete* (in the sense of Cook) iff for all AL and I, if I is *expressive* with respect to AL and PL, then

$$\models_I \{P\} S \{Q\} \Leftrightarrow \vdash_{H, Th(I)} \{P\} S \{Q\}.$$

4. Expressibility

We say that I is *expressive* with respect to AL and PL iff for all $S \in PL$ and Q there is a formula of AL that expresses the *weakest precondition for partial correctness* (called the weakest liberal precondition in Dijkstra (1976)) $WP[S](Q) = \{\sigma \mid \forall \sigma' \, [(\sigma, \sigma') \in M[S] \rightarrow Q[\sigma']]\}$. If I is expressive with respect to AL and PL, then it is not difficult to prove that $\models_I \{WP[S](Q)\} S \{Q\}$ and that if $\models_I \{P\} S \{Q\}$ then $\models_I P \rightarrow WP[S](Q)$.

Expressibility is important because it guarantees the existence of invariants for loops and recursive procedures. For example, it is easy to show that

$$\models_I WP[\textbf{while } b \textbf{ do } S](Q) \equiv (b \wedge WP[S](WP[\textbf{while } b \textbf{ do } S](Q)) \vee (\neg b \wedge Q).$$

From this identity it follows that

$$\models_I \{WP[\textbf{while } b \textbf{ do } S](Q) \wedge b\} S \{WP[\textbf{while } b \textbf{ do } S](Q)\} \tag{1}$$

and

$$\models_I WP[\textbf{while } b \textbf{ do } S](Q) \wedge \neg b \rightarrow Q. \tag{2}$$

By using the **while** axiom and the rule of consequence, we immediately obtain

$$\models_I \{WP[\textbf{while } b \textbf{ do } S](Q)\} \textbf{ while } b \textbf{ do } S \{Q\}.$$

This type of reasoning (cf. Clarke (1979*b*)) shows that $WP[\textbf{while } b \textbf{ do } S](Q)$ can always be used as the invariant of a **while** loop with postcondition Q and is the essence of the relative completeness proof for a simple programming language containing the **while** statement as the only control structure.

We could have equally defined expressibility in terms of the *weakest precondition for total correctness*

$$\mathrm{WT}[S](Q) = \{\sigma \mid \exists \sigma' [(\sigma, \sigma') \in M[S] \wedge Q[\sigma']]\}$$

or in terms of the *strongest post-condition*

$$\mathrm{SP}[S](P) = \{\sigma' \mid \exists \sigma [P[\sigma] \wedge (\sigma, \sigma') \in M[S]]\}.$$

It is shown in Clarke (1979*a*) that all of these definitions lead to the same concept.

THEOREM 1. *The following are equivalent.*

(1) I *is* WP-*expressive with respect to* PL *and* AL.

(2) I *is* WT-*expressive with respect to* PL *and* AL.

(3) I *is* SP-*expressive with respect to* PL *and* AL.

In establishing relative completeness results for looping constructs it is more convenient to work with the weakest pre-condition for partial correctness. For recursive procedures, on the other hand, the strongest post-condition generally is more useful.

Not every choice of AL, PL, and I gives expressibility. Cook demonstrates this for the case where the assertion language is Presburger arithmetic. Wand (1978) gives another example of the same phenomenon. More realistic choices of AL, PL, and I do give expressibility, however. If AL is the full language of number theory and I is an interpretation in which the symbols of number theory receive their usual interpretations, then I is expressive with respect to AL and PL. Also, if the domain of I is finite, then expressibility is assured. Recently, German & Halpern (1983) and Urzyczyn (1983) have independently obtained a strong characterization of those interpretations that are expressive.

THEOREM 2. *Suppose that* PL *is an* acceptable *programming language with recursion and that* I *is a* Herbrand-definable *interpretation that is expressive for* AL *and* PL. *Then* I *is either finite or* strongly arithmetic.

The *acceptability* of the programming language is a mild technical assumption that ensures that the language is closed under certain reasonable programming constructs, and that given a program, it is possible to effectively ascertain its step-by-step computation in interpretation I by asking quantifier-free questions about I. An interpretation I over a type Σ *is Herbrand-definable* (cf. Clarke (1983)) if every element $d \in \mathrm{Dom}(I)$ is the meaning of some term of the Herbrand universe over type Σ. An interpretation I is said to be *strongly arithmetic* (cf. Clarke (1983)) if there exist first-order formulas $Z(x)$ (for zero), $S(x, y)$ (for successor), $A(x, y, z)$ (for addition), and $M(w, y, z)$ (for multiplication) and a bijection $J: \mathrm{Dom}(I) \to N$, which makes I isomorphic to a standard model of arithmetic.

5. INCOMPLETENESS RESULTS

Are there any programming language constructs for which it is impossible to obtain good Hoare axiomatizations? An obvious place to start our search is with more complicated parameter passing mechanisms. In this section we consider the problem of obtaining a sound and complete proof system for an ALGOL-like language that allows procedures as parameters of procedure calls.

THEORM 3. *It is impossible to obtain a Hoare proof system* H *that is sound and complete in the sense of Cook for a programming language* PL *that allows*:

(1) *procedures as parameters of procedure calls*;

(2) *recursion*;

(3) *static scope*;

(4) *global variables*;

(5) *internal procedures as parameters of procedure calls.*

Proof of theorm 3 follows immediately from lemmas 1 and 2. Note that all of the features (1)–(5) are found in ALGOL 60. Moreover, the result holds even if the language PL is restricted so that *self-application* (for example, calls of the form **call** P(..., P, ...)) is not permitted. Thus, the result also applies to PASCAL, where procedures are restricted so that actual procedure parameters must be either formal procedure parameters or names of procedures with no procedure formal parameters.

LEMMA 1. *The halting problem is undecidable for programs in a programming language* PL *with features* (1)–(5) *for all finite interpretations* I *with card* (Dom(I)) $\geqslant 2$.

The proof of the lemma uses a modification of a technique of Jones & Muchnick (1978) and is fully described in Clarke (1979*a*). Note that the lemma does not hold for flowchart schemes or *while* schemes. In each of these cases if I is finite, the program can be viewed as a finite state machine and we may test for termination (at least theoretically) by watching the execution sequence of the program to see whether any program state is repeated. For recursion one might expect that the program could be viewed as a type of push-down automaton (for which the halting problem is also decidable). This is not so if we allow procedures as parameters. The static scope execution rule, which states that procedure calls are interpreted in the environment of the procedure's declaration rather than in the environment of the procedure call, allows the simulation program to access values normally buried in the run-time stack without first 'popping the top' of the stack. This additional power can be used to simulate an arbitrary Turing machine.

LEMMA 2. *If* PL *has a Hoare proof system that is sound and complete in the sense of Cook, then the halting problem for* PL *must be decidable for all finite interpretations.*

Proof. Suppose that PL has a Hoare proof system that is sound and complete in the sense of Cook. Thus, for all AL and I if (*a*) T is a complete proof system for AL and I and (*b*) I is expressive with respect to PL and AL, then

$$\models_{I} \{P\}\, S\, \{Q\} \Leftrightarrow \vdash_{H,T} \{P\}\, S\, \{Q\}.$$

Assume further that the halting problem for PL is undecidable for some particular finite interpretation I. Observe that in this case T may be chosen in a particularly simple manner; in fact, there is a decision procedure for the truth of formulas in AL relative to I. Note also that AL is expressive with respect to PL and I, since I is finite. Thus, both hypotheses (*a*) and (*b*) are satisfied. From the definition of partial correctness, we see that {*true*} S {*false*} holds iff S diverges for the initial values of its global variables. We conclude that the set of programs S such that $\models_{I}$ {*true*} S {*false*} holds is not recursively enumerable. On the other hand, since

$$\models_{I} \{true\}\, S\, \{false\} \Leftrightarrow \vdash_{H,T} \{true\}\, S\, \{false\},$$

we can enumerate those programs S such that $\models_I \{true\}\, S\, \{false\}$ holds: simply enumerate all possible proofs and use the decision procedure for T to check applications of the rule of consequence; this, however, is a contradiction.

If sharing (which intuitively means referring to the same program variable by two or more different names) and self application are disallowed, a sound and relatively complete Hoare proof system may be obtained by modifying any one of the five features of theorem 3. So if we change from *static scope* to *dynamic scope*, a complete set of axioms may be obtained for (1) procedures with procedure parameters, (2) recursion, (4) global variables, and (5) internal procedures as parameters; or if we disallow internal procedures as parameters, a complete system may be obtained for (1) procedures with procedure parameters, (2) recursion, (3) static scope, and (4) global variables.

Techniques similar to that used in theorem 3 have also been used (Clarke 1979*a*) to obtain incompleteness results for programming languages that include any of the features: (*a*) call-by-name parameters passing in the presence of recursive procedures, functions, and global variables; (*b*) coroutines with local recursive procedures that can access global variables; (*c*) unrestricted (PL/1-like) pointer variables with retention; (*d*) unrestricted pointer variables with recursion; and (*e*) label variables with retention.

6. The characterization problem

The incompleteness results are established by observing that if a programming language PL has a sound and relatively complete proof system for all expressive interpretations, then the halting problem for PL must be decidable for finite interpretations. Lipton (1977) considered a form of converse: if PL is an *acceptable* programming language and the halting problem is decidable for finite interpretations, then PL has a sound and relatively complete Hoare logic for expressive and effectively presented interpretations. Lipton actually proved a partial form of the converse. He showed that given a program S and the effective presentation of I, it is possible to enumerate all the partial correctness assertions of the form $\{true\}\, S\, \{false\}$ that are true in I. From this it easily follows that we can enumerate all true quantifer-free partial correctness assertions, since we can encode quantifier-free tests into the programs. But, it does not follow that we can enumerate all first-order partial correctness assertions, since an acceptable programming language will not in general allow first-order tests.

Clarke *et al.* (1983) consider acceptable programming languages that permit recursive procedure calls. They also require that the interpretation be Herbrand-definable. Under these assumptions they are able to extend the results of Clarke (1979*a*) and Lipton (1977), significantly. They are able to eliminate the requirement that pre- and post-conditions be quantifier-free and that the interpretation be effectively presented. They further show that the set of partial correctness assertions true in I is actually (uniformly) decidable in Th(I) provided that the halting probelm for P is decidable for finite interpretations. Lipton's proof, on the other hand, produces an enumeration procedure for partial correctness assertions and, thus, shows only that the set of true partial correctness is r.e. in Th(I). We sketch below a proof of the main theorem of Clarke *et al.* (1983).

Theorem 4. *Let* PL *be an acceptable programming language with recursion. Then the following are equivalent.*

(1) *There is an effective procedure that for expressive, Herbrand-definable interpretations* I *will decide which first-order partial correctness assertions are true in* I *when given an oracle for* Th(I).

(2) PL *has a decidable halting problem for finite interpretations*

Sketch of proof. The fact that (1) ⇔ (2) followed from lemma 2. Proof that (2) ⇒ (1) is considerably more complicated. Assume that PL is an acceptable programming language with recursion and that I is both expressive and Herbrand-definable. By theorem 2 we know that I is either finite or strongly arithmetic. Assume further that we are given an oracle for Th(I). We must provide an effective procedure for deciding which partial correctness assertions are true in I. The decision procedure will actually consist of two procedures M_1 and M_2, which are dovetailed. Both M_1 and M_2 are sound in the sense that they generate only true partial correctness triples; in addition, M_1 will be complete if I is strongly arithmetic, and M_2 will be complete if I is finite.

Let AX be a finite set of axioms for first-order arithmetic. We could take, for example, the nine axioms for zero, successor S(x, y), addition A(x, y, z), multiplication M(x, y, z), and less-than L(x, y, z) given in ch. 2 of Shoenfield (1967). There will, of course, be non-standard models for AX, so this set of axioms will not be complete for all of standard arithmetic. Nevertheless, an interpretation that satisfies AX will have a standard part consisting of those elements of the domain of the forms $S^k(0)$ for some integer k. In general, there is no first-order formula that defines the standard part, but under the hypothesis above we will show that the standard part can be defined.

The first step is to define inductively an encoding of Herbrand terms of type Σ. The details of the encoding are straightforward, and we refer the reader to Clarke *et al.* (1983) for details. We will use the binary predicate symbol H to denote this encoding. Thus, we want H(u, d) to be true iff u is the encoding of a Herbrand term with value d. To achieve this goal, we give an axiom ENC for H and prove that if I satisfies AX and ENC, then $\models_I H(S^k(0), d)$ iff k is the encoding of a Herbrand term whose value in I is d.

By using the encoding relation H we can explicitly give a formula that defines the standard part of I.

LEMMA 3. *If* I *satisfies* AX, ENC, *and is Herbrand-definable then* $\mathrm{Std}(x) \equiv \exists d \forall z(H(z, d) \Rightarrow x < z)$ *defines the standard part of* I.

We can now describe the construction of M_1, which will guess formulas Z(x), S(x, y), L(x, y), A(x, y, z), M(x, y, z), and H(x, y) and check using the oracle for Th(I) that AX and ENC hold in I when written in terms of these formulas. We then define Std(x) as in lemma 3 check $\models_I \forall x[\mathrm{Std}(x)]$. If not, M_1 continues guesses. But if $\forall x[\mathrm{Std}(x)]$ does hold in I, then we have effectively found formulas that make I strongly arithmetic.

LEMMA 4. *Suppose we can effectively find formulas* Z(x), S(x, y), A(x, y, z) *and* M(x, y, z) *of type S that make* I *strongly arithmetic. Then for each* P ∈ PL *we can effectively find a formula* A'_p *of type* Σ *that is equivalent to* A_p *in* I.

Now given a pair of first-order formulas P and Q, and a program S, M_1 will construct the formula

$$\forall \bar{x}, \bar{y}[P(\bar{x}) \wedge A'_S(\bar{x}, \bar{y}) \Rightarrow Q(\bar{y})]$$

and consult the oracle for Th(I). If this formula is true, M_1 will output {P} S {Q}; otherwise it will output ¬({P} S {Q}).

By making use of theorem 2, the construction of M_2 can be made much simpler than the version in Clarke *et al.* (1983). The first step is to determine how many elements are in Dom(I).

P_2 will successively generate formulas of the form $F_n = \exists x_1 x_2 \ldots x_n \forall x[x = x_1 \lor x = x_2 \lor \ldots \lor x = x_n]$ for $n = 1, 2 \ldots$ and submit them to the oracle for Th(I). If I is finite, then the answer *true* will be obtained for some formula F_n, indicating that Dom(I) has no more than n elements. For this case every element of Dom(I) must be the value of some Herbrand term of depth $n+1$ or less. Let $t_1, t_2, \ldots, t_m$ be the Herbrand terms of depth $n+1$ or less. Consider a particular partial correctness formula {P} S {Q}. We rename the bound variables of P and Q so that all are distinct. We next replace every subformula of P and Q of the form $\forall x[W]$ by

$$(x = t_1 \rightarrow W) \land (x = t_n \rightarrow W)$$

and every subformula of the form $\exists x[W]$ by

$$(x = t_1 \land W) \lor \ldots \lor (x = t_n \land W)$$

to obtain a new quantifier-free partial correctness triple {P′} S {Q′}, which will be true in I iff the original triple {P} S {Q} is true in I. If LOOP is a program that always diverges, then S′

if ¬ P′ **then** LOOP **else begin** S; **if** Q′ **then** LOOP **end**

will also be a program and will diverge on all of its inputs iff {P′} S {Q′} is true in I. Thus, by using our decision procedure for the halting problem of PL on finite interpretations we can determine whether the original triple {P} S {Q} is true or false in I.

This completes the sketch of the proof of theorem 4. Grabowski (1984) has developed a modification of the proof above, which appears to avoid the hypothesis of Herbrand-definability that we have previously required in interpretations. However, Grabowski's version of the theorem does not handle total correctness.

The deficiencies of the characterization theorem and its proof are clear. The proof system that is produced is an enumeration procedure and could not be used in practice. Moreover, the proof system does not follow the syntax of the programming language in the same way that Hoare's original system does. This is disturbing since the theorem may guarantee a proof system for a programming language for which no natural Hoare system is known. These problems, however, are precisely the ones mentioned in the introduction as being suitable for further research; we will discuss them in detail in the next section.

7. Research directions

7.1. *Natural axiomatizations for new programming languages*

Although it is difficult to say precisely what makes a proof system natural or whether one system is more natural than another, certainly no one would claim that theorem 4 leads to a natural Hoare proof system. Since the present version of the characterization theorem may predict that a certain programming language should have a good Hoare proof system, even though no natural system has been found, it would seem to be of little use. We conjecture, however, that whenever this happens, additional research will always lead to a natural proof system; perhaps by extending the existing notions of what is permitted in a Hoare axiomatization. A good example is the language L4, which is obtained from the programming language in theorem 3 when global variables are disallowed. Since L4 has generated a great deal of interesting research and since it also illustrates a number of new ideas we consider it in some detail below.

In Clarke (1979*a*) it was argued that if use of global variables was disallowed, then denesting of internal procedures would be possible. Thus, the proof system given for the latter case in Clarke (1979*a*) could also be adapted for use with L4. This argument was shown to be incorrect by Olderog (1982). Since globally declared procedures can still be called from within an internal procedure declaration even if global variables have been disallowed, complete denesting is not always possible. For example, it is impossible to denest the internally declared procedure q in the program segment below. (We use the convention that parameters appearing after the colon in a parameter list are procedure parameters.)

```
begin proc p(: f); begin proc q; begin...f; ...end q;
                       ...p(: q);...
                       ...f;...
                   end p;
      proc r; begin...end r;
      p(: r)
end
```

Previous languages involving procedures were relatively easy to axiomatize, since they all had the *finite range* property. Informally, this property states that for each program, there is a bound on the number of distinct *procedure environments*, or associations between procedure names and bodies, that can be reached. L4 does not have this property, however. This is significant since all previous axiom systems for procedures were based on the ALGOL 60 copy rule semantics for procedure execution and since Olderog (1983) was able to show that none of these axiom systems can deal adequately with infinite range.

For several years the question of whether there existed a natural Hoare proof system for L4 that was sound and complete in the sense of Cook remained open. Langmaack (1979) proved that the halting problem for L4 was decidable and hence, by the characterization theorem given in §6, such a proof system should exist (although perhaps not a natural one!). Olderog (1982) and Damm & Josko (1982) devised proof systems for L4, which were based on the use of a higher order assertion language and the addition of *relation variables* to the programming language. Their systems did not completely solve the problem, however; in both of these papers, the axiom system is assumed to include all of the formulas valid in a certain higher order theory related to the interpretation. Moreover, because of the addition of relation variables to the programming language, their proofs required a stronger notion of expressiveness than was used originally by Cook.

A natural proof system that only uses a first order assertion language and the standard notion of expressiveness has recently been given by German *et al.* (1983). To deal with infinite range, they introduce a class of generalized partial correctness assertions, which permit implication between partial correctness assertions, universal quantification over procedure names, and universal quantification over environment variables. By using these assertions it is possible to relate the semantics of a procedure with the semantics of procedures passed to it as parameters.

For example, let p be the procedure

proc p(x: r); **begin** r(x); r(x) **end**

which calls the formal procedure r twice on the variable parameter x. For an arithmetic domain, p satisfies the formula

$$\forall r, v(\{y = y_0\}\, r(y)\, \{y = y_0 \cdot v\} \rightarrow \{x = x_0\}\, p(x\colon r)\, \{x = x_0 \cdot v^2\}).$$

Intuitively, this formula says that for all procedures r and domain values v, if the call r(y) multiples y by v, then for the same procedure r and value v, the call p(x: r) multiplies x by v^2. Observe how the environment variable v, appearing in the post-conditions of the calls r(y) and p(x: r), is used to express the relation between the semantics of r(y) and p(x: r).

It is not obvious that this approach is sufficient to specify all procedures; indeed, this is the essence of the relative completeness proof. The proof is based on the existence of *abstract interpreter programs*, which can be shown to exist whenever the interpretation is Herbrand-definable and the programming language is acceptable in the sense of §4. Roughly speaking, an interpreter program receives as inputs a number of ordinary variables containing an encoding of a relation to be computed and a number of other variables to which the relation is to be applied. The interpreter then modifies the second set of variables according to the relation. Using interpreter programs, we can transform any L4 program into a program without procedures passed as parameters by adding additional ordinary variables to pass values that encode the procedures.

Many of the techniques introduced in German *et al.* (1983) appear to have applications beyond L4. For example, the more general partial correctness assertions and the way the relative completeness proof is structured may be helpful with other languages that have infinite range de Bakker *et al.* (1981).

7.2. *Syntax-directed proof systems*

Certainly the most important research problem is to develop a version of the characterization theorem that provides some insight as to when a syntax-directed proof system can be obtained. One could even argue that any version of the theorem that fails to address this issue does not really capture the spirit of Hoare logic. An important first step towards developing such a theorem has recently been made by Olderog, who has obtained an interesting characterization of the formal call trees of programs in those sublanguage of Pascal for which a sound and relatively complete Hoare axiomatization can be obtained. His theorem also guarantees that a particular syntax-directed proof system will be sound and relatively complete for those sublanguages.

Let PL_{Pas} be the language obtained from Dijkstra's guarded command language by adding blocks and a Pascal-like procedure mechanism in which actual procedure parameters of a procedure call must either be formal procedure parameters or names of procedures with no formal procedure parameters. Thus, self application is not possible with programs in PL_{Pas}. We refer the reader to Olderog (1983) for the formal syntax and semantics of this class of programs.

By the incompleteness theorem of §5 there is no sound and relatively complete proof system for the full language; however, there may be complete proof systems for sublanguages of $PL \subseteq PL_{Pas}$. Olderog gives a Hoare proof system H_0, which is sound for all of PL_{Pas} and then proves the following surprising result.

THEOREM 5. *For every admissible* $PL \subseteq PL_{Pas}$ *the following are equivalent.*

(1) *There exists a sound and relatively complete Hoare logic in the sense of theorem* 4 *for* PL.

(2) *The halting problem of* PL *is decidable under finite interpretations.*

(3) *All programs in* PL *have* regular *formal call trees.*

(4) *The Hoare proof system* H_0 *is sound and relatively complete for* PL.

A sublanguage $PL \subseteq PL_{Pas}$ is *admissible* if PL is r.e. and closed under program transformations that leave procedure structure invariant. A tree T over a finite alphabet is *regular* if the set of paths in T is a regular language or, equivalently, if there are only finitely many different patterns of subtrees. The *formal call tree* of a program S records the order in which the procedures of S are called in all possible executions of S. The formal call tree for the program skeleton in §7.1 is shown in figure 1 and is clearly non-regular. Hence, it follows by the Olderog theorem that any programming language, PL, containing the program must fail to have a sound and relatively complete Hoare proof system. Note that this does not contradict the results of German *et al.* (1983), since any admissible language that contains this program will also contain programs that access non-local variables, and hence the proof system of German *et al.* (1983) would not be expected to be complete.

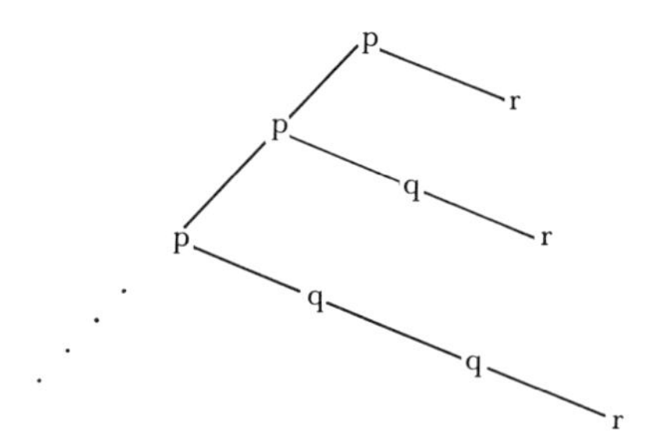

FIGURE 1. The formal call tree for the program skeleton in §7.1.

7.3. *The problem with total correctness*

What happens when we attempt to extend the characterization theorem to apply to total correctness assertions as well as partial correctness assertions? Under the same hypothesis as in the previous proof it is possible to show that the set of true total correctness assertions is (uniformly) decidable in Th(I) iff the halting problem for PL is decidable for finite interpretations. Moreoever, the set of true total correctness assertions is (uniformly) r.e. in Th(I) even if the halting problem for PL is *not decidable* for finite interpretations (Clarke *et al.* 1983). This last result unexpectedly suggests that good axiom systems for total correctness may exist for a wider class of programming languages than for partial correctness and is, therefore, rather disturbing.

Proof of the result above is similar to the proof of the characterization theorem in §6. As in the previous proof, this proof breaks into two cases depending on whether the interpretation is finite or infinite and strongly arithmetic. The infinite case is just like the infinite case for partial correctness except that we ask the oracle for Th(I) about the formula

$$\forall \bar{x} \exists \bar{y} \,(P(\bar{x}) \Rightarrow A^{I}_{S}(\bar{x}, \bar{y}) \wedge Q(\bar{y}))$$

to determine whether the total correctness assertion $\langle P \rangle \, S \, \langle Q \rangle$ is true or false.

For the finite interpretation we can use the same trick as in the previous theorem to make the pre- and post-conditions quantifier-free. We then use the decision procedure for the halting problem of PL programs to determine if the program S′ shown below halts on all of its inputs.

if P **then begin** S; **if** ¬ Q **then** LOOP **end**

Alternatively, since there are only a finite number of domain elements and since we can find a finite set of Herbrand terms such that every domain element is the value of some term in the set, we can run S′ on all possible combinations of its inputs. If S′ halts on all of them, then we enumerate the triple $\langle P \rangle \, S \, \langle Q \rangle$.

We note that this anomaly does not occur if we require that the negation of a total correctness assertion also be a legal total correctness assertion. For example, we could augment first-order logic with a special operator for the *weakest precondition for total correctness*:

$$\langle\text{formula}\rangle ::= \langle\text{atomic formula}\rangle \mid \text{WT}[\langle\text{program}\rangle](\langle\text{formula}\rangle) \mid \neg\langle\text{formula}\rangle$$
$$\mid \langle\text{formula}\rangle \vee \langle\text{formula}\rangle \mid \exists\langle\text{var}\rangle[\langle\text{formula}\rangle]\rangle.$$

Atomic formulas will have the same syntax as for standard first-order logic. The syntax of programs will not be given; however, programs are assumed to be deterministic, and all booleans in programs must be atomic formulas. Thus, in contrast to dynamic logic Pratt (1976), we do not permit booleans to be arbitrary WT-formulas.

Let f be a formula and let S be a program. We write $I, \sigma \models f$ iff f is true in interpretation I and state σ. The obvious definition is used in all of the clauses for ⟨formula⟩ except the one for WT. We define $I, \sigma \models \text{WT}[S](f)$ iff $I, M[S](\sigma) \models f$. A WT-formula f is *true in* I ($I \models f$) iff $I, \sigma \models f$ for all states σ.

THEOREM 6. *Assume that* PL *is an acceptable programming language with recursion and that* I *is Herbrand-definable and expressive with respect to* AL *and* PL. *Then the set of* WT-*formulas that are true in* I *is uniformly r.e. in* Th (I) *iff the halting problem for* PL *is decidable for finite interpretations.*

Proof. Assume that PL has an undecidable halting problem for some finite interpretation I. Since finite interpretations are expressive, it follows that there will always be a formula P for WT[S](Q) that does not itself involve WT. However, it is impossible to effectively enumerate such formulas given S and Q. Thus, we cannot have a sound and relatively complete proof system for a logic that can express $\text{WT}[S](Q) \equiv P$ when P and Q do not involve WT. For the converse we actually prove that if the halting problem for PL is decidable for finite interpretations, then the set of WT-formulas that are true in I is uniformly decidable in Th(I).

Assume that I is Herbrand-definable and expressive and that the halting problem for PL is decidable for finite interpretations. Given an oracle for Th(I), the construction used in the proof of theorem 4 can also be used to find a formula of AL that expresses WT[S](Q) whenever Q is a formula of AL and S is a program in PL.

In case I is arithmetical, we can use the formula $\exists \bar{y}[A'_S(\bar{x}, \bar{y}) \Rightarrow Q(\bar{y})]$, where $A'_S(\bar{x}, \bar{y})$ is the AL formula that expresses the input–output relation of S.

In explaining the finite case we use the same notation as that in theorem 4. Assume that S has global variables $v_1, v_2, \ldots, v_k$. Let $S'(a_{i_1}, \ldots a_{i_k})$ be the program

```
begin
        v1 := a_i1 ;
        .
        .
        .
        vk := a_ik ;
        S;
        if ¬ Q' then LOOP
end
```

where each a_{i_j} is one of the terms $t_1, \ldots, t_n$ and Q′ is the quantifier-free formula that is equivalent to Q. Next, determine whether S′ will halt for each possible combination of $a_i, \ldots, a_{i_n}$. The formula for the weakest precondition will be the disjunction of all those clauses $v_1 = a_{i_1} \wedge v_2 = a_{i_2} \wedge \ldots \wedge v_k = a_{i_k}$ that correspond to initial states in which S′ will halt.

Thus, given an arbitrary WT-formula, we can transform it to an equivalent formula of AL not involving WT. Start with the most deeply nested occurrence of WT, say $WT[S_1](Q_1)$, where Q_1 is a formula of AL and does not involve WT. By the observation above, we can replace $WT[S_1](Q_1)$ by an equivalent AL formula Q_2 not involving WP. We continue to repeat this process until all occurrences of WT are eliminated. We then ask the oracle for Th(I) about the truth of f*, where f* is the universal closure of f.

7.4. *More powerful notions of expressibility*

Another obvious question is whether a more powerful notion of expressibility might permit sound and relatively complete proof systems to be obtained for a wider class of programming languages than is currently the case with Cook's original definition. The answer is, trivially, yes. If, for example, we use a notion of expressibility that requires interpretations to be strongly arithmetical, then only the infinite case in theorem 4 will apply. Since the infinite case does not use the hypothesis that the halting problem is decidable for finite interpretations, the relative decision procedures could be adapted, for example, to apply to the full language PL_{Pas}. This is unlikely to lead to a very natural proof technique because of the encoding that is necessary to obtain the formula $A_S^I(x, y)$ from program S.

Alternatively, we could simply compile PL_{Pas} into an assembly language where the run-time stack is encoded as the value of an integer variable, where the only control structures are the conditional and the **while** statement, and where assignments can use standard arithmetical operations of addition, multiplication, etc. This, however, is contrary to the spirit of high level programming languages. If the proof of a recursive program requires explicit reasoning about the low-level implementation of the language by means of the run-time stack, then why not simply replace the recursive procedures themselves by stack operations. The purpose of recursion in programming languages is to free the programmer from the details of implementing recursive constructs.

If a programming language requires an unnatural use of encoding to get an axiomatization, then perhaps it is too powerful to reason about effectively. The incompleteness results of §5, which depend only on finite interpretations, show that certain programming language features cannot have natural axiomatizations. In fact, we would argue that finite interpretations are often more useful than infinite interpretations for judging whether an axiomatization is natural, since they preclude the possibility that domain elements can be used to encode complicated run-time data structures such as the run-time stack or linked lists of activation records. Moreover, all of the standard partial-correctness rules (for example, the assignment axiom, the **while** statement rule, etc.) work just as well for finite interpretations as for infinite ones.

We do not mean to imply that there is nothing to be learned from further study of expressiveness. We suggest, however, a different direction for research on this topic. Although expressiveness has been assumed by many previous researchers to get a complete axiomatization, the use they have made of this assumption (for example, to generate the existence of loop invariants) seems more natural than its use in the proof of the characterization theorem in §6. So, we believe that perhaps the hypothesis of expressiveness should be weakened or restricted in some way. We note, however, that such a weakening would not affect the incompleteness results of §5.

8. Conclusion: implications for language design

The fact that not every programming language can be described adequately by means of Hoare axioms does not mean that this method for reasoning about programs is less useful than operational or denotational methods. On the contrary, it is exactly because Hoare Logic is more restrictive in descriptive power that it turns out to be so useful for reasoning about programs. The increased flexibility of more operational approaches is obtained at a high price; the necessary attention to low level implementation details usually makes high-level reasoning about programs unacceptably cumbersome.

That some programming languages would be extremely hard to specify in this manner should be expected. It has been known for some time that certain language constructs make informal reasoning about a program's behaviour quite difficult; this same complexity would also be expected to complicate a Hoare proof system for such a language. In this respect the programming languages of §5 are particularly pathological since arbitrary Turing machine computations can be simulated by the control structures of the language even in a finite interpretation.

Perhaps, the existence of a sound and relatively complete Hoare Logic could be used as a criterion for the design of programming languages suitable for program verification. At the very least such a criterion would force language designers to devise programming languages with simple, clean control structures and to consider carefully the possible unexpected interactions of adding another control structure to an already existing language.

This research was partly supported by N.S.F. Grant no. MCS-82-16706.

References

de Bakker, J. W., Klop, J. W., Meyer, J.-J. C. 1981 Correctness of programs with function procedures. *Tech. Rep.* no. IW 170/81. Amsterdam: Mathematisch Centrum.

Clarke, E. M. 1979*a* Programming language constructs for which it is possible to obtain good Hoare-like axioms. *J. Ass. comput. Mach.* **26**, 129–147.

Clarke, E. M. 1979*b* Program invariants as fixedpoints. *Computing* **21**, 273–294.

Clarke, E. M. Jr, German, S. & Halpern, J. Y. 1983 Effective axiomatization of Hoare logics. *J. Ass. comput. Mach.* **30**, 612–636.

Cook, S. A. 1978 Soundness and completeness of an axiom system for program verification. *SIAM J. Comput.* **7**, 70–90.

Damm, W. & Josko, B. 1982 A sound and relatively complete Hoare-logic for a language with higher type procedures. *Tech. Rep. Bericht*, no. 77. RWTH Aachen: Lehrstuhl fur Informatik II.

Dijkstra, E. W. 1976 *A discipline of programming*. Englewood Cliffs, N.J.: Prentice Hall.

German, S. M., Clarke, E. M. & Halpern, J. Y. 1983 Reasoning about procedures as parameters. In *Proc. CMU Conference on Logics of Programs*, pp. 206–221. New York: Ass. comput. Mach.

German, S. M. & Halpern, J. Y. 1983 On the power of the hypothesis of expressiveness. *IBM Research Tech. Rep.* no. RJ 4079.

Grabowski, M. 1984 On the relative completeness of Hoare logics. In *Proc. 14th Ass. comput. Mach. Symp. on Principles of Programming Languages*, pp. 258–262. New York: Ass. comput. Soc.

Hoare, C. A. R. 1969 An axiomatic basis for computer programming. *Commun. Ass. comput. Mach.* **12**, 576–583.

Jones, N. D. & Muchnick, S. S. 1978 Complexity of finite memory programs with recursion. *J. Ass. comput. Mach.* **25**, 312–321.

Langmaack, H. 1979 On termination problems for finitely interpreted ALGOL-like programs. *Tech. Rep. Bericht* nr. 7904. Kiel: Inst. f. Inform. u. Prakt. Math., Christian-Albrechtst-Univ.

Lipton, R. J. 1977 A necessary and sufficient condition for the existence of Hoare logics. In *18th IEEE symp. on Foundations of Computer Science, 1–6, LNCS 85, 1977*, pp. 363–373.

Olderog, E.-R. 1982 Correctness of PASCAL-like programs without global variables. Mathematisches Forschungsinstitut Oberwolfach.

Olderog, E.-R. 1983 A characterization of Hoare's logic for programs with Pascal-like procedures. In *Proc 15th Ass. comput. Mach. Symp. on Theory of Computing*, pp. 320–329. New York: Ass. comput. Mach.
Pratt, V. R. 1976 Semantical considerations of Floyd–Hoare logic. In *Proc. 17th IEEE symp. on Foundations of Computer Science*, pp. 109–121. London: IEEE.
Shoenfield, J. R. 1968 *Mathematical logic*. Reading, Massachusetts: Addison Wesley.
Urzyczyn, P. 183 A necessary and sufficient condition in order that a Herbrand interpretation is expressive relative to recursive programs. Institute of Mathematics, University of Warsaw.
Wand, M. 1978 A new incompleteness result for Hoare's system. *J. Ass. comput. Mach.* **25**, 167–168.

Discussion

P. Aczel (*Mathematics Department, Manchester University, U.K.*). What does the *possession of a sound and relatively complete Hoare-type axiomatization* mean for the proof of correctness of real programs? Is there hope of doing it completely automatically, or even with the injection of suitable formulas, for example loop invariants, by a human? If so is the same true for Professor Clarke's non-syntax directed axioms?

E. M. Clarke. When we have a *sound and relatively complete axiomatization*, we know that our proof rules are adequate for reasoning about any possible combination of the various constructs of the programming language. We have reduced the problem of verifying a program to the problem of finding invariants and proving theorems in the assertion language. These problems may be quite difficult, but at least we know that in principle we will not get into trouble when a programmer uses some feature of the language in an unusual way.

P. Aczel (*Mathematics Department, Manchester University, U.K.*). In using Hoare style proof rules to verify programs by hand the predicates, i.e. the pre-conditions and post-conditions of correctness assertions, need only be formulated in precise, but perhaps informal, standard mathematical language. On the other hand the notion of relative completeness of the proof rules requires the involvement of formal languages for expressing these predicates.

In view of the fact that this involvement is seemingly cancelled out by relativizing to arbitrary expressive formal languages, would it not be better to avoid their use in the first place when formulating the notion of completeness of the proof rules? Much of the syntactic detail could then be banished from the completeness proofs.

E. M. Clarke. I agree with you to some extent. We could simply treat a predicate as a collection of program states and not concern ourselves with the syntactic representation of predicates. This approach was used by de Bakker & Meertens (1973). They were able to show the soundness and completeness of proof rules for the simple looping control structures and for parameterless recursive procedures. It seems to me, however, that this approach breaks down when we attempt to handle more complicated language features such as blocks with local variable declarations or recursive procedures with variable parameters. One of the rules for procedures states that execution of statement S leaves P invariant (i.e. P{S} P) provided that all of the variables free in P are inactive in S. This rule seems to require that we know something about the syntactic representation of P. There are many other similar rules in the literature.

Reference

de Bakker, J. W. & Meertens, L. G. L. T. 1973 *On the completeness of the inductive assertion method*. Amsterdam: Mathematisch Centrum.

J. V. TUCKER (*Department of Computer Studies, University of Leeds, U.K.*). I will comment on the technical idea of completeness, and on the role of completeness theorems in the theory of program verification.

Hoare logics concern control structures at a given level of data abstraction; this data abstraction is specified by a set, T, of axioms for the operations invoked in the programs of interest. A soundness theorem confirms that a formal proof of a specified program {p} S {q}, in Hoare logic based on T, guarantees the validity of {p} S {q} for every implementation I satisfying the specification T. However, the 'converse' idea of completeness, in the sense of Cook, considers the validity of {p} S {q} in a *single* implementation I of T, rather than its validity for the class of *all* implementations of T as might be expected for a data type specification. It is known that this latter completeness property also fails to obtain for first-order Hoare Logics in general.

The theorems about completeness in the sense of Cook have further deficiencies. First, the use of the set Th(I), of all true first-order statements about I, as an oracle, spoil the axiomatic nature of Hoare logics. For example, in the important case of arithmetic N, the set Th(N) is highly non-computable (being of Turing degree of unsolvability O^{ω}; infinitely more complex than the halting problem for the Turing machine, as it were). Secondly, the expressiveness concept becomes awkward to apply for two-sorted data types. For example, it is known that two independent copies of N can form a two-sorted structure that is not first-order expressive. Thus, proving programs with two types of variable can be problematical in first-order Hoare logic.

How should these completeness theorems be interpreted? I think that a completeness theorem for a given syntax-directed Hoare logic merely confirms that, in some limited sense, the logic possesses sufficient rules for its underlying programming constructs. A completeness theorem for a general Hoare logic, in Professor Clarke's sense, confirms that some logical system with sufficient rules is possible. As we have seen, in Professor Clarke's very interesting lecture, for some language constructs that is the meagre extent of our present knowledge.

I believe that a different attitude to completeness is also important. In general, a completeness theorem for a logical system L with respect to some semantics M can be interpreted as a confirmation that L syntactically or proof-theoretically characterizes M. Thus, the lack of a general completeness theorem for a consistent Hoare logic implies that the semantics of the programming language is not the semantics about which the logic is reasoning. If a Hoare logic is used to define a programming language (as was originally envisaged in the writings of Floyd, Hoare and Wirth) then various non-standard semantics of the language must be examined. I have worked on these problems of completeness with Dr J. A. Bergstra (Centre for Mathematics and Computer Science, Amsterdam).

In conclusion, I am tempted to speculate that research into the 'model theory' of Hoare logics will create a more agreeable conceptual framework for the attractive characterization theorems of Professor Clarke and his collaborators.

Reference

Bergstra, J. A. & Tucker, J. V. 1982 *J. Comput. Syst. Sci.* **25**, 267–284.

E. M. CLARKE. The use of the Th(I) in relative completeness proofs is simply a technical device for factoring out the complexity of proving theorems in the assertion language from the more general problem of proving programs correct. It permits us to investigate the adequacy of the

Hoare axioms for reasoning about the various constructs of the programming language. With this limited objective in view, I do not see why it should 'spoil the axiomatic nature of the Hoare Logic'.

I agree that interesting technical problems with expressiveness occur for two-sorted types. I very much enjoyed Dr Tucker's paper on this topic.

I also agree with Dr Tucker's interpretation of the incompleteness results for certain programming languages in terms of the existence of non-standard semantics for those languages.

J. C. SHEPHERDSON (*School of Mathematics, University of Bristol, U.K.*). Can Professor Clarke give a definition of what is meant by 'syntax-directed' rules?

E. M. CLARKE. I think that it would not be terribly difficult to give a definition of the term *syntax-directed proof rule*. For example, one could imagine a very general definition using an *attribute grammar* for the programming language under consideration. An attribute grammar is a context-free grammar extended by attaching attributes to the symbols of the grammar. Associated with each production of the grammar is a set of semantic equations where each equation defines one attribute as the value of semantic function applied to other attributes in the production. For proof rules in a Hoare logic the attributes would be first-order formulas involving pre- and post-conditions of statements associated with the various symbols of the grammar.

The problem of actually finding a sound and relatively complete syntax-directed proof system for a given programming language seems much harder, and apart from Olderog's work little progress has been made on this question.

Deductive learning

By L. G. Valiant

Aiken Computation Laboratory, Harvard University, Cambridge, Massachusetts 02138, *U.S.A.*

A non-technical discussion of a new approach to the problem of concept learning in the context of artificial devices is given. Learning is viewed as a process of acquiring a program for recognizing a concept from an environment that does not reveal an explicit description of the program but only suggests it by such means as identifying positive examples of it. The proposed model makes possible a study of learning that reconciles three requirements: the classes of concepts that can be learnt are relevant for general purpose knowledge; they can be characterized; the process of learning them is computationally feasible.

1. Introduction

We consider the following computational model of knowledge. A robot receives information from the outside world via a set of primitive Boolean variables $x_1, \ldots, x_n$. Its task is to recognize whether various predicates or *concepts* are exemplifed in the information presented. The knowledge base of the robot is a set of programs $f_1, \ldots, f_m$ that compute Boolean functions $F_1 \ldots, F_m$ respectively, one corresponding to each concept. These programs may use each other as subroutines. They can take as input parameters both the primitive variables and the output of other programs.

The question we ask is: how can the robot acquire a program for a further function F_{m+1} if no source for providing an explicit listing of that program is available? In this paper we describe such a process of *program acquisition without being programmed* as *learning*. This is a central issue in artificial intelligence. A primary goal there is to provide machines with human-like skills for which satisfactory algorithms are often unknown. Even when such algorithms are known the problem of adding one to a knowledge base that is already very complex and difficult to understand may present difficulties.

Our purpose here is to formulate and discuss a rigorous approach to understanding such learning processes. A first aim would be to delimit the class of functions that are learnable from those that are not. In this model the impediment to learnability is computational complexity. If members of a class of programs can be acquired by learning only in exponentially many steps then this class will not be learnable in practice. On the positive side we expect that the model will provide particular proposals for realistic learning systems. A more complete treatment of our approach appears elsewhere (Valiant 1984).

Learning is often associated with the notion of induction. This association emphasizes the fact that if we are deriving a general principle from a limited number of examples, say, then there is, inevitably, some element of inspiration or guesswork involved, since the information available is simply insufficient for a deduction to be made with certainty.

In our title we use the word deductive to emphasize the contrary point. Human learning often shows remarkable properties of convergence. In large populations there is a high degree of agreement on the meaning of thousands of words as they relate to everyday situations. This suggests that highly reliable program acquisition may be feasible even in the absence of explicit programming. Hence it is reasonable to insist that our study of learning be disciplined by insistence on fast convergence.

One motivation of this study is encapsulated in the informal notion of an 'optimal learning situation'. Here a robot eager to learn, already possessing much knowledge as well as the best general purpose learning strategies, wishes to learn its next new concept from a teacher that understands the concept well and is willing to go to any lengths to impart to the robot a recognition algorithm for the concept, short of providing an explicit description of such a program.

To give a precise meaning to the above we have to define the *learning protocol*, the manner of interaction that is allowed between the learner and teacher. This will typically include the teacher making positive or negative identifications of the concept for various inputs, and, possibly, the teacher answering questions posed by the learner. We call this study that of *learnability* because its aims include that of understanding the maximal limits of the learning phenomenon that are feasible with reasonable learning protocols.

To represent knowledge and programs we shall use propositional calculus expressions. On the one hand they are so simple and central in knowledge representation that it is difficult to imagine how the learning issue can be understood without considering them. As we shall see, however, the task of learning even in this limited context poses serious problems. It would appear to be over ambitious to attempt much more before the questions raised here are better understood.

The study of learning that we suggest is, in the first instance, a theoretical one in the spirit of, say, computability theory. Whether it will ever be efficacious to make artificial systems with general purpose learning capabilities depends on whether efficient strategies exist and can be discovered for classes of programs that are substantial enough. It may turn out that even if very good strategies exist, they only start being usable when a very large knowledge base has been built. In that case the validation of such strategies for practical purposes would involve major challenges for the experimenter.

Extensive bibliographies on previous work on inductive inference and machine learning are given by Angluin & Smith (1982) and Michalski *et al.* (1983).

2. A PROBLEM OF FORMULATION

We consider propositional expressions in a set of propositional variables $p_1, \ldots, p_t$. An extremely simple kind of expression is a product or *monomial*. For example, $f = p_2 \bar{p}_4 p_5$ is a monomial. It takes the value 'true' or '1' if p_2 and p_5 are both true and p_4 false, whatever values the other variables take. The expression f is 'false' if p_2 is false or if p_5 is false or if p_4 is true or if any combination of these conditions holds.

It is realistic to consider that t is very large. A system may have large numbers of primitive inputs and of functions that are programmed or previously learnt. Each single function may be dependent on only a small fraction of the t variables.

A *positive example* of a function or expression will be a vector of truth assignments to the variables that makes the function or expression true. Thus $(p_1 = 1, p_2 = 1, p_4 = 0, p_5 = 1)$ will be a positive example of the particular expression f but $(p_2 = 0, p_4 = 0, p_5 = 1, p_6 = 1)$ and

($p_2 = 1$, $p_4 = 0$) will not be. The omission of a variable p_i, or equivalently setting $p_i = *$, denotes that the value of p_i is *undetermined*. It is important to allow for undetermined variables because in realistic situations confirmations of a concept may be obtained from the values of a small set of the variables. The values of some of the remaining variables may not be obtainable. For example, in recognizing an 'elephant' the colour, size, location, etc., may all be relevant but it may be possible to make a positive identification even when the values of some of the variables are unknown.

Suppose that a robot is presented with a large number N of vectors that are identified as positive examples of f. The task of the robot is to deduce reliably an expression that equals or in some sense approximates f. The question of defining a plausible learning mechanism even for such apparently trivial expressions as monomials is problematic and was previously unsolved. The difficulty lies in giving a definition of learning that is both realistic and computationally feasible.

A first attempt at a definition may be to insist that f be deducible from any set of N distinct positive examples. This, however, is unrealistically optimistic and may require N to be exponentially large in terms of t. For example, suppose that $f = p_1$ say and $N = 2^{\frac{1}{2}t}$; then an unfortunate choice of examples would assign $p_1 = p_2 = \ldots = p_{\frac{1}{2}t} = 1$ and would vary over all combinations of assignments to the remaining variables. These examples clearly reveal little about the nature of f.

A second attempt may be to define some natural probabilistic distribution for the relative probability of occurrence of the various vectors. For example, we could say that all the 2^{t-1} vectors consistent with $f = p_1$ have the same probability of occurring. This model would make unfortunate choices of examples unlikely and would therefore solve the problem technically. Unfortunately in the real world this assumption will nearly always be totally false. The actual distributions for the various concepts of interest may bear no relation to each other and will not be known *a priori* in general.

3. A probabilistic model

The solution proposed to the above predicament is a very simple one: assume that vectors of variable values do occur in nature with some fixed probabilistic distribution. Allow this distribution, however, to be completely *arbitrary* and unknown. Furthermore require of the learner only the ability to deduce an expression that approximates f in that if a vector is drawn randomly from the distribution then the deduced expression may disagree with f on this vector, but the probability of this happening is small. Thus, pursuing the example $f = p_1$ of the previous section, suppose that $p_2 = 1$ in 99% of positive examples of f. Then a learner who has not seen a positive example with $p_2 = 0$ or p_2 undetermined, may deduce that $f = p_1 p_2$. Our definitions tolerate this inaccuracy because the learner's program $p_1 p_2$ will in that case indeed be equivalent to p_1 for 99% of the time in real-world examples of the concept.

The deduction algorithm for the expression we assume above is a simple one: let the deduced expression be the product of all p_i or $\bar{p}_i$ that are determined to be true in *all* the positive examples seen by the learner.

Now without knowing anything about the distribution the following is provable. For any number $h > 1$, if $2h(t + \log_2 h)$ positive examples are drawn from the distribution, then with probability at least $1 - h^{-1}$ the deduced expression g will have the property: (i) for any vector v for which g is true f is also true; (ii) if a vector v for which f is true is drawn at random with probability determined by the distribution of such positive examples of f, then v will make g true with probability at least $1-h^{-1}$.

The possibility of proving such results suggests the general definition of what it means for a class of expressions, or more generally programs, to be learnable. Suppose that X is a class of programs. For a typical member $f \in X$ we denote the size of f by the parameter s, and its arguments by $p_1, \ldots, p_t$. We denote an assignment of truth values to $p_1, \ldots, p_t$ by the vector $v \in \{0, 1, *\}^t$. We denote by D and $\bar{D}$, respectively, the arbitrary probability distributions over $\{v \mid f \text{ is true on } v\}$ and $\{v \mid f \text{ is not true on } v\}$. Thus D(v) denotes the relative probability of occurrence of v among vectors that make f true. $\bar{D}(v)$ is the corresponding distribution for the complement set. Note that if f is not true on input v it may be either false or undefined.

The class X is *learnable* with respect to a learning protocol L if there is a deduction procedure using L such that

(i) the procedure runs in time polynomial in s, t and in an adjustable parameter h, and

(ii) for all $f \in X$ and all D, $\bar{D}$ the algorithm will deduce, with probability at least $1-h^{-1}$, a program $g \in X$ having the properties:

(*a*) $\Sigma\{D(v) \mid f \text{ is true but } g \text{ is not true on } v\} \leqslant h^{-1}$;

(*b*) $\Sigma\{\bar{D}(v) \mid f \text{ is not true but } g \text{ is true on } v\} \leqslant h^{-1}$.

In the example cited earlier the learning protocol consists of a supply of positive examples. The learner is allowed to call a procedure EXAMPLES, which always returns the value of a vector v such that f is true on v. The probability that a particular v is provided is exactly D(v).

The definition given of learnability allows for *two-sided error*. In the example we gave of learning single monomials, it is clear that if $f(v) \neq 1$ it is impossible that $g(v) = 1$. In this case, and in all the other cases so far considered (Valiant 1984), learning can be achieved with only *one-sided error*. Learnability with one-sided error is defined in the same way as for two-sided error, except that condition (ii) (*b*) is replaced by 'for all v if g is true on v then so is f'. This is an important advantage because it allowed us to omit mentioning $\bar{D}$. While it may be reasonable to discuss the distribution of the attributes of elephants, we may prefer not discussing the distribution of the attributes of non-elephants.

The most interesting class of propositional expressions that we can show to be learnable (with one-sided error) is the class of k-CNF *expressions* with at most k literals (negated or unnegated variables) in each clause. For example $(p_1+\bar{p}_3)(p_2+p_3)(p_2+\bar{p}_3)$ is a 2-CNF expression. 3-CNF expressions are already complex in the sense that it is NP-hard to determine whether such an expression has the value zero for all vectors v. Nevertheless the following theorem can be proved.

THEOREM 1. *For every positive integer* k *the class of* k-CNF *expressions is learnable with respect to the positive examples learning protocol.*

The expressions that appear to be easiest to understand for humans are disjunctive normal form (or sum of product) expressions, such as $p_1 p_3 p_4 + p_2 p_4$. An expression is *monotone* if no variable occurs negated. A very immediate question that is currently unresolved is whether monotone DNF expressions are learnable with respect to the positive examples protocol.

4. Oracles

The idea of learning from positive or negative examples is appealing because the teacher has only the minimal role of making the identifications. Unfortunately the classes of expressions that we can show to be learnable from examples alone are very limited. It is therefore necessary to ask how we can formulate more active forms of teaching in the context of an optimal learning situation. The solution we propose is that of introducing various *oracles*. Each oracle can answer questions of a specified nature about the concept to be learnt. The learning protocol allows the learner to pose questions and receive answers to them.

A simplest oracle is one of *necessity*. Given a vector of truth assignments to a subset of the variables it will determine whether the vector is a positive example or not. Note that if a vector is a positive example then so will also any vector obtained from it by making some undetermined variables determined. The power of such an oracle is illustrated by the fact that if the learner has to decide whether the correct expression sought is p_1 or $p_1 p_2$ it can simply input '$p_1 = 1$' to the oracle and will get a positive answer if the correct formula is p_1, and a negative one if it is $p_1 p_2$. The following theorem can be proved.

Theorem 2. *The class of monotone disjunctive normal form expressions is learnable with respect to the protocol that allows positive examples and the necessity oracle.*

The size measure in theorem 2 is the number of symbols in the expression. When negations are allowed, if the size measure is redefined appropriately a similar result can be proved. An interesting open question is whether monotone CNF expressions with no bound on clause size are learnable via positive examples and the necessity oracle.

One can define a variety of other oracles for kinds of questions that a person understanding a concept may be expected to be able to answer. For example a *possibility* oracle would tell given a vector whether it is possible to make the expression true by giving the undetermined variables some suitable values. Thus the assertion 'large = 1' is a vector for which it is possible but not necessary that the described thing is an elephant. An oracle of *relevant possibility* would tell, given a vector, whether by making determined some undetermined variables, one can obtain a vector that is (necessarily) a positive example, but such that making any determined variable undetermined in it would not give a (necessarily) positive example. Thus 'large = 1' is relevantly possible if in *some* conjunctive criterion for elephants the question of largeness cannot be dropped.

One can say informally that an oracle is reasonable if it gives insight into the learning process. Oracles that give explicit answers about the syntactic description of the program to be learnt are not reasonable because they are thinly disguised programming languages.

5. Limits of learnability

It is conceivable that all programs, when described as Boolean circuits, say, are learnable. There is, however, substantial circumstantial evidence from cryptography that this is not so and that the class of learnable programs is very restricted. One task of cryptography is to find encoding schemes such that an enemy that has access to even a large sample of previous messages and their encodings is unable to replicate the encoding algorithm. Our notion of learnability, at least when restricted to protocols using examples alone, requires the converse property. We require that from the input–output behaviour of any member of a class of programs the particular program be easily replicated. Furthermore in encoding schemes no member of the class should be deducible, while in a learnable class we expect them all to be deducible. Hence the widely conjectured existence of encoding schemes that are computationally simple suggests that learnable classes of programs may be extremely limited.

In the light of the above observation the question arises as to how the acquisition of complex programs or skills should be viewed. The view we propose is that while simple programs can be learnt, in our sense, in anything more complicated a programming element becomes essential. It is conceivable, for example, that given the state of knowledge and learning strategies of a particular robot the concept of 'elephant' is not learnable for it. It may be, however, that the notion of 'trunk' is learnable and that, once that concept is learnt, 'elephant' becomes learnable also. Such intervention by the teacher in identifying and sequencing intermediate concepts we classify as programming.

This research was supported in part by National Science Foundation Grant MCS-83-02385.

References

Angluin, D. & Smith, C. H. 1982 A survey of inductive inference: theory and methods. *Yale University, Computer Science Department Tech. Rep.* no. 250.

Michalski, R. S., Carbonell, J. G. & Mitchell, T. M. 1983 *Machine learning: an artificial intelligence approach.* Palo Alto, California: Tioga.

Valiant, L. G. 1984 A theory of the learnable. In *Proc. 16th Ass. Comput. Mach. Symp. on Theory of Computing*, pp. 436–445. New York: Association for Computing Machinery.

Discussion

J. C. Shepherdson (*School of Mathematics, University of Bristol, U.K.*). Professor Valiant emphasized that he was talking about *deductive inference*. Do his results apply also to other kinds of inference, for example to machines that make random guesses on the way to fixing on a program? Could he argue that they do, because a random element could always be replaced by a pseudo-random element that could be computed in polynomial time?

L. G. Valiant. The word *deductive* was intended to emphasize that the formulation constrains the learning process to converge quickly and in a demanding manner. The formulation contains a probabilistic element arising from the probabilistic distribution on the example space and, as it happens, already allows for the possibility that additionally there is randomizaton in the learning procedure itself. Although I have not found an application for this idea it is certainly worth pursuing. Whether true randomness can be replaced by pseudo-randomness in the context of polynomial time algorithms is still an open problem.

Programming as a mathematical exercise

By J. R. Abrial
26 rue des Plantes, 75014 Paris, France

This paper contains a formal framework within which logic, set theory and programming are presented together.

These elements can be presented together because, in this work, we no longer regard a (procedural) programming notation (such as PASCAL) as a notation for expressing a computation; rather, we regard it as a mere extension to the conventional language of logic and set theory. The extension constitutes a convenient (economical) way of expressing certain relational statements.

A consequence of this point of view is that the activity of program construction is transformed into that of proof construction.

To ensure that this activity of proof construction can be given a sound mechanizable foundation, we present a number of theories in the form of some basic deduction and definition rules. For instance, such theories compose the two logical calculi, a weaker version of the standard Zermelo–Fraenkel set theory, as well as some other elementary mathematical theories leading up to the construction of natural numbers. This last theory acts as a paradigm for the construction of other types such as sequences or trees. Parallel to these mathematical constructions we axiomatize a certain programming notation by giving equivalents to its basic constructs within logic and set theory. A number of other non-logical theories are also presented, which allows us to completely mechanize the calculus of proof that is implied by this framework.

0. Introduction

In the past few years, specification of computer programs has become the subject of intense activity among computer scientists; numerous specification languages and similar methods have been proposed to 'solve this problem' (see, for example, Jones (1980)). After some years of activity in this area, we have now reached the conclusion that the problem is not so much that of stating (specifying) what a computer program is supposed to do; but rather studying the *mathematical framework* within which each program is supposed to behave. For instance, the specification of a sorting program is not sufficient to construct one; it is certainly necessary to also study certain mathematical properties enjoyed by sorted sequences and by permuted ones.

Experience shows that the number of logical and mathematical tools to be used in the construction of most computer programs is quite small. In fact, such tools are essentially made up of the two logical calculi, the elementary mathematical entities (sets, relations, functions) and, finally, the first mathematically constructed types (finite subsets, natural numbers, finite sequences, finite trees). As can be seen, these are in no way comparable to what needs to be mastered by the professional mathematician.

However, once the mathematical framework in question has been established, and once the program has been formally specified within this framework, the development process by which a corresponding real program can be reached is by no means a trivial task (Jones 1980; Bjørner & Jones 1982). This is the reason why an increasing number of people think, as we do, that the gap must be bridged between a program specification (that is, a declarative statement expressing a *relation* between a program input and some output) and a program content (that is, an algorithmic statement expressing the transformation by finite means of a program input into some output). To do so, it has been proposed to make specifications possibly computable (R. Kowalski and D. A. Turner, this symposium). Compared with Professor Hoare's contribution to this symposium, what we envisage in this paper is slightly different. *We propose to make programs not necessarily executable.* In other words, we no longer regard a programming language as a notation for expressing a computation (however abstract the corresponding computer might be); rather, we regard it as a notation for expressing a relation. That some of these relations are indeed computable is then simply a happy accident.

Of course, all specifications (that is, all logical and set-theoretic relational statements) cannot fit into this 'programming' notation. This is the reason why the activity of program construction has not disappeared; it has even, we think, been clarified in that it now consists of transforming certain formal statements into others, related to the former by equivalence or implication. Such transformations can be done owing to the mathematical framework established, at the initial stage, together with the first specification of the program. In other words, and to summarize at this point, the activity of program construction has been transformed into that of *proof construction*, to be done in the realm of logic and set theory.

This paper is intended to present a *unified theoretical basis* within which this activity of 'program' construction can be developed. As already stated, this basis is essentially made up of logic and set theory together with a 'programming' notation, the constructs of which have equivalent counterparts in logic and set theory. The purpose of such a formal basis is, among others, to ensure that the activity of 'program' construction, that is, again, that of proof construction, can be *mechanically aided*. To do so, we shall also present a number of small extra theories, the role of which is to formalize what is usually written, in the form of English comments besides formal statements (i.e. that certain variables are not free in a formula, that all variables of a declaration are distinct from each other, that some expression is to be substituted for some variable in a formula, etc.). Among these small theories, one is of particular importance: the theory of variable declarations (also called schema (Morgan & Sufrin 1984)), which allows simplification and unification of set theory and programming.

The theory of sets presented here is, in a sense, weaker than the standard set theory of Zermelo and Fraenkel (herinafter called Z.F.); a noticeable difference lies in the absence of the axiom of pairing (there exists a set, the members of which are two given sets) and in that of the axiom of union (there exists a set, the members of which are the members of the members of a given set). As a consequence, the concept of ordered pair cannot be defined by using the traditional trick of Kuratowski, nor can the construction of natural numbers be done, as usual, by a cumulative hierarchy. The reason for these limitations is our intent to give to each formalized object a *type*, constructed from more elementary types through the only operations of Cartesian product, power set, set comprehension and set-theoretic fixpoint.

In fact, the theory of types presented here is just a part of set theory. It starts with the (Whitehead) constructive (fixpoint) definition of the set of finite subsets of a set, which allows one to define eventually the concept of infinity (an infinite set is one that is not a member of the set of its finite subsets); we then postulate (as in Z.F.) the existence of an infinite set. The corresponding axiom, however, does not take an existential form; rather it is expressed through a *symbol*, 'U', denoting the infinite set in question. This set constitutes, together with the empty

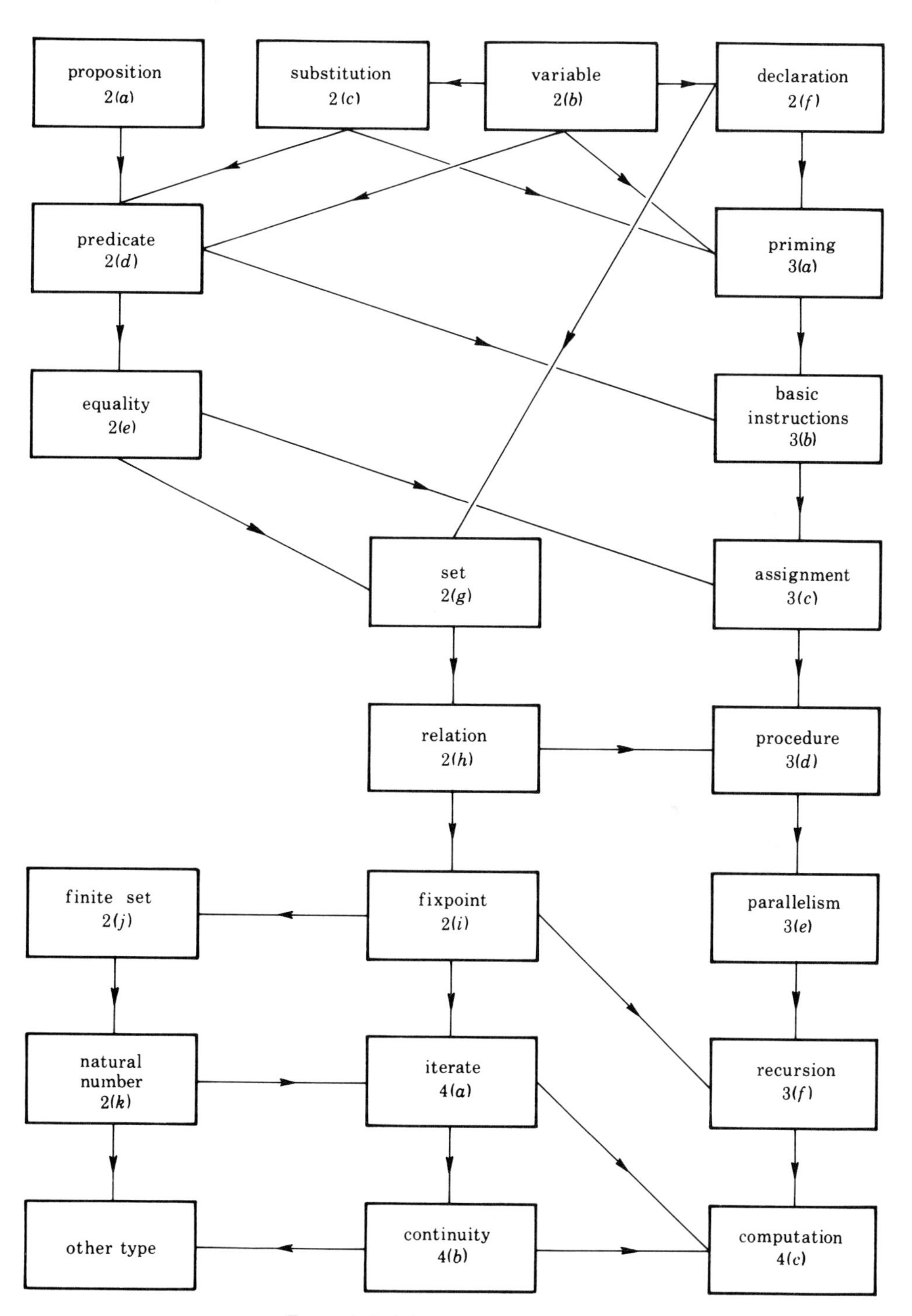

FIGURE 1. Relations between the theories.

set, our only given set. We then construct (again, as a fixpoint) the set of natural numbers as a certain subset of the power set of 'U'. From this point on, other types such as finite sequences and finite trees are easily definable.

Parallel to this presentation of logic and set theory, we define the first constructs of the 'programming' notation (namely guarding, sequencing, alternation, and local variables) (Dijkstra 1975). All these constructs are expressed solely in terms of logic (i.e. propositional calculus and predicate calculus). The 'programming language' is then extended to include an assignment and a '**skip**' (no-op) operation. These, of course, are expressed in terms of equality. A further extension deals with more 'advanced' concepts such as procedures, procedure calls (with various modes of parameter passing), parallelism and recursion. These are expressed in terms of set theory.

As will be seen later, we have carefully and intentionally avoided the possibility of writing spurious 'programs'. For instance, procedures cannot have global variables (although parameters can be passed to them 'by reference'). This precludes the 'dangerous' phenomenon of aliasing, by which the same programming variable can be reached through different paths.

It should be noted that the definition of this 'programming' notation in terms of logic and set theory *does not constitute a form of denotational semantics* (Scott & Stratchey 1970). Again, we should bear in mind that this notation is just a convenient (i.e. economical) way of formally writing certain statements of logic and set theory. This is precisely the reason that we feel it so important to clarify (and, perhaps, simplify) the definition of set theory.

Figure 1 summarizes the relations that exist between the various theories we shall present in later sections.

The remainder of this paper comprises four sections. In the first of them, we shall present some metalinguistic considerations. Section 2 contains logic and set theory. In §3 we present a theory of programming, and a theory of computation is given in §4.

1. Some metalinguistic considerations

In this section we shall present various rules that allow one to correctly 'read' a formal theory. Mostly, such rules correspond to well accepted traditions in logic and in formal mathematics. Our purpose is only to make precise practices that are often implicitly followed by the working logician and mathematician.

This section is divided into four subsections covering the following topics: (*a*) lexical considerations, (*b*) syntactical considerations, (*c*) metatheoretic considerations, describing the structures of deduction rules and of definitions that constitute a theory, (*d*) linguistic considerations, describing conventions for the well-formedness of linguistic constructs.

These considerations will purposely take the form of rather 'dry' statements, as one might find them in the description of the rules of a game. The hurried reader may skip this section (at his own risk!).

(*a*) *Lexical considerations*

(i) A formula is a non-empty sequence made up of any symboi *except for* ' ', '$\vdash$', '$\triangleq$' (blank, turnstile, definition).

(ii) In a formula, each individual symbol is meaningful, *the only exception* being bold lower case letters. In fact, one or more such letters, arranged in a continuous sequence, stand (collectively and in that order) for an individual symbol. In what follows, by extension, we shall call such a sequence also a symbol. For instance, 'P', '→', '**proc**' and '**rec**' are all symbols.

(*b*) *Syntactical considerations*

(i) All symbols have an arity that is one of 0, 1 or 2.

(ii) Upper case and non-italic letters are symbols of arity 0 (but there exist other symbols of arity 0).

(iii) In a formula, all symbols of arity 1 are prefixed, *except the symbol* '′' (prime), which is postfixed.

(iv) In a formula, all symbols of arity 2 are infixed.

(v) All symbols have the same priority of 0, *except six symbols, which are*: '|', ';', ':', '[', '{' and '′' (bar, semicolon, colon, left square bracket, left curly bracket, prime).

(vi) When priority is the same, association is from left to right. For instance, the formula '$P \wedge Q \to R \vee P$' is to be understood '$((P \wedge Q) \to R) \vee P$'. Parentheses (i.e. '(' and ')') can always be added to enhance readability or to circumvent the left to right rule.

(vii) The three symbols '|', ';' and ':' have priority −3, −2 and −1 respectively (and, as we shall see, arity 2). For instance, the formula '$X:S;Y:S \to T;Z:T|P \vee Q$' is to be understood '$(((X:S);(Y:(S \to T)));(Z:T))|(P \vee Q)$'.

(viii) The two symbols '{' and '[' have priority 1 (and, as we shall see, arity 1 and 2 respectively). Moreover, these symbols have corresponding closing symbols '}' and ']'. For instance, the formula '$P[S/X] \vee Q[S/X]$' is to be understood '$(P[(S/X)) \vee (Q[(S/X))$'.

(ix) The symbol '′' has priority 1 (and, as we have seen, arity 1).

(*c*) *Metatheoretical considerations*

A theory is defined by means of a finite number of rules of two different kinds: deduction rules and definition rules.

(i) A deduction rule is made up of two parts: first, the antecedent, which comprises zero, one or more formulae separated by a 'blank' symbol and secondly, the consequent, which is made of a single formula. Antecedent and consequent are separated by the turnstile symbol '⊢'. For instance, the following are deduction rules:

$$\text{`}P \quad P \to Q \vdash Q\text{'}, \quad \text{`}\vdash (P \vee P) \to P\text{'}.$$

(ii) A definition rule is also a rule comprising two parts: the antecedent (as for deduction rules) and the definition. Antecedent and definition are separated by the turnstile symbol '⊢'. The definition part comprises two formulae separated by the definition symbol '≙'. For instance, the following are definition rules:

$$\text{`}X\backslash A \vdash A[S/X] \triangleq A\text{'}, \quad \text{`}\vdash P \wedge Q \triangleq \sim(\sim P \vee \sim Q)\text{'}.$$

(iii) A rule, be it a deduction or a definition, stands for an infinite number of other rules called its *instances*. An instance of a rule can be obtained mechanically by simultaneously replacing all occurrences of some (or all) upper case non-italic letters contained in it by corresponding formulae. For instance, the rule '$P \vee Q \quad (P \vee Q) \to (Q \vee P) \vdash Q \vee P$' is an instance of the rule '$P \quad P \to Q \vdash Q$' because the former has been obtained by simultaneously replacing all occurrences of 'P' and 'Q' in the latter by '$P \vee Q$' and '$Q \vee P$' respectively.

(*d*) *Well-formedness*

(i) Five non-logical theories, which are fully described in Appendix 1, are mainly concerned with the following unary symbols: '**pred**', '**term**', '**vrbl**', '**decl**', and '**inst**'.

(ii) Formulae such as '**pred**(P)', '**term**(T)', '**vrbl**(X)', '**decl**(D)' and '**inst**(I)' are respectively to be read 'P is a well formed predicate', 'T is a well formed Term', 'X is a well formed variable', 'D is a well formed declaration', 'I is a well formed instruction'.

(iii) From now on, and to simplify other theories, we shall suppose that occurrences of certain upper case letters in a rule imply that certain corresponding formulae such as those described are implicitly present in its antecedent. The association between these unary symbols and the upper case letters is given in table 1.

TABLE 1. ASSOCIATION BETWEEN UNARY SYMBOLS AND UPPER CASE LETTERS

pred	P	Q	R	—
term	S	T	U	V
vrbl	X	Y	Z	N
decl	D	E	F	—
inst	I	J	K	—

For instance, a rule such as '$\vdash (S = T) \rightarrow (P[S/X] \rightarrow P[T/X])$' stands for the more complete rule:

$$\text{'}\mathbf{pred}(P)\quad \mathbf{term}(S)\quad \mathbf{term}(T)\quad \mathbf{vrbl}(X) \vdash (S = T) \rightarrow (P[S/X] \rightarrow P[T/X])\text{'}.$$

2. LOGIC AND SET THEORY

In this section we introduce logic and set theory through a number of embedded theories, starting with propositional calculus and ending with natural numbers. Each theory will correspond to a separate subsection organized as follows.

We shall first explain informally what the subject of the theory is. To do so, we shall introduce the specific symbols of the theory together with their English meaning. We shall also explain the main properties of each symbol. All this will be formalized through a series of rules that constitute the theory.

As already mentioned (see §1 (*c*)), we have two kinds of rules: deduction rules and definition rules. Each deduction rule may have an antecedent, in which case it is a rule of inference, or no antecedent, in which case it is an axiom. We have already mentioned (see §1 (*d*)) that the formulae involved in the antecedent of a rule may quite well be non-logical statements (i.e. statements that do not belong to the language of logic or set theory).

The definition part of a definition rule introduces a (symmetric) *syntactic equivalence* between the formulae that lie on each side of the '$\triangleq$' symbol. Thus in this paper, a definition rule (which can be *basic*, that is given in a theory, or *derived*, that is proved within a theory) means more than the simple introduction of an abbreviation, which is traditionally implied by the word 'definition'. Moreover a definition rule may also have an antecedent; in this case, the syntactic equivalence implied by the definition is subjected to a number of conditions that must be checked before applying the definition in a proof. For instance, the following definition rule (in fact a derived definition rule of predicate calculus):

$$\text{'}X \backslash P \vdash EX.(P \wedge Q) \triangleq P \wedge (EX.P)\text{'}$$

means that the formula '$EX.(P \wedge Q)$' may be replaced by '$P \wedge (EX.P)$' (and *vice versa*) in the midst of any logical formula; this transformation, however, is subjected to the condition '$X \backslash P$', which means 'X is not free in P'. As can be seen, '$X \backslash P$' is not a logical statement. It is, however, a formal statement to which there corresponds a theory, the theory of variables (see §2 (*b*)), which allows one to formally prove statements of this kind.

In some theories, the introduction of new symbols may necessitate the extension of previously defined theories.

Each section will finish with statements of the most useful results of the theory. These statements take the form of other (derived) deduction or definition rules. To keep this paper to a reasonable length, we have decided not to give any formal proof. Instead, we occasionally give some hints.

(*a*) *Propositional calculus*: P

Propositional calculus formalizes elementary reasonings involving the four basic Boolean connectives. The theory presented here is known as the Hilbert–Ackermann system; however, these authors recognized that it was essentially due to A. N. Whitehead and B. Russell. We have only added conditional definition P6, which cannot be proved within the logical system alone.

symbol	$\sim$	$\vee$	$\rightarrow$	$\wedge$
arity	1	2	2	2

Main rules

P1 $\vdash P \rightarrow (P \vee Q)$
P2 $\vdash (P \vee Q) \rightarrow (Q \vee P)$
P3 $\vdash (P \vee P) \rightarrow P$
P4 $\vdash (Q \rightarrow R) \rightarrow ((P \vee Q) \rightarrow (P \vee R))$
P5 $P \quad P \rightarrow Q \vdash Q$
P6 $P \rightarrow Q \quad Q \rightarrow P \vdash P \triangleq Q$

Abbreviations

P7 $\vdash P \rightarrow Q \triangleq {\sim} P \vee Q$
P8 $\vdash P \wedge Q \triangleq {\sim}({\sim} P \vee {\sim} Q)$

Among the standard results of propositional calculus, two seem to be quite significant. These are the rule of excluded middle and the rule of double negation.

$\vdash P \vee {\sim} P$
$\vdash P \triangleq {\sim}{\sim} P$

(*b*) *Theory of variables*: V

The theory of variables (our first non-logical theory), axiomatizes expressions or assertions such as 'a variable that does not occur free in formulae A and B' or 'the variable X is not free in A' or 'the variables X and Y are distinct variables'. To do so, we introduce two symbols of arity 2, '^' and '\'. The formula 'A^B' is the formal translation of the first quoted English sentence; consequently 'A^B' *is* a variable. The formula '$X \backslash A$' corresponds to the second quoted sentence. When 'A' is 'Y', we obtain '$X \backslash Y$', which corresponds to the formal translation of the third quoted sentence.

As can be seen in Appendix 1, if 'X' and 'Y' are well formed variables and if 'X' is distinct from 'Y' (i.e. 'X\Y') then 'X,Y' *is also a well formed variable*. Consequently, we have to explain in this theory under which circumstances the variable 'X,Y' is not free in the formula 'A'. This is obviously when both 'X' and 'Y' are not themselves free in 'A'.

symbol	ˆ	\	,
arity	2	2	2

Main rules

V1 $\vdash A\hat{}B \triangleq B\hat{}A$
V2 $\vdash A\hat{}(B\hat{}C) \triangleq (A\hat{}B)\hat{}C$
V3 $\vdash (A\hat{}B)\backslash A$
V4 $\vdash X\backslash Y \triangleq Y\backslash X$
V5 $X\backslash A \quad Y\backslash A \vdash (X,Y)\backslash A$

Unless otherwise stated, all symbols that we shall introduce will be subjected to one of the following rules depending upon their arity. In these rules, 'ω' stands for any such symbol.

V6 $\vdash X\backslash\omega$
V7 $X\backslash A \vdash X\backslash\omega A$
V8 $X\backslash A \quad X\backslash B \vdash X\backslash(A\omega B)$

Note that rule V7 is already applicable to '$\sim$' and rule V8 to '$\vee$'.

(*c*) *Theory of variable substitution*: S

The theory of variable substitution (again, a non-logical theory) axiomatizes expressions such as 'the formula A where the term S has been substituted for all free occurrences of the variable X'. To do so, we introduce the symbol '[' (which, as has been seen already (see §1 (*b*)), is a symbol of arity 2, priority 1 and with a corresponding closing symbol ']'), and the symbol '/' so that the formula 'A[S/X]' is the formal translation of the above quoted sentence.

The first rule of this theory explains the essence of substitution, namely that 'S' substituted for 'X' in 'X' is 'S'. We, then, give general rules showing under which circumstances a substitution has no effect (i.e. when the variable is substituted for itself, when the variable is not free in the formula). Finally, we give rules for successive substitutions as well as for simultaneous ones.

symbol	[	/
arity	2	2

Main rules

S1 $\vdash X[S/X] \triangleq S$
S2 $\vdash A[X/X] \triangleq A$
S3 $X\backslash A \vdash A[S/X] \triangleq A$
S4 $Y\backslash A \vdash A[Y/X][S/Y] \triangleq A[S/X]$
S5 $X\backslash Y \quad X\backslash T \vdash A[S/X][T/Y] \triangleq A[T/Y][S[T/Y]/X]$
S6 $X\backslash Y \quad Y\backslash S \vdash A[(S,T)/(X,Y)] \triangleq A[S/X][T/Y]$

Extensions to theory V

V9 $X\backslash S \vdash X\backslash A[S/X]$
V10 $X\backslash A \quad X\backslash S \vdash X\backslash A[S/Y]$

As for theory V, *and unless otherwise stated*, all symbols that we shall introduce thereafter will be subjected to one of the following rules depending upon their arity. In these rules 'ω' stands for any such symbol.

S7 $\vdash (\omega A)[S/X] \triangleq \omega(A[S/X])$
S8 $\vdash (A\omega B)[S/X] \triangleq (A[S/X])\ \omega(B[S/X])$

The main result of this theory is the commutativity of simultaneous substitution. It can be stated as

$$X\backslash Y \vdash A[(S,T)/(X,Y)] \triangleq A[(T,S)/(Y,X)].$$

This result can be proved by using rules S4, S5 and S6 together with the auxiliary variables '$A\hat{}S\hat{}X$' and '$(A\hat{}T\hat{}Y)\hat{}(A\hat{}S\hat{}X)$'.

(*d*) *Predicate calculus*: Q

Predicate calculus formalizes reasonings that involve objects. Formulae denoting objects are called terms. For the moment, well formed terms are variables only (see Appendix 1 for a complete definition of well formed terms).

symbol	*E*	*A*	.
arity	1	1	2

Main rules

Q1 $\vdash P[S/X] \rightarrow (EX . P)$
Q2 $P \vdash AX . P$
Q3 $X\backslash Q \vdash (AX . (P \rightarrow Q)) \rightarrow ((EX . P) \rightarrow Q)$

Abreviations

Q4 $X\backslash Y \vdash E(X,Y) . P \triangleq EX . (EY . P)$
Q5 $\vdash AX . P \triangleq \sim(EX . \sim P)$

Extension to theory V

V11 $\vdash X\backslash(EX . P)$
V12 $X\backslash P \vdash X\backslash(EY . P)$

Extension to theory S

S9 $Y\backslash X \quad Y\backslash S \vdash (EY . P)[S/X] \triangleq EY . P[S/X]$

Rule V11 defines the *scope* of the quantifier '*E*' by explaining that the variable 'X' is not free in '*E*X . P'. Rule S9 explains under which circumstances a substitution can be performed within a quantified formula, namely when the quantified variable, here 'Y', is not free in the substituting term 'S'.

Among the many results that can be proved within predicate calculus, four seem to be particularly useful. They deal with the distribution of the quantifier 'E' (resp. 'A') over the Boolean connectives '$\vee$' and '$\wedge$', with the commutativity of ',' within the quantifier 'E' (resp. 'A'), and with changes of variable within quantified formulae.

$$\vdash E\mathrm{X}.(\mathrm{P} \vee \mathrm{Q}) \triangleq (E\mathrm{X}.\mathrm{P}) \vee (E\mathrm{X}.\mathrm{Q})$$
$$\mathrm{X}\backslash\mathrm{P} \vdash E\mathrm{X}.(\mathrm{P} \wedge \mathrm{Q}) \triangleq \mathrm{P} \wedge (E\mathrm{X}.\mathrm{Q})$$
$$\mathrm{X}\backslash\mathrm{Y} \vdash E(\mathrm{X},\mathrm{Y}).\mathrm{P} \triangleq E(\mathrm{Y},\mathrm{X}).\mathrm{P}$$
$$\mathrm{X}\backslash\mathrm{Y} \quad \mathrm{Y}\backslash\mathrm{P} \vdash E\mathrm{Y}.(\mathrm{P}[\mathrm{Y}/\mathrm{X}]) \triangleq E\mathrm{X}.\mathrm{P}$$

(e) *Equality theory*: E

Equality theory introduces, as expected, the equality symbol '$=$', which is not to be confused with the definition metasymbol '$\triangleq$'.

symbol	$=$	$\neq$
arity	2	2

Main rules

E1 $\mathrm{X}\backslash\mathrm{S} \vdash E\mathrm{X}.((\mathrm{X} = \mathrm{S}) \wedge \mathrm{P}) \triangleq \mathrm{P}[\mathrm{S}/\mathrm{X}]$

E2 $\vdash (\mathrm{S},\mathrm{T}) = (\mathrm{U},\mathrm{V}) \triangleq (\mathrm{S} = \mathrm{U}) \wedge (\mathrm{T} = \mathrm{V})$

Abbreviation

E3 $\vdash \mathrm{S} \neq \mathrm{T} \triangleq \sim(\mathrm{S} = \mathrm{T})$

As can be seen, we have not defined equality theory using the more traditional rules

$$\vdash (\mathrm{S} = \mathrm{T}) \rightarrow (\mathrm{P}[\mathrm{S}/\mathrm{X}] \rightarrow \mathrm{P}[\mathrm{T}/\mathrm{X}])$$
$$\vdash \mathrm{S} = \mathrm{S}$$

instead of rule E1. The reason for this choice is not only because these results can be proved (Hao Wang) from E1, but also because we wanted to emphasize the importance of rule E1 in what follows.

(f) *Theory of declarations*: D

The theory of declarations is our last non-logical theory. It formalizes the concept of declaration.

An elementary declaration is made of a variable together with a term that is called the *type* of the variable; this association is expressed by the binary symbol ':'. Two declarations can be combined (put together) by using the binary symbol ';'. Moreover, a declaration can be restricted by a predicate by using the symbol '|'. The theory of declarations is first concerned with the basic properties of these symbols.

symbol	:	;	|
arity	2	2	2

Main rules (part 1)

D1 $\vdash \mathrm{D};(\mathrm{E};\mathrm{F}) \triangleq (\mathrm{D};\mathrm{E});\mathrm{F}$

D2 $\vdash \mathrm{D};(\mathrm{E}|\mathrm{P}) \triangleq (\mathrm{D};\mathrm{E})|\mathrm{P}$

D3 $\vdash (\mathrm{D}|\mathrm{P});\mathrm{E} \triangleq (\mathrm{D};\mathrm{E})|\mathrm{P}$

D4 $\vdash (\mathrm{D}|\mathrm{P})|\mathrm{Q} \triangleq \mathrm{D}|(\mathrm{P} \wedge \mathrm{Q})$

As can be seen, a declaration can always be put in a *normalized form* made up of the left association of the combinations of all its elementary declarations followed by conjunction of all their restrictions.

We now introduce two more symbols, namely 'α' and 'σ', which, when applied to a declaration, yield its *alphabet* and *signature* respectively. The alphabet of a declaration is a variable comprising the individual variables of its elementary declarations. The signature of a declaration is a predicate involving a new binary symbol '$\in$', the *membership symbol.*

symbol	α	σ	$\in$
arity	1	1	2

Main rules (*part* 2)

D5 $\vdash \alpha(X:T) \triangleq X$
D6 $\vdash \alpha(D;X:T) \triangleq (\alpha D),X$
D7 $\vdash \alpha(D|P) \triangleq \alpha D$
D8 $\vdash \sigma(X:T) \triangleq X \in T$
D9 $\vdash \sigma(D;E) \triangleq (\sigma D) \wedge (\sigma E)$
D10 $\vdash \sigma(D|P) \triangleq (\sigma D) \wedge P$

As can be seen, alphabets are only defined for normalized declarations so that two declarations having the same normalized form have the same alphabet.

Finally, we introduce yet another form of declaration, the *empty* declaration, denoted by the symbol '**skip**'. Its obvious axiomatic properties are given.

symbol	**skip**
arity	0

Main rules (*part* 3)

D11 $\vdash$ **skip**$;D \triangleq D$
D12 $\vdash D;$**skip** $\triangleq D$
D13 $\vdash \sigma($**skip**$)$

We now extend the theory of variables to deal with variables of the form '$\alpha(D;E)$' or '$\alpha($**skip**$)$'.

Extension to theory V

V13 $\vdash \alpha(D;E)\backslash A \triangleq (\alpha D,\alpha E)\backslash A$
V14 $\vdash \alpha($**skip**$)\backslash A$
V15 $\vdash \alpha($**skip**$), X \triangleq X$
V16 $\vdash X,\alpha($**skip**$) \triangleq X$

As can be seen, '$\alpha($**skip**$)$' is the 'non-variable'. We also extend predicate calculus so that quantification may be applied to declarations as well.

Extension to theory Q

Q6 $\vdash ED\,.\,P \triangleq E(\alpha D)\,.\,(\sigma D \wedge P)$
Q7 $\vdash E\alpha(D;E)\,.\,P \triangleq E(\alpha D,\alpha E)\,.\,P$
Q8 $\vdash AD\,.\,P \triangleq \sim ED\,.\,\sim P$

The following results can be proved.

$$\vdash \alpha(D;E)[(S,T)/(\alpha D,\alpha E)] = U \triangleq (\alpha D,\alpha E)[U/\alpha(D;E)] = (S,T)$$
$$\vdash E\alpha(\mathbf{skip}) \,.\, P \triangleq P$$
$$\vdash A\alpha(\mathbf{skip}) \,.\, P \triangleq P$$

To prove the first of these results one may use rules V13, Q7 and E1.

(*g*) *Set theory*: T

Set theory, as defined here, involves essentially two kinds of terms introduced by the unary symbols '{' and '*P*'. (Remember (§1 (*b*)) that '{' is a symbol of arity 1 having a closing symbol '}'.) A term such as '{T|D}', where 'T' is a (well formed) term and 'D' is a (well formed) declaration (see Appendix 1 for the rigorous definition of well-formedness) is to be read 'the set of objects of the form T indexed by D'. A term such as '*P*T' is to be read 'the set of all subsets of T'.

The purpose of this theory is to give equivalents for predicates such as '$S \in \{T|D\}$' and '$S \in PT$'. Of course, set equality is also axiomatized as usual, by using the operation of set inclusion '$\subset$'. Finally, we axiomatize the empty set '$\varnothing$'.

symbol	{	*P*	$\varnothing$
arity	1	1	0

Main rules

T1 $\vdash (S \subset T) \wedge (T \subset S) \rightarrow (T = S)$
T2 $\alpha D \backslash S \vdash S \in \{T|D\} \triangleq ED \,.\, (S = T)$
T3 $\vdash S \in PT \triangleq S \subset T$
T4 $\vdash S \notin \varnothing$

We shall now define a number of abbreviations for set inclusion, set comprehension, singleton, Cartesian product and non-membership.

symbol	$\subset$	$\times$	$\notin$
arity	2	2	2

Abbreviations

A1 $X \backslash S \quad X \backslash T \vdash S \subset T \triangleq A(X:S) \,.\, (X \in T)$
A2 $\vdash \{D\} \triangleq \{\alpha D|D\}$
A3 $\vdash \{T\} \triangleq \{T|\mathbf{skip}\}$
A4 $\vdash S \times T \triangleq \{X:S;Y:T\}$
A5 $\vdash S \notin T \triangleq \sim (S \in T)$

The main result at this point shows that a set such as '{T|D}' can be typed whenever the term 'T' can itself be typed. Other traditional results have to do with the simpler forms of set as defined in A2 and A4.

$$\alpha D \backslash S \vdash (AD \,.\, (T \in S)) \rightarrow (\{T|D\} \in PS)$$
$$X \backslash S \vdash T \in \{X:S|P\} \triangleq (T \in S) \wedge P[T/X]$$
$$\vdash (U,V) \in (S \times T) \triangleq (U \in S) \wedge (V \in T)$$

It is also necessary to extend the theory of variables and the theory of substitution. This is done in an obvious way as follows.

Extension to theory V

$$\text{V17} \quad \vdash \alpha D\backslash\{T|D\}$$
$$\text{V18} \quad X\backslash T \quad X\backslash D \vdash X\backslash\{T|D\}$$

Extension to theory S

$$\text{S10} \quad \alpha D\backslash X \quad \alpha D\backslash S \vdash \{T|D\}[S/X] \mathrel{\hat{=}} \{T[S/X]|D[S/X]\}$$

(*h*) *Theory of relations and functions*: R

We shall now introduce the symbols '$\nrightarrow$' and '$\rightarrow$' to define, as usual, the set of all partial functions and the set of all total functions from one set to another. To conveniently formalize the set of partial functions, we use another binary symbol, '$\lceil$', which, when applied to a predicate and to a variable, as in '$P\lceil X$', is to be read 'predicate P is functional in X'. Finally, we introduce the quantifier 'λ' used to define total functions by abstraction.

symbol	$\nrightarrow$	$\rightarrow$	$\lceil$	λ
arity	2	2	2	1

Main rules

$$\text{R1} \quad Y\backslash P \quad Z\backslash P \vdash P\lceil X \mathrel{\hat{=}} A(Y,Z)\,.\,(P[Y/X] \wedge P[Z/X] \rightarrow (Y = Z))$$
$$\text{R2} \quad \vdash S \nrightarrow T \mathrel{\hat{=}} \{Z\!:\!P(S\times T)|A(X\!:\!S)\,.\,((X,Y\in Z)\lceil Y)\}$$
$$\text{R3} \quad \vdash S \rightarrow T \mathrel{\hat{=}} \{Z\!:\!S\nrightarrow T|A(X\!:\!S)\,.\,(EY\,.\,(X,Y\in Z))\}$$
$$\text{R4} \quad \vdash \lambda D\,.\,T \mathrel{\hat{=}} \{\alpha D,T|D\}$$

We shall now extend set theory to formalize the notion of a total function *evaluation*. If 'Y' is a total function from 'S' to 'T', then the term 'Y[X]' (where 'X' is supposed to be a member of 'S') is called the *value* of 'Y' at 'X'.

Extension to theory T

$$\text{T5} \quad \vdash A(X\!:\!S;Y\!:\!S\rightarrow T)\,.\,(X,Y[X]\in Y)$$

The main results at this point concern the typing of a function evaluation, that of a function defined by lambda abstraction, and the correspondence between evaluation and term substitution.

$$\vdash A(Y\!:\!S\rightarrow T;X\!:\!S)\,.\,(Y[X]\in T)$$
$$\alpha D/S \vdash (AD\,.\,(T\in S)) \rightarrow (\lambda D\,.\,T \in (\{D\}\rightarrow S))$$
$$\alpha D/S \vdash (AD\,.\,(T\in S)) \rightarrow (A(X\!:\!\{D\})\,.\,((\lambda D\,.\,T)[X] = T[X/\alpha D])$$

The last result is of particular importance; it shows under which circumstances one is able to equate a lambda-abstraction evaluation (i.e. '$(\lambda D\,.\,T)[X]$') with the substitution of the actual parameters (i.e. 'X') for the formal ones (i.e. 'αD') in its body (i.e. '$T[X/\alpha D]$'). This is (1) when the body in question is well typed for all typed values of the formal parameters (i.e. '$AD\,.\,(T\in S)$') and (2) when the actual parameters agree with the type of the formal ones (i.e. '$A(X\!:\!\{D\})$').

(*i*) *Set-theoretic fixpoint*: FP

In this extension to set theory, we introduce four symbols, namely '$\cap$', 'ϕ', 'M' and 'μ', which correspond respectively to the concepts of intersection of a set of sets, fixpoint and monotonicity of a set function, and minimalization.

symbol	$\cap$	ϕ	M	μ
arity	1	1	1	1

Main rules

FP1 $\vdash A(Z:PPS|Z \neq \varnothing).(\cap Z = \{X:S|A(Y:Z).(X \in Y)\})$
FP2 $\vdash A(Y:PS \to PS).(\phi Y = \cap\{X:PS|Y[X] \subset X\})$
FP3 $\vdash MS \triangleq \{Z:PS \to PS|A(X:PS;Y:PS|X \subset Y).(Z[X] \subset Z[Y])\}$
FP4 $\vdash \mu(X:PS).T \triangleq \phi(\lambda(X:PS).T)$

The main result (Tarski 1955) at this point shows that the fixpoint of a monotonic set function (definition FP3) is indeed a 'fixed-point', that it is the smallest of them, and consequently, that any subset of it, provided it is also a fixpoint, is indeed equal to it.

$\vdash A(Y:MS).(Y[\phi Y] = \phi Y)$
$\vdash A(Y:MS;X:PS|X = Y[X]).(\phi Y \subset X)$
$\vdash A(Y:MS;X:PS|X \subset \phi Y|X = Y[X]).(X = \phi Y)$

The last result is important because it allows one to reason by *induction* to prove universal properties for sets defined by the fixpoint operator 'ϕ' applied to monotonic set functions (Burstall 1969; Park 1969).

(*j*) *Finite subsets of a set*: F

The previous theory has given us the tools that allow us to define inductively the set of all finite subsets of a given set. For this, we only need to introduce the operation '^' of adding an element to a set. The set '*F*S' of finite subsets of 'S' is then defined as the smallest subset of '*P*S', which contains the empty set '$\varnothing$' and which is closed under the operation defined by the symbol '^'.

symbol	^	F
arity	2	1

Main rules

F1 $\vdash A(X:S;Y:PS).(X\hat{}Y = \{Z:S|(Z = X) \vee (Z \in Y)\})$
F2 $\vdash FS \triangleq \mu(Z:PPS).(\varnothing\hat{}\{X\hat{}Y|X:S;Y:Z\})$

The main result here concerns the possibility of proving properties of '*F*S' by induction.

$\vdash \varnothing \in FS$
$\vdash A(X:S;Y:FS).(X\hat{}Y \in FS)$
$P[\varnothing/Y] \quad A(X:S;Y:FS|P).P[X\hat{}Y/Y] \vdash A(Y:FS).P$

An infinite set is one that is not a member of its finite subsets. An interesting property of infinite sets is that they are indeed infinite; in other words, the set difference between an infinite set and one of its finite subsets *is never empty*.

$\vdash S \notin FS \to (A(Y:FS).(\{X:S|X \notin Y\} \neq \varnothing))$

(*k*) *Natural numbers*: N

To construct the natural numbers, one must postulate the existence of an infinite set. We shall suppose that such a set is (God) given to us; its name is 'U'.

Although we can define the natural numbers without it, it is also convenient to suppose that, for each *non-empty* set 'S', there exists a *privileged member of it*, denoted by 'τS'. These elements constitute the last two rules of set theory.

symbol	U	τ
arity	0	1

Extension to theory T

T6 $\vdash U \notin FU$
T7 $\vdash S \neq \varnothing \rightarrow (\tau S \in S)$

Given a finite subset 'X' of 'U' we define its successor 'σ' by adding to it the privileged element of the set difference between 'U' and 'X'. We already know (§2 (*j*)) that such a set difference is not empty because 'U' is infinite and 'X' is one of its finite subsets. The set 'N' of natural numbers is then defined to be the smallest subset of 'FU', which contains the empty set (that is, '0') and which is closed under the successor operation 'σ'.

symbol	σ	N	0
arity	1	0	0

Main rules

N1 $\vdash A(X{:}FU)\,.\,(\sigma X = (\tau\{Y{:}U \mid Y \notin X\}\hat{}X))$
N2 $\vdash 0 \triangleq \varnothing$
N3 $\vdash N \triangleq \mu(X{:}PFU)\,.\,(0\hat{}\{\sigma Y \mid Y{:}X\})$

As expected, the main results are the five 'axioms' of Peano.

$\vdash 0 \in N$
$\vdash A(X{:}N)\,.\,(\sigma X \in N)$
$\vdash A(X{:}N)\,.\,(\sigma X \neq 0)$
$\vdash A(X{:}N; Y{:}N \mid X \neq Y)\,.\,(\sigma X \neq \sigma Y)$
$P[0/X] \quad A(X{:}N \mid P)\,.\,P[\sigma X/X] \vdash A(X{:}N)\,.\,P$

The four arithmetic operations can then be defined as well as the minimum of a non-empty subset of 'N'. Other types, such as finite sequences and finite trees, are also easily definable.

3. Theory of programming

As for logic and set theory, the theory of programming is made up of a series of embedded theories. The first of them is an extension to the theory of variables (§2 (*b*)). We then find various theories within which the features of the 'programming' notation are gradually introduced.

(*a*) *Theory of priming*

In this section we extend the 'variable language' by introducing the unary symbol ''' (prime) (remember (§2 (*b*)) that it is a postfixed symbol of priority 1). If 'X' is a well formed variable then so is 'X′'. The variable 'X′' is distinct from 'X' and if 'X' and 'Y' are distinct variables then so are 'X′' and 'Y′'. The priming of the variable 'X,Y' is 'X′,Y′'.

symbol ′
arity 1

Extension to theory V

V19 $\vdash X \backslash X'$
V20 $\vdash X \backslash Y \triangleq X' \backslash Y'$
V21 $\vdash (X,Y)' \triangleq X',Y'$

By extension, the priming of a declaration corresponds to that of its alphabet.

Extension to theory D

D14 $\vdash D' \triangleq D[(\alpha D)'/\alpha D]$

An 'interesting' result is the following.

$\vdash$ **skip**′ $\triangleq$ **skip**

(*b*) *Theory of programming*: *basic structures*

An instruction (of the 'programming' notation) is an incomplete predicate that can only be completed by a declaration. This is accomplished by an operation denoted by the binary symbol 'π'.

Given a declaration 'D' and an instruction 'I', 'DπI' is a predicate that indicates how the values stored in the memories bearing the same names and types as those of the variables declared in 'D', are to be affected by the execution of 'I'.

(The use of expressions such as 'value stored', 'memory', 'execution' constitutes an obvious abuse of language. As already mentioned in the introduction, the proposed 'programming' notation does not constitute a genuine programming language; rather, it is a notation for writing certain logical and set-theoretic statements. However, and because certain features of this notation look like those of some existing programming languages, we have taken the liberty of explaining them *informally* in operational terms.)

More precisely, 'DπI' is a predicate involving the variables 'αD' and 'αD′'. The former denotes the values stored in the corresponding memories *just before* the execution of 'I' (these values are members of the set '{D}') and the latter denotes the values stored in the *same* memories *just after* the execution of 'I' (these values are also members of '{D}'). The predicate 'DπI' is obviously independent of the order of the elementary declarations in 'D'.

We now introduce the basic 'control' structures of the notation. Again, we shall give some informal explanation in terms of 'execution' as if these control structures were genuine programming features.

When the predicate 'P' holds, the execution of 'P→I' has the same effect as that of the instruction 'I'. When 'P' does not hold, however, the execution of 'P→I' does not give any result (which is *not* the same as having no effect).

The execution of 'I;J' corresponds as usual, to the execution of the instruction 'I' followed by that of the instruction 'J'. If one of the two does not give any result, then their sequential composition does not give any result either.

The effect of the execution of '$I\Box J$' is that of the execution of instruction 'I' *or* that of the execution of instruction 'J', the choice between the two being arbitrary. If one of the two does not give any result, then the effect of their non-deterministic alternation is that of the other. In this respect, the non-determinism involved in this alternation is said to be 'angelic'.

Finally, in the execution of '**loc**(D) . I', the instruction 'I' may use the variables declared in 'D' as local memories. Note that a non-initialized memory has nevertheless a value stored in it; this value is unknown. Again, we have here a very unrealistic situation.

symbol	$\Box$	$\rightarrow$	;	**loc**
arity	2	2	2	1

Main rules

I1 $\vdash (D\pi I) \rightarrow \sigma(D;D')$
I2 $\vdash (D;E)\pi I \triangleq (E;D)\pi I$
I3 $\vdash D\pi(P \rightarrow I) \triangleq P \wedge (D\pi I)$
I4 $\vdash D\pi(I;J) \triangleq EX.((D\pi I)[X/\alpha D'] \wedge (D\pi J)[X/\alpha D])$
I5 $\vdash D\pi(I\Box J) \triangleq (D\pi I) \vee (D\pi J)$
I6 $\vdash D\pi(\mathbf{loc}(E).I) \triangleq E\alpha(E;E').((D;E)\pi I)$

It should now be clear that the English expression 'instruction I does not give any result (in the context of the declaration D)' is formalized by '$\sim(D\pi I)$ is a tautology'. The main and obvious results concern the associativity of ';', the commutativity of '$\Box$' and the distributivity of ';' over '$\Box$'.

$\vdash D\pi(I;J;K) \triangleq D\pi(I;(J;K))$
$\vdash D\pi(I\Box J) \triangleq D\pi(J\Box I)$
$\vdash D\pi((I\Box J);K) \triangleq D\pi((I;K)\Box(J;K))$
$\vdash D\pi(I;(J\Box K)) \triangleq D\pi((I;J)\Box(I;K))$

Note that the instruction '**loc**(**skip**|P) . I' has the effect of imposing that the predicate 'P' is an *invariant* of instruction 'I'.

(c) *Assignment*

At first, assignment may seem to be easy to formalize: given a variable 'X' and a term 'T', the execution of '$X \leftarrow T$' modifies the contents of the memories associated with the individual variables in 'X' by storing in them values corresponding to the evaluation of 'T'. What we have to formalize, however, is not the instruction '$X \leftarrow T$', which is, as already mentioned, an incomplete predicate; rather, we have to give an equivalent to the predicate '$D\pi(X \leftarrow T)$'. If some variables in 'X' are not declared in 'D', we cannot say anything about this predicate. On the other hand, if some variables declared in 'D' do not occur in 'X', we have to say something about them, namely that *they are not modified by the execution of this instruction.* Note that the values stored initially, and the final values as well, must belong to the set '{D}'. We shall also formalize the instruction '**skip**', which has no effect on any memory whatsoever.

symbol	$\leftarrow$	**skip**
arity	2	0

Extension to theory I

$$\text{I7} \quad \vdash D\pi(\mathbf{skip}) \triangleq \sigma D \wedge (\alpha D' = \alpha D)$$
$$\text{I8} \quad A(D;E).(\sigma(D;E))[T/\alpha D] \vdash (D;E)\pi(\alpha D \leftarrow T) \triangleq \sigma D \wedge (\alpha D' = T) \wedge (E\pi(\mathbf{skip}))$$

The main result at this point concerns the sequential composition of an assignment with another instruction.

$$\vdash (D;E)\pi(\alpha D \leftarrow T;I) \triangleq \sigma D \wedge ((D;E)\pi I)[T/\alpha D]$$

Note that '$(\mathbf{skip})\pi(\mathbf{skip})$' is a tautology.

(*d*) *Procedures and procedure calls*

Given an instruction 'I' and a declaration 'D', the construct '**proc**(D) . I' is a procedure. The formal parameters of this procedure are specified in the declaration 'D'. The body of the procedure is the instruction 'I'.

Given a procedure 'S' and a variable 'X', the construct 'S[X]' is an instruction that is the call of the procedure 'S'. The actual parameters of this call are those individual variables occurring in 'X'. (Thus, actual parameters are passed 'by reference').

A procedure such as '**proc**(D) . I' *is a binary relation*; more precisely, it is the subset of '{D} × {D}', the members of which are such that the predicate 'DπI' holds. This definition dictates that of 'DπS[X]': if 'X' is exactly 'αD' then 'DπS[X]' is equivalent to the membership of the pair '(αD,αD′)' to the binary relation 'S', provided, however, that 'S' is a binary relation of the right type, namely '*P*({D} × {D})' (we shall abbreviate this set by '*R*D'). If some variables in 'D' are not in 'X', then we have a '**skip**' action on these variables, as for assignment. Finally, if some variables in 'X' are not declared in 'D', we cannot say anything about the predicate 'DπS[X]'.

symbol	**proc**	[	*R*
arity	1	2	1

Extension to theory I

$$\text{I9} \quad \vdash \mathbf{proc}(D).I \triangleq \{\alpha D,\alpha D' \mid (D;D' \mid D\pi I)\}$$
$$\text{I10} \quad \alpha D \backslash S \quad AE.(S \in RD) \vdash (D;E)\pi S[\alpha D] \triangleq ((\alpha D,\alpha D') \in S) \wedge (E\pi(\mathbf{skip}))$$

Extension to theory A (*abbreviations for set theory*)

$$\text{A6} \quad \vdash RD \triangleq P(\{D\} \times \{D\})$$

Note that we can unify procedure calls and assignments, as the predicate '$\sigma D \wedge (\alpha D' = T)$' involved in rule I8 can be rewritten '$(\alpha D,\alpha D') \in (\lambda D.T)$' (provided '$\lambda D.T$' is a genuine total function from '{D}' to '{D}'). As a consequence, we have the definition:

$$\text{I11} \quad \vdash \alpha D \leftarrow T \triangleq (\lambda D.T)[\alpha D].$$

(It should be clear that the formula '$(\lambda D.T)[\alpha D]$', being a term and at the same time an instruction, is nevertheless not ambiguous. This is so because these distinct usages of the same formula never occur within the same linguistic context.) To deal directly with guarded assignments, we have the special case

$$\text{I11}' \quad \vdash P \rightarrow (\alpha D \leftarrow T) \triangleq (\lambda(D \mid P).T)[\alpha D].$$

As can be seen, we cannot deal with procedures having global variable assignments. In fact, no genuine predicate can ever be transformed into a construct such as '$D\pi I$', where 'I' would contain an assignment to a variable not declared in 'D' (there does not exist any rule, the backwards application of which would lead to such a construct). Consequently, no 'procedure' such as '**proc**(D) . I' can ever be *constructed* that would contain an assignment to a variable not declared in 'D'.

Actual parameters are systematically passed 'by reference'. The effect of passing actual parameters 'by value' can be obtained for actual parameters corresponding to formal parameters occurring at the end of the declaration. If 'S' is a procedure, the construct '$S[X;T]$' is a procedure call with actual parameters 'X' passed 'by reference' and actual parameters 'T' passed 'by value'. The corresponding definition is

$$\text{I12} \quad \vdash S[\alpha D;T] \triangleq \mathbf{loc}(E).(\alpha E \leftarrow T; S[\alpha(D;E)]).$$

Note that the fact that the actual parameters called 'by value' should correspond to the last parameters in formal parameter declaration is not really a limitation, as the order of these parameters may easily be rearranged within an *ad hoc* procedure.

The main result of this theory is the obvious identity

$$\vdash D\pi(\mathbf{proc}(D).I)[\alpha D] \triangleq D\pi I$$

(*e*) *Parallelism*

Parallelism (simultaneous execution) is not defined for instructions in general; rather it is defined for procedure calls. For this reason, in this section, we shall call a procedure call a *process.* Given two processes '$S[\alpha(D;E)]$' and '$T[\alpha(E;F)]$', their parallel execution denoted by the symbol '$\|$' is also a process.

symbol	$\|$
arity	2

$$\text{I13} \quad \vdash (S[\alpha(D;E)])\|(T[\alpha(E;F)]) \triangleq U[\alpha A]$$

where

U is $\{\alpha A, \alpha A' | (A;A' | B \wedge C)\}$
A is $(D;E;F)$
B is $(D;E)\pi S[\alpha(D;E)]$
C is $(E;F)\pi T[\alpha(E;F)]$

The variables in the common declaration 'E' are acting as *communication channels* between the two processes. When 'E' is '**skip**', the two processes do not communicate.

(*f*) *Recursion and loop*

If 'I' is an instruction and 'X' is a variable, then the construct '**rec**(X) . I' is another instruction; the execution of this instruction corresponds to the execution of 'I' within which occurrences of calls to 'X' are replaced by '**rec**(X) . I' itself!

(The limitation of informal 'operational' explanations appears now quite clearly; this English description of what '**rec**(X) . I' is supposed to be is obviously extremely vague, if not misleading.)

To give an equivalent to the predicate '$D\pi(\mathbf{rec}(X).I)$', we consider the function '$\lambda(X{:}RD).(\mathbf{proc}(D).I)$'; this is a function of type '$RD \rightarrow RD$'; consequently the fixpoint (§2 (*i*)) of this function is a member of 'RD', that is, a binary relation from '$\{D\}$' to '$\{D\}$'. The predicate '$D\pi(\mathbf{rec}(X).I)$' corresponds to the 'call' of this relation.

We also define the '**loop**' of an instruction 'I' as a certain recursion on 'I'.

symbol	**rec**	**loop**
arity	1	1

Extension to theory I

I14 $\vdash \mathbf{proc}(D).(\mathbf{rec}(X).I) \hat{=} \mu(X{:}RD).(\mathbf{proc}(D).I)$

I15 $\vdash D\pi\mathbf{loop}(I) \hat{=} D\pi(\mathbf{rec}(X).((I;X[\alpha D])\Box(\sim(E\alpha D'.(D\pi I))\rightarrow\mathbf{skip})))$

We can use previous results of the theory of functions (§2 (*h*)) and of the theory of set-theoretic fixpoint (§2 (*i*)) to prove the expected results

$(\lambda(X{:}RD).A) \in M(\{D\}\times\{D\}) \vdash B \hat{=} A[B/X]$

where

A is $\mathbf{proc}(D).I$

B is $\mathbf{proc}(D).(\mathbf{rec}(X).I)$

$C \vdash D\pi\mathbf{loop}(I) \hat{=} D\pi((I;\mathbf{loop}(I))\Box(\sim(E\alpha D'.(D\pi I))\rightarrow\mathbf{skip}))$

where

C is $(\lambda(X{:}RD).(\mathbf{proc}(D).(I;X[\alpha D]))\in M(\{D\}\times\{D\})$

4. Theory of computation

In this last section we shall formally define the concept of *computation*. To do so, we shall introduce the concept of nested substitution (§4.1) and that of set-theoretic continuous function (§4.2). In the last subsection we shall see what is meant by a computable instruction.

(*a*) *Nested iterated substitution*: IT

The main purpose of this section is to formally define the concept of *nested iterated substitutions*. Given a term 'T', a natural number 'N', another term 'U', and a variable 'X', the construct $T[N\downarrow(U/X)]$ corresponds to '$T[T[\ldots T[U/X]\ldots/X]/X]$', where the innermost substitution is embedded '$N-1$' times. For instance, '$T[2\downarrow(U/X)]$' is '$T[T[U/X]/X]$', '$T[3\downarrow(U/X)]$' is '$T[T[T[U/X]/X]/X]$', etc.

To give a rigorous definition to such a construct we first need to define the iterate '**itrt**' of a total function from a set to itself. Given such a function 'Y', '**itrt**(Y)' is another function that, when applied to a number 'N', yields the 'Nth' iterate of 'Y' (this is denoted by '$Y\uparrow N$'). The definition of '**itrt**' uses that of the identity function on a set 'S' (this is denoted by 'IS') and that of the composition '$\circ$', of two total functions.

symbol	I	$\circ$	**itrt**	$\uparrow$	$\downarrow$
arity	1	2	1	2	2

Main rules

IT1 $\vdash IS \triangleq \lambda(X:S).X$
IT2 $\vdash A(X:S\to T;Y:T\to U).(Y\circ X = (\lambda(Z:S).Y[X[Z]]))$
IT3 $\vdash A(Y:S\to S).(\mathbf{itrt}(Y) = A)$
where A is $\mu(Z:P(N\times(S\to S))).((0,IS)\hat{}\{\sigma N,(Y\circ X)\,|\,(N,X):Z\})$
IT4 $\vdash A(Y:S\to S,N:N).(Y\uparrow N = (\mathbf{itrt}(Y))[N])$

Extension of theory S

S11 $\vdash T[N\downarrow(U/X)] \triangleq ((\lambda(X:S).T)\uparrow N)[U]$

The expected intuitive results are

$\vdash A(Y:S\to S).(\mathbf{itrt}(Y)\in(N\to(S\to S)))$
$\vdash A(Y:S\to S).(Y\uparrow 0 = IS)$
$\vdash A(Y:S\to S;N:N).(Y\uparrow\sigma N = (Y\circ(Y\uparrow N)))$
$\vdash A\to(T[0\downarrow(U/X)] = U)$
$\vdash A\to(A(N:N).(T[\sigma N\downarrow(U/X)] = T[T[N\downarrow(U/X)]/X])$
where A is $(A(X:S).(T\in S))\wedge(U\in S)$.

The first of these results is a consequence of rule IT3. It can be proved by mathematical induction and by using the fourth Peano axiom, which states that the successor function 'σ' is 'one–one' on 'N'.

(*b*) *Set-theoretic continuous functions*: C

When a set function (i.e. a function from '*P*S' to itself) is *continuous*, its fixpoint (§2(*i*)) can be equated to certain iterates. More precisely, when the set function in question is defined by lambda abstraction (§2(*h*)), its fixpoint is equal to the (infinite) union of all the nested substitutions of the empty set in its body.

To define '*C*S', the set of continuous set functions built on 'S', we need to introduce the union '$\cup$' of a set of sets and also the set of increasing infinite sequences of subsets of a set 'S' (this is denoted by '**inc**(S)').

symbol	$\cup$	**inc**	*C*
arity	1	1	1

Main rules

C1 $\vdash A(Z:PPS).(\cup Z = \{X:S|E(Y:Z).(Z\in Y)\})$
C2 $\vdash \mathbf{inc}(S) \triangleq \{Y:N\to PS|A(N:N).(Y[N]\subset Y[\sigma N])\}$
C3 $\vdash CS \triangleq \{Y:PS\to PS|A(X:\mathbf{inc}(S)).A\}$
where A is $\cup\{Y[X[N]]|N:N\} = Y[\cup\{X[N]|N:N\}]$

Note how the operations '$\cup$' and '[' commute in the definition of '*C*S'. The main result (Kleene 1952) is the one given at the beginning of this section.

$$(\lambda(X:PS).T)\in CS\vdash\mu(X:PS).T \triangleq \cup\{T[N\downarrow(\varnothing/X)]|N:N\}$$

This result can be put in another form.

$$(\lambda(X:PS).T)\in CS \vdash U\in(\mu(X:PS).T) \mathrel{\hat{=}} E(N:N).(U\in T[N\downarrow(\varnothing/X)])$$

In other words the membership of a term 'U' to a fixed-point defined set is equivalent to an *existential quantification* (over the natural number) of the membership of the same term to a term obtained by nested substitution.

Another important result (J. W. de Bakker & D. Scott, 'A theory of programs' (unpublished notes (1969))) allows one to prove universal properties of fixpoints of continuous functions.

(*c*) *Computation*

In this subsection, at last, we deal with the concept of *computation*. As expected, this concept is related to that of proof; when all other means have been exhausted, the only way to prove a conjecture might be to undertake an exhaustive search (a computation) through the problem space.

Where the conjecture in question takes the form of an *existential quantification*, the exhaustive search is, by definition, guaranteed to be successful *if the conjecture is provable*.

If we look at the various forms taken by the predicate '$D\pi I$' (§3) for the various instructions 'I' of the 'programming' notation, we see that the only one that is not an existential form is '$D\pi(\mathbf{rec}(X).I)$' (and of course '$D\pi(\mathbf{loop}(I))$', as it is defined in terms of it). All other predicates 'invoke' similar predicates through existential quantifications (or by simple Boolean connections; this is so for '$D\pi(P\rightarrow I)$' or '$D\pi(I\Box J)$').

We shall see that, provided a certain condition (of continuity) is met, we can also give an existential (computable) form to the predicate '$D\pi(\mathbf{rec}(X).I)$'.

To do so, we need to extend the 'programming' notation by introducing four more instructions. First, the instruction replacement instruction, the construct '$I[J/X]$', where 'I' *and* 'J' are instructions, is an instruction, the execution of which corresponds to that of 'I', except that 'J' is executed upon 'encountering' the variable 'X'. Second, the nested generalization of the previous instruction; this is denoted by '$I[N\downarrow(J/X)]$'. Third, the 'Nth' iterate of instruction 'I', denoted by '$I\uparrow N$'. Finally, the '**break**' instruction, *which never gives any result*!

symbol	**break**
arity	0

Extension to theory I

I16	$\vdash D\pi(I[J/X]) \mathrel{\hat{=}} (D\pi I)[\mathbf{proc}(D).J/X]$
I17	$\vdash D\pi I[N\downarrow(J/X)] \mathrel{\hat{=}} (D\pi I)[N\downarrow(\mathbf{proc}(D).J/X)]$
I18	$\vdash D\pi(I\uparrow N) \mathrel{\hat{=}} D\pi(I;X[\alpha D])[N\downarrow(\mathbf{skip}/X)]$
I19	$\vdash \sim(D\pi(\mathbf{break}))$

Now the main and well known result, a direct consequence of the result of the previous section, is

$$A\vdash D\pi(\mathbf{rec}(X).I) \mathrel{\hat{=}} E(N:N).(D\pi I[N\downarrow(\mathbf{break}/X)])$$

where A is $(\lambda(X:RD).(\mathbf{proc}(D).I))\in C(\{D\}\times\{D\})$.

For the loop instruction, this result reduces to

$$B \vdash D\pi(\mathbf{loop}(I)) \triangleq E(N:N) . C$$

where

C is $D\pi(I{\uparrow}N) \wedge \sim(ED . (D\pi I))[\alpha D'/\alpha D]$
B is $(\lambda(X:RD) . (\mathbf{proc}(D) . (I;X[\alpha D]))) \in C(\{D\} \times \{D\})$.

5. Conclusion

In this paper, we have presented a foundation for logic, set theory and programming. We have obviously not proved any new result (we have not proved any result at all!). Our only (limited) goal was to present this material in a certain style, characterized by a high degree of formalism together with a number of English explanations at the same time. We think that such a style, where the extremes are brought together, is perhaps indispensable for presenting this kind of work.

In being *completely formal* (Bourbaki 1970) we had in mind the possible mechanization of that part of proof writing that is *completely clerical* and thus extremely tedious and error prone. In fact, we have very serious reasons (Milner, this symposium; Abrial 1984) to believe that a mechanized 'proof assistant' (PA) already exists, or can be easily constructed, and that *all* (missing) proofs in this paper can be written with it.

We now discuss some requirements for the proof assistant. It should first offer a series of housekeeping facilities to allow an interactive user to enter new symbols (their arity, their priority), to create new theories, to enter (and check for syntax correctness) new *basic* deduction or definition rules, and finally to retrieve the material just entered. In this respect, it would only mechanize what has been done (and checked!) by hand in this paper.

A second series of facilities concerns the entering of a new *derived* deduction or definition rule. In fact, to accept such a rule, PA requires a proof. It is, however, able to assist the user in accomplishing this unavoidable task (note that a rule, once accepted by PA, can be used like any other already-entered rule).

In operating the first facilities of this second series, the user provides the proof assistant with a set of formulae together with an existing deduction rule. It is then able to automatically generate the consequent of each instance (see §1 (*c*)) of the given rule, having the given set of formulae as an antecedent. This facility corresponds to the most elementary step taken in the making of a formal proof. A similar facility could be offered for definition rules; upon providing PA with a set of antecedent formulae together with a definition rule and a formula to be transformed, it is able to automatically generate all possible transformations of the given formula compatible with instances of the given rule that have the given set of formulae as an antecedent.

Other modes of operation are mere variants of the two previous facilities. In operating these variants, we provide the proof assistant with *less and less information*. For instance, the user could give only the name of a theory instead of that of a rule. It would then be required to try all possible rules in this theory (experience shows that if theories are not too big, a dozen rules or so, then some elementary criterions easily discard most non-pertinent rules). Another (separate) variant would consist in providing the proof assistant with more formulae than strictly necessary to build a possible antecedent. It would then be required to choose among these candidates, the formulae which would fit the given rule. A third variant uses both previous variants together. A fourth variant would consist of applying repeatedly all definition rules (backwards or forwards) of a theory until no rule is applicable (This variant is particularly useful for a change of variables).

As can be seen, the proof assistant, although 'artificial', is not particularly 'intelligent' (sometimes it can even prove to be a little too enthusiastic in expressing its services!). We think, nevertheless, that it can be of some help in constructing proofs, thus in *constructing programs.*

In this respect, the important thing to keep in mind is that definition rules are able to work on *both sides*. Almost all rules of the theory of programming (§3) are definition rules; when applying them from left to right, we assign meanings to 'programs' (Floyd 1967). However, and perhaps more important, when we apply them from right to left, we also assign 'programs' to meanings.

I am particularly indebted to Tony Hoare; many ideas in this paper are obviously his. The importance of program construction was made clear to me by Michel Sintzoff. Bernard Sufrin convinced me eventually of the importance of the concept of schema. Countless discussions with Cliff Jones have had a great influence on the content of this paper.

During the last five years, several people have been kind enough to comment on some preparatory works to this paper, among whom are D. Scott, D. Gries, R. Milne, R. Burstall, S. Schuman, I. Sorensen, T. Clement, L. Morris, M. Goldsmith, B. Meyer, A. Guillon, C. Morgan, J. C. Shepherdson, as well as some other anonymous commentators. Their remarks have all been studied carefully and profitably.

Last, I warmly thank Cathy de Rudder for her remarkable typing (and patience). This paper could never have been finished on time without her.

Appendix 1. Well-formedness

Well formed predicates

$\vdash \mathbf{pred}(\mathrm{P}[\mathrm{S}/\mathrm{X}])$
$\vdash \mathbf{pred}(\sim \mathrm{P})$
$\vdash \mathbf{pred}(\mathrm{P} \vee \mathrm{Q})$
$\vdash \mathbf{pred}(E\mathrm{X}\,.\,\mathrm{P})$
$\vdash \mathbf{pred}(\mathrm{S} = \mathrm{T})$
$\vdash \mathbf{pred}(\mathrm{S} \in \mathrm{T})$
$\vdash \mathbf{pred}(\sigma \mathrm{D})$
$\vdash \mathbf{pred}(\mathrm{D} \pi \mathrm{I})$

Well formed terms

$\vdash \mathbf{term}(\mathrm{T}[\mathrm{S}/\mathrm{X}])$
$\vdash \mathbf{term}(\mathrm{X})$
$\vdash \mathbf{term}(\mathrm{S},\mathrm{T})$
$\vdash \mathbf{term}\{\mathrm{T}|\mathrm{D}\}$
$\vdash \mathbf{term}(P\mathrm{S})$
$\vdash \mathbf{term}(\varnothing)$
$\vdash \mathbf{term}(\mathrm{S}[\mathrm{T}])$
$\vdash \mathbf{term}(U)$
$\vdash \mathbf{term}(\tau \mathrm{S})$

Well formed variables

$\vdash \mathbf{vrbl}(A\hat{\ }B)$
$X\backslash Y \vdash \mathbf{vrbl}(X,Y)$
$\vdash \mathbf{vrbl}(\alpha D)$
$\vdash \mathbf{vrbl}(X')$

Well formed declarations

$X\backslash T \vdash \mathbf{decl}(X:T)$
$\alpha E\backslash D \quad \alpha D\backslash E \vdash \mathbf{decl}(D;E)$
$\vdash \mathbf{decl}(D|P)$
$\vdash \mathbf{decl}(\mathbf{skip})$
$\alpha D'\backslash D \vdash \mathbf{decl}(D')$
$\vdash \mathbf{decl}(D[X/\alpha(E;D;F)])$

Well formed instructions

$\vdash \mathbf{inst}(I[S/X])$
$\vdash \mathbf{inst}(P \rightarrow I)$
$\vdash \mathbf{inst}(I;J)$
$\vdash \mathbf{inst}(I \square J)$
$\vdash \mathbf{inst}(\mathbf{loc}(D) . I)$
$\vdash \mathbf{inst}(\mathbf{skip})$
$\vdash \mathbf{inst}(X \leftarrow T)$
$\vdash \mathbf{inst}(S[X])$
$\vdash \mathbf{inst}((S[X]) \parallel (T[Y]))$
$\vdash \mathbf{inst}(\mathbf{rec}(X) . I)$
$\vdash \mathbf{inst}(\mathbf{loop}(I))$
$\vdash \mathbf{inst}(I[J/X])$
$\vdash \mathbf{inst}(I[N \downarrow (J/X)])$
$\vdash \mathbf{inst}(I \uparrow N)$
$\vdash \mathbf{inst}(\mathbf{break})$

References

Abrial, J. R. 1984 The mathematical construction of a program. In *Science of computer programming*, p. 4.
Bjørner, D. & Jones, C. B. 1982 *Formal specification and software development*. Englewood Cliffs, N.J.: Prentice-Hall.
Bourbaki, N. 1970 *Théorie des ensembles*. Paris: Hermann.
Burstall, R. M. 1969 Proving properties of programs by structural induction. *Computer J.* **12**, 41–48.
Dijkstra, E. W. 1975 Guarded commands, non-determinacy and formal derivation of programs. *Communs Ass. comput. Mach.* **18** (8).
Floyd, R. W. 1967 Assigning meanings to programs. In *Proc. Symp. Appl. Math.* (ed. J. T. Schwartz), vol. 19, pp. 19–31. Providence, Rhode Island: American Mathematical Society.
Jones, C. B. 1980 *Software development – a rigorous approach*. Englewood Cliffs, N.J.: Prentice-Hall.
Kleene, S. C. 1952 Introduction to meta-mathematics. New York: Van Nostrand.
Morgan, C. & Sufrin, B. 1984 Specification of the UNIX filing system. *IEEE Trans. software Engng* (In the press.)
Park, D. 1969 Fixpoint induction and proofs of program properties. *Mach. Intell.* **5**. Edinburgh University Press.
Scott, D. & Stratchey, C. 1970 Towards a mathematical semantics for computer languages. *Tech. Monogr.* PRC-6. Oxford University Press.
Tarski, A. 1955 A lattice-theoretical fixpoint theorem and its application. *Pacif. J. Math.*

Discussion

J. C. Shepherdson (*School of Mathematics, University of Bristol, U.K.*). Is there not a danger when one makes one's first specification in a completely formal language that one may make a mistake in the very first step, that of translating the informal everyday language specification of a program into this language? Is it not safer to proceed in stages, first expressing the specification in a very rich and friendly language?

J. R. Abrial. I certainly agree with Professor Shepherdson that the brutal *translation* of our first specification written in the 'informal every day language' into another one written in a 'completely formal language' is obviously a mistake, and that it is certainly safer to first express our specification in a 'very rich and friendly language'.

However, I do not think that we have to reason in terms of 'translation' from one language, be it 'everyday' or 'very rich and friendly', into another 'completely formal' one. The term 'translation' is too narrow. What we have to do is to obtain a *mathematical representation* of our informally stated problem, and such a representation must be easily understandable. Such a desirable mathematical representation is certainly not the result of a translation process; rather it is the result of deep understanding of the mathematical properties of our problem.

Obviously we have to learn how to write such mathematical representations. For instance, I do not think that predicate calculus is the best tool for such an activity. Far better, in my opinion, is to place ourselves directly within the realm of set theory, where such concepts as functions and relations and their operations are available, and where such mathematical objects as natural numbers, sequences and trees and their operations are usable. Obviously such concepts and objects offer possibilities that are very 'rich' and 'formal' at the same time (i.e. we can formally prove properties of mathematical representations written with such tools).

In fact Professor Shepherdson's question raises an important point. For many years, the issue of language (programming, specification, query, relational, natural, etc.) and that of translation has hidden what is, in my opinion, the real problem; namely that of aproaching the activity of program construction from a mathematical point of view.

J. S. Hillmore (*Polytechnic of North London Computing Service, London, U.K.*). Could Mr Abrial act as a spokesman both for himself and for the previous speakers, and explain the relevance of this theoretical work to those of us who write real programs and also to those of us who teach others to write real programs?

J. R. Abrial. Sorry, I can only act as a spokesman for myself. Firstly, I must say that the subject of this symposium was not the writing of real programs nor the teaching of how to write such programs; it is, as you know: 'Mathematical Logic and Programming Languages'. As a consequence, I felt that I had to concentrate mostly on the main subject, although I have agreed with you for many years that the questions you raise are of utmost importance.

In my paper, I have tried to embed a certain programming notation within a completely formal treatment of logic and set theory. In other words, the thesis of my paper is that programming is nothing but a certain part of logic and set theory rewritten in a convenient way.

This *theoretical* thesis has very important consequences on the *practical* activities you mention.

It means, for instance, that we could teach future programmers mathematical logic and some part of axiomatic set theory as a prerequisite for programming courses. In one way or another we have to teach students how to *reason rigorously while constructing their programs.* Excellent textbooks, such as Jones (1980) or Gries (1981), are already available to help support such teachings.

I am convinced that real programming will never become a mature technical activity unless real programmers use a genuinely mathematical approach to construct their programs. It may take some time for such ideas to spread among the software community.

Reference

Gries, D. 1981 *The science of programming.* Berlin: Springer.

R. L. Constable (*Computer Science Department, Edinburgh University, U.K.*). Mr Abrial's program of research is quite similar to that of de Bruijn's AUTOMATH project, begun in 1968, and to that of Edinburgh LCF, begun in 1975, and to FOL at Stanford. For instance, LCF has a formalized account of substitution, which is then used in building new user-defined proof rules, as Robin Milner explained earlier in this symposium. Mr Abrial's ideas for a theory of programs and data types seem quite similar to those in the Cornell work on programming logics, *ca.* 1978. All of these projects already have built computer systems to help with the details of proof construction. In what ways do Mr Abrial's ideas go beyond those in the established projects? In what way is his set theory superior to that defined in AUTOMATH, which provides an explicit theory of functions (as typed lambda terms) in each of its theories?

J. R. Abrial. I must admit that for some reason I have not been able to become familiar with the work you mention. As a consequence, it is quite probable that the ideas in my paper do not go beyond those in established projects that started so long ago, and that the set theory presented is in no way superior to that defined in AUTOMATH.

My main sources of inspiration were Bourbaki's treatise on set theory, Hoare's work on the axiomatization of programming languages and Dijkstra's '**do...od**' non-deterministic language.

Programs are predicates

By C. A. R. Hoare, F.R.S.

Programming Research Group, Oxford University Computing Laboratory,
8–11 *Keble Road, Oxford OX*1 3*QD, U.K.*

A computer program is identified with the strongest predicate describing every relevant observation that can be made of the behaviour of a computer executing that program. A programming language is a subset of logical and mathematical notations, which is so restricted that products described in the language can be automatically implemented on a computer. The notations enjoy a number of elegant algebraic properties, which can be used for optimizing program efficiency.

A specification is a predicate describing all permitted observations of a program, and it may be expressed with greatest clarity by taking advantage of the whole language of logic and mathematics. A program P meets its specification S iff

$$\models P \Rightarrow S.$$

The proof of this implication may use all the classical methods of mathematics and logic.

These points are illustrated by design of a small language that includes assignments, conditionals, non-determinism, recursion, input, output, and concurrency.

1. Introduction

It is the aim of the natural scientist to discover mathematical theories, formally expressed as predicates describing the relevant observations that can be made of some physical system. A physical system is fully defined by the strongest predicate that describes it. Such predicates contain free variables, standing for values determined by observation, for example 'a' for acceleration, 'v' for velocity, 't' for time, etc.

The aim of an engineer is complementary to that of the scientist. He starts with a specification, formally expressible as a predicate describing the desired observable behaviour of a system or product not yet in existence. Then, with a limited set of tools and materials, within a limited timescale and budget, he must design and construct a product that meets that specification. The product is fully defined by the strongest specification that it meets.

For example, an electronic amplifier may be required to amplify its input voltage by a factor of ten. However, a condition of its correct working is that the input voltage must be held in the range 0 to 1 V. Furthermore, a margin of error of up to one volt is allowed on the output. This informal specification may be formalized as a predicate, with free variables:

V_i, standing for the i*th* observed input voltage;
$\tilde{V}_i$, standing for the i*th* observed output voltage.

Then the specification is

$$\forall i.\,(i \leqslant j \Rightarrow 0 \leqslant V_i \leqslant 1) \Rightarrow |\tilde{V}_j - 10 \times V_j| \leqslant 1.$$

Table 1 (*a*) and (*b*) show the first six observations made of two different amplifiers. The first observation of each amplifier shows it working with perfect accuracy at the midpoint of its range. The second observation is only just within the margin of tolerance. On the third observation the amplifier reveals its 'non-determinism': it does not always give the same output voltage for the same input voltage. On the fourth observation something goes wrong. For 4 (*a*) it is the amplifier that has gone wrong, because the five volt output is outside the permitted margin of error. Even if every subsequent observation is satisfactory, this product has not met its specification, and should be returned to its maker. For 4 (*b*), it is the observer who is at fault in supplying an excessive input of 1.3 V. As a result, the amplifier breaks, and its subsequent behaviour is entirely unconstrained: no matter what it does, it continues to meet its original specification. So on the sixth observation, it is the observer who returns to his Maker.

TABLE 1. OBSERVATIONS MADE OF TWO DIFFERENT AMPLIFIERS

observation number	(*a*) V	(*a*) $\tilde{V}$	(*b*) V	(*b*) $\tilde{V}$
1	0.5	5	0.5	5
2	0.4	5	0.4	5
3	0.5	4	0.5	4
4	0.3	5	1.3	13
5	0.6	6	0.6	6
6	0.7	7	0.7	997

The serious point of this example is to illustrate the usefulness of material implication in a specification. The consequent of the implication describes the desired relation between the inputs and the outputs of the system. The antecedent describes the assumptions that must be satisfied by the inputs of the system for it to continue working. If the assumptions are falsified, the product may break, and its subsequent (but not its previous) behaviour may be wholly arbitrary. Even if it seems to work for a while, it is completely worthless, unreliable, and even dangerous.

A computer programmer is an engineer whose main materials are the notations and structures of his programming language. A program is a detailed specification of the behaviour of a computer executing that program. Consequently, a program can be identified abstractly with a predicate describing all relevant observations that may be made of this behaviour. This identification assigns a meaning to the program (Floyd 1967), and a semantics to the programming language in which it is expressed.

These philosophical remarks lead to the main thesis of this paper, namely that programs are predicates. However, the converse claim would be incorrect, because any predicate that is wholly unsatisfiable (for example the predicate false) cannot correspond to a program. If it did, the behaviour of a computer executing that program would be wholly unobservable! Consequently, every observation of that behaviour would satisfy every specification! A product that satisfies every need is known as a *miracle*. Since such a product is also in principle unobservable, philosophical considerations lead us to suppose that it does not exist. Certainly any notation in which such a miracle could be expressed would not be an implementable programming language. There are also obvious practical reasons for ensuring that all predicates expressible as programs are in some sense computable, and can be computed at a cost that is controllable by the programmer and acceptable to his client.

The design of a programming notation requires a preliminary selection of what are the relevant observable phenomena, and a choice of free variables to denote them. A meaning must then be given to the primitive components of the language, and to the operators that compose programs from smaller subprograms. Ideally, these operators should have pleasant algebraic properties, which permit proof of the identity of two programs whenever they are indistinguishable by observation. The achievement of these ideals is far from easy: so the language introduced in the next section for illustrative purposes has been kept very simple. It includes non-determinism, output, input, recursion, concurrency, assignment, and conditional.

2. A SIMPLE PROGRAMMING LANGUAGE

The first and simplest predicate that is expressible in our simple programming language is the predicate 'true'. This predicate is satisfied by *all* observations. If this is the *strongest* specification of a product, then there is no constraint whatever on the behaviour or misbehaviour of the product. The only customer who is certain to be satisfied with this product is one who would be satisfied by *anything*. Thus the program 'true' is the most useless of all products, just as a tautology is the most useless of scientific theories.

Now the most useless of computer programs is one that immediately goes into an infinite loop or recursion. Such a program is clearly broken or unstable, and can satisfy only the most undemanding customer. Thus we identify the infinitely looping program with the predicate 'true'. This may be a controversial decision; but in practice the ascription of a meaning to a divergent program is arbitrary, because no programmer will ever deliberately want to write a program that runs any risk of looping forever.

Non-determinism

The first and simplest operator of our programming language is disjunction. If P and Q are programs, the program $(P \vee Q)$ behaves either like P or like Q. There is no way of controlling or predicting the choice between P and Q; the choice is arbitrary or non-deterministic. All that is known is that each observation of $(P \vee Q)$ must be an observation of the behaviour of P or of Q or of both.

The algebraic properties of disjunction are very familiar: it is idempotent, symmetric, associative, etc. Furthermore, it is *distributive* (through disjunction) and *strict* in the sense that

$$p \vee \text{true} = \text{true} \vee P = \text{true}.$$

This means that if either P or Q may break then so may $(P \vee Q)$. To an engineer, a product that *may* break is as bad as one that *does*, because you can never rely on it.

Processes

Now we must be more specific about the nature of the objects described by programs in our simple language. These objects are called *processes*; a process should be regarded as a 'black box' connected to its environment by two wires. One of the wires is used for input of discrete messages, and the other for output (figure 1). A process engages in an unbounded sequence of communications, each of which is either an input from the input wire or an output to the output wire (but not both). If the environment is not ready for the communication, the process waits for it to become so, and vice versa. There is no 'buffer' in the wire; the act of communication requires simultaneous synchronized participation of both the sender and the receiver.

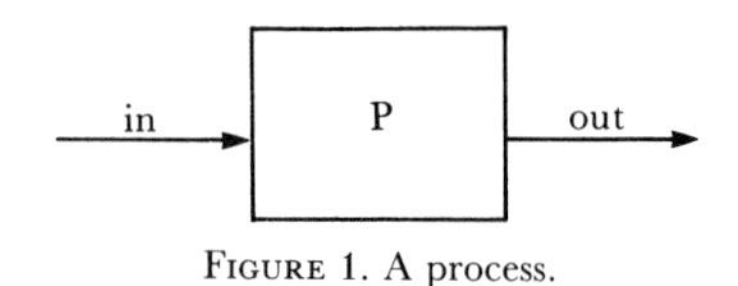

FIGURE 1. A process.

We postulate that the passing of a message on either wire is an observable aspect of the behaviour of the process. Imagine that there is a tape recorder attached to each of the wires, recording each message as it passes, but not recording the length of the gaps between the messages. At any moment, we can observe the current content of each of the two tapes. We introduce the free variable 'in' to stand for the current content of the tape recorder on the input wire, and 'out' to stand for the sequence of messages recorded from the output wire.

We also postulate that the internal state of a process cannot be directly observed: the black box has no openable lid. However, we assume that we can observe, by a green light perhaps, whether the process is working properly. This will be indicated by the value of a free Boolean variable 'stable', which takes as value either true or false. If ever 'stable' goes false, the machine is broken, and anything may happen (beware!).

Specifications

To formulate specifications, we need some notations to describe sequences of messages:

$\langle\ \rangle$ is the empty sequence, containing no messages. This is the value of both variables 'in' and 'out' if they are observed at the very start of the process;

$|s|$ is the length of s.

If s is a sequence other than $\langle\ \rangle$,

s_0 is the first message of s,

s' is the result of removing the first message of s,

$s^\dagger$ is the result of removing the last message of s (truncation).

If s and t are sequences,

$s\hat{\ }t$ is the result of concatenating s and t in this order

$s \leqslant t \triangleq \exists u.\ s\hat{\ }u = t$, i.e. s is an initial segment of t.

This is clearly a partial order with bottom $\langle\ \rangle$.

Using these notations, we can describe the behaviour of certain simple processes. For example, a process that just copies messages from its input to its output is always stable, and every observation of it shows the output sequence either exactly equal to the input sequence or one shorter:

$$\text{COPY} \triangleq \text{stable} \wedge (\text{out} = \text{in} \vee \text{out} = \text{in}^\dagger).$$

This copying process must always output each message immediately after inputting it. A more general buffering process relaxes this constraint. For example, a double buffer may be specified:

$$\text{BUFF2} \triangleq \text{stable} \wedge \text{out} \in \{\text{in}, \text{in}^\dagger, \text{in}^{\dagger\dagger}\}.$$

An unbounded buffer ensures that the output is always a copy of some initial segment of the input sequence

$$\text{BUFF} \triangleq \text{stable} \wedge \text{out} \leqslant \text{in}.$$

Thus we see how predicates with free variables 'in', 'out' and 'stable' (together with conventional mathematical notations) can effectively describe and specify the behaviour of processes. But *none* of these notations can feature in our simple programming language; nor can they be included in any other programming language, since they can be used to express unsatisfiable predicates, such as

$$\text{in} \leqslant \text{out} \wedge \text{out} \leqslant \text{in} \wedge \text{in} \neq \text{out}$$

or unimplementable predicates like

$$\text{stable} \wedge |\text{in}| \geqslant 3,$$

which requires a process to input three messages before it starts! Our programming language must therefore be restricted to notations defined in the remaining paragraphs of this section. The restrictions will also ensure that no process can ever stop, so it will be impossible to implement the specification: $\text{stable} \wedge |\text{in}|+|\text{out}| \leqslant k$.

Output

Let P be a predicate exactly describing the behaviour of a process, and let e be a term composed of (say) constants, variables, and a fixed selection of primitive recursive functions. We introduce the notation

$$!e \rightarrow P$$

to describe the process that first outputs the value of e on its output wire, and then behaves as described by P.

The very first observation of the behaviour of $(!e \rightarrow P)$ is that it is stable and that the sequences of input and output messages are both empty. In every subsequent observation, the output sequence is nonempty, and its first message has value e. Furthermore, on removing the first message from the output sequence, the resulting observation will be an observation of the behaviour of P. These remarks explain the definition:

$$\begin{aligned} !e \rightarrow P(\text{in}, \text{out}, \text{stable}) \triangleq\ & \text{out} = \text{in} = \langle\ \rangle \wedge \text{stable} \\ & \vee \text{out} \neq \langle\ \rangle \leqslant \text{out}_0 = e \wedge P(\text{in}, \text{out}', \text{stable}). \end{aligned}$$

This operator is distributive but not strict:

$$!e \rightarrow (P \vee Q) = (!e \rightarrow P) \vee (!e \rightarrow Q).$$

As an example, we give

$$\begin{aligned} (!x \rightarrow \text{COPY}) = (&(\text{in} = \text{out} = \langle\ \rangle \wedge \text{stable}) \\ & \vee (\text{out} \neq \langle\ \rangle \wedge \text{out}_0 = x \\ & \wedge \text{stable} \wedge \text{out}' \in \{\text{in}, \text{in}^{\dagger}\})). \end{aligned}$$

Notice how the output has introduced the free variable x into the formula.

Input

Let P(x) be a predicate (possibly containing the variable x among its free variables) that describes exactly the behaviour of a process as a function of the initial value of x. Then we introduce the notation

$$?x \rightarrow P(x)$$

to describe the process that first inputs a value on its input wire, and then behaves like P(v), where v is the value it has just input.

The initial observation of the behaviour of $(?x \rightarrow P(x))$ is exactly the same as that of a process that starts with an output. In every subsequent observation, the input sequence is nonempty. Furthermore, on removing the first message from the input sequence, the resulting observation will be an observation of $P(in_0)$, i.e. the process that results from setting the initial value of x to in_0. These remarks explain the definition:

$$\begin{aligned}?x \rightarrow P(x, in, out, stable) \triangleq & ((out = in = \langle\ \rangle \wedge stable) \\ & \vee (in \neq \langle\ \rangle \wedge P(in_0, in', out, stable))).\end{aligned}$$

This operator is distributive, and binds the variable specified:

$$\begin{aligned}&(?x \rightarrow (P(x) \vee Q(x))) = ((?x \rightarrow P(x)) \vee (?x \rightarrow Q(x))) \\ &(?x \rightarrow P(x)) = (?y \rightarrow P(y)) \text{ when x is not free in } P(y) \\ &\qquad\qquad\qquad\qquad\qquad\quad \text{and y is not free in } P(x).\end{aligned}$$

As an example we give

$$\begin{aligned}(?x \rightarrow (!x \rightarrow COPY)) &= ((in = out = \langle\ \rangle \wedge stable) \\ &\quad \vee in \neq \langle\ \rangle \wedge (in' = out = \langle\ \rangle \wedge stable \\ &\qquad\qquad \vee (out \neq \langle\ \rangle \wedge out_0 = in_0 \\ &\qquad\qquad\quad \wedge stable \wedge out' \in \{in', in'^{\dagger}\}))) \\ &= stable \wedge (in = out = \langle\ \rangle \\ &\qquad \vee |in| = 1 \wedge out = \langle\ \rangle \\ &\qquad \vee out_0 = in_0 \wedge out' \in \{in', in'^{\dagger}\}) \\ &= COPY.\end{aligned}$$

Note how the input has eliminated the free variable x from the formula. Note also that COPY is the solution for ξ in the equation

$$\xi = (?x \rightarrow (!x \rightarrow \xi)).$$

Recursion

Let ξ be a variable standing for an unknown process. Let $P(\xi)$ be a formula containing ξ, but otherwise containing only the notations of our simple programming language: disjunction, output, input, and the constant 'true'. Consider now the equation

$$\xi = P(\xi).$$

This may be taken as a recursive definition of a process with name ξ and body $P(\xi)$. Every time ξ is encountered in the body, it stands for another copy of the whole body $P(\xi)$. The predicate that is the weakest solution to this equation will be denoted

$$\mu\xi \,.\, P(\xi).$$

But does such a solution exist? D. S. Scott has shown how to answer this question. Consider the sequence of predicates

$$\text{true}, P(\text{true}), P(P(\text{true})), \ldots, P^n(\text{true}), \ldots$$

and define

$$\mu\xi \,.\, P(\xi) \triangleq \forall n \geqslant 0 \,.\, P^n(\text{true}).$$

The fact that this is the weakest solution to the equation given above depends on the fact that $P(\xi)$ is a *continuous* function of ξ, in the sense that it distributes over the universal quantification of descending chains of predicate, i.e.

$$P(\forall n \geqslant 0 \,.\, Q_n) = \forall n \geqslant 0 \,.\, P(Q_n) \text{ whenever } \models Q_{n+1} \Rightarrow Q_n \text{ for all } n.$$

The continuity of all programs expressed in our simple language is assured by the fact that each operator of the language is continuous, and the composition of continuous operators is also continuous. We therefore have good reason to insist that all future operators introduced into the language must also be continuous.

The simplest example of recursion is the infinite loop

$$\mu\xi \,.\, \xi = \forall n \geqslant 0 \,.\, \text{true} = \text{true}.$$

A more interesting example is the program that copies messages from its input to its output

$$\mu\xi \,.\, (?x \rightarrow !x \rightarrow \xi) = \forall n \geqslant 0 \,.\, P_n,$$

where $P_0 = \text{true}$

and $P_{n+1} = (?x \rightarrow !x \rightarrow P_n)$.

The first few terms of the series are

$$\begin{aligned} P_1 = (&\text{in} = \text{out} = \langle\,\rangle \wedge \text{stable} \\ &\vee \text{in} \neq \langle\,\rangle \wedge (\text{in}' = \text{out} = \langle\,\rangle \wedge \text{stable} \\ &\qquad\qquad\qquad \vee \text{out} \neq \langle\,\rangle \wedge \text{out}_0 = \text{in}_0 \wedge \text{true})), \end{aligned}$$

$$\begin{aligned} P_2 = (&\text{in} = \text{out} = \langle\,\rangle \wedge \text{stable} \\ &\vee \text{in}' = \text{out} = \langle\,\rangle \wedge \text{stable} \\ &\vee \text{in}' = \text{out}' = \langle\,\rangle \wedge \text{in}_0 = \text{out}_0 \wedge \text{stable} \\ &\vee \text{in}'' = \text{out}' = \langle\,\rangle \wedge \text{in}_0 = \text{out}_0 \wedge \text{stable} \\ &\vee \text{in}'' = \text{out}'' = \langle\,\rangle \wedge \text{in}_0 = \text{out}_0 \wedge (\text{in}')_0 = (\text{out}')_0). \end{aligned}$$

In general, P_n describes the first 2n communications of a process that correctly copies the first n messages from the input to the output and then breaks. We therefore guess the general form

$$\begin{aligned} P_n = (&|\text{in}| + |\text{out}| < 2n \Rightarrow \\ &\quad \text{stable} \wedge (\text{out} = \text{in} \vee \text{out} = \text{in}^\dagger)) \\ &\wedge (|\text{in}| + |\text{out}| = 2n \Rightarrow \text{out} = \text{in}). \end{aligned}$$

Finally, we draw the conclusion (which was obvious all along) that

$$\begin{aligned}\mu\xi(?x \rightarrow !x \rightarrow \xi) &= \forall n \geqslant 0 \,.\, P_n \\ &= \text{stable} \wedge (\text{out} = \text{in} \vee \text{out} = \text{in}^\dagger) \\ &= \text{COPY}.\end{aligned}$$

A simpler way to prove this identity is to show that the predicate COPY is a solution to the defining equation of the recursion, i.e.

$$\text{COPY} = (?x \rightarrow !x \rightarrow \text{COPY}).$$

The fact that this is the *weakest* solution is a consequence of the fact that it is the *only* solution. A program $P(\xi)$ is said to be *guarded* for ξ if every possible occurrence of ξ is preceded by an input or output operation. Thus

$$(!x \rightarrow \xi) \vee (?y \rightarrow !x \rightarrow \xi) \quad \text{is guarded,}$$

but $$(!x \rightarrow \xi) \vee \xi \quad \text{is not guarded.}$$

If $P(\xi)$ is guarded for ξ, then the equation

$$\xi = P(\xi)$$

has an unique solution $\mu\xi \,.\, P(\xi)$.

Chain

If P and Q are processes, we define $(P \gg Q)$ as the result of connecting the output wire of P to the input wire of Q (see figure 2). Communications along this connecting wire cannot

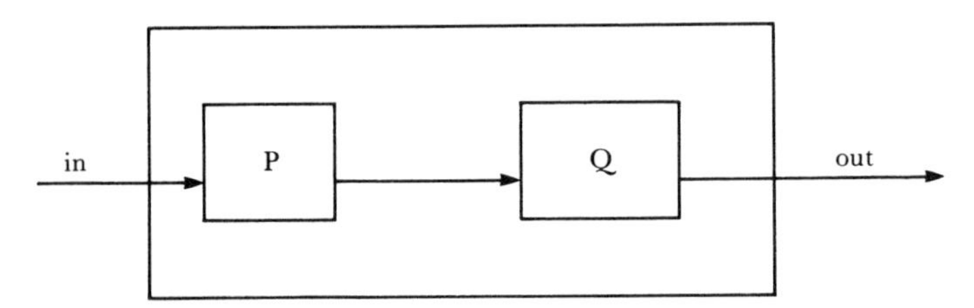

FIGURE 2. A chain.

be observed from the environment; they occur automatically whenever P is ready to output and Q is ready to input. All communication on the input wire of $(P \gg Q)$ is performed by P and all output to the environment is performed by Q. $(P \gg Q)$ is itself a process, and may be chained to other processes:

$$(P \gg Q) \gg R.$$

A simple example of a chain is formed by two instances of the COPY process connected to each other to make a double buffer:

$$\begin{aligned}(\text{COPY} \gg \text{COPY}) &= \text{stable} \wedge \exists b \,.\, b \in \{\text{in}, \text{in}^\dagger\} \wedge \text{out} \in \{b, b^\dagger\} \\ &= \text{stable} \wedge \text{out} \in \{\text{in}, \text{in}^\dagger, \text{in}^{\dagger\dagger}\} \\ &\triangleq \text{BUFF2}.\end{aligned}$$

A more spectacular example is a program that implements an unbounded buffer by chaining a recursive instance of itself:

$$\begin{aligned}\mu\xi\,.\,(?x \rightarrow (\xi \gg (!x \rightarrow \mathrm{COPY})))&\\ &= \mathrm{stable} \wedge \mathrm{out} \leqslant \mathrm{in}\\ &\triangleq \mathrm{BUFF}.\end{aligned}$$

A chain that does nothing but internal communication is just as broken as one that is engaged in an infinite recursion:

$$(\mu\xi\,.\,!0 \rightarrow \xi) \gg (\mu\xi\,.\,?x \rightarrow \xi) = \mathrm{true}.$$

Instead of giving an explicit definition of the chaining operator as a predicate, let us list the algebraic properties we would like it to have. Clearly it should be continuous and distributive; it should also be strict, so that it breaks whenever either of its operands is broken; finally, it should obey the following four laws, which describe the expected behaviour of input and output. First, when the left operand outputs and the right operand inputs, both these actions take place simultaneously; the communication cannot be observed, but its effect is to copy the value of the expression from the outputting to the inputting process. These remarks are formalized in the law

$$(!e \rightarrow P) \gg (?x \rightarrow Q(x)) = P \gg Q(e). \tag{1}$$

If either operand of $\gg$ starts with a communication with the other, but the other starts with an external communication, then the external communication takes place first, and the other process must wait:

$$(!e \rightarrow P) \gg (!f \rightarrow Q) = !f \rightarrow ((!e \rightarrow P) \gg Q), \tag{2}$$

$$(?x \rightarrow P(x)) \gg (?y \rightarrow Q(y)) = ?z \rightarrow (P(z) \gg (?y \rightarrow Q(y))), \tag{3}$$

where z is chosen not to occur in Q(y). The last of the four laws states that when *both* operands start with an external communication, then either communication may occur first, the choice being non-determinate:

$$\begin{aligned}(?x \rightarrow P(x)) \gg (!f \rightarrow Q) = {} & (?z \rightarrow (P(z) \gg (!f \rightarrow Q)))\\ & \vee (!f \rightarrow ((?x \rightarrow P(x)) \gg Q))).\end{aligned} \tag{4}$$

If P and Q are finite in the sense that they contain no recursions, then the collection of laws given are complete, in the sense that $(P \gg Q)$ can be reduced to 'normal' form that does not contain $\gg$. Thus for finite processes, the meaning of the chaining operator (if it has one) is uniquely defined by these laws. The continuity condition for $\gg$ ensures that chaining is uniquely defined for processes containing recursion as well. The proof of this depends on the fact that every process can be expressed as an universal quantification of a descending chain of finite processes. This fact also permits proof of other desirable properties of chaining, for example that it is associative.

The discovery of an explicit definition of the chaining operator is not simple. A first attempt at a definition can be based on the fact that if at any time there exists some sequence b of messages that could have passed on the internal channel, then the current trace of the external channels is a possible observation of the chain. So we make a preliminary definition:

$$\begin{aligned}&P(\mathrm{in}, \mathrm{out}, \mathrm{stable}) \gg_0 Q(\mathrm{in}, \mathrm{out}, \mathrm{stable})\\ &\quad \triangleq \exists b\,.\,P(\mathrm{in}, b, \mathrm{stable}) \wedge Q(b, \mathrm{out}, \mathrm{stable}).\end{aligned}$$

But $\gg_0$ is neither strict nor continuous, and so cannot be the right definition of $\gg$.

To ensure continuity, we need to describe the conditions under which the chain may break as a result of engaging in an infinite sequence of internal communications, a phenomenon known as 'infinite chatter':

$$\text{CHATTER} \triangleq \forall n \geqslant 0\,.\,\exists b\,.\,|b| > n \wedge P(\text{in}, b, \text{true}) \wedge Q(b, \text{out}, \text{true}).$$

To ensure strictness, we need to identify those cases when the chain diverges as a result of divergence of just one of its operands. These cases are characterized by the fact that 'stable' is false (in fact this was the main reason why the variable 'stable' was introduced into the formal system).

$$\begin{aligned}\text{UNSTAB1} \triangleq \exists b\,.\,&P(\text{in}, b, \text{false}) \wedge Q(b, \text{out}, \text{true})\\ &\vee P(\text{in}, b, \text{true}) \wedge Q(b, \text{out}, \text{false})).\end{aligned}$$

Finally, we need to ensure that once the chain breaks it remains broken forever, i.e. it degenerates to the bottom process 'true'. To do this we introduce a modal operator ($\Diamond R$) to mean 'there was a time when R was true':

$$\begin{aligned}&\Diamond R(\text{in}, \text{out}, \text{stable}) \triangleq\\ &\quad \exists a \leqslant \text{in}\,.\,\exists b \leqslant \text{out}\,.\,R(a, b, \text{stable}).\end{aligned}$$

At last we can formulate the definition of the chaining operator

$$P \gg Q \triangleq (P \gg_0 Q \vee \Diamond\text{CHATTER} \vee \Diamond\text{UNSTAB1}).$$

That this definition has all the required algebraic properties is only a conjecture: the proof would depend on the fact that the operands of $\gg$ are not arbitrary predicates but are restricted to the notations of our simple programming language.

Assignment

Let x be a list of distinct variables, and let e be a list of the same number of expressions, and let P(x) be a program describing the behaviour of a process as a function of the initial values of x. We then define

$$(e \succ\!\!- x \to P(x)) \triangleq P(e),$$

i.e. the result of simultaneously substituting each variable in the list x by the corresponding expression in the list e, making sure that free variables of e remain free after the substitution. We assume for simplicity that all expressions of e are defined for all values of the variables they contain, so that if y is a list of distinct fresh variables

$$e \succ\!\!- x \to P(x) = (\exists y\,.\,y = e \wedge P(y)) = (\forall y\,.\,y = e \Rightarrow P(y)).$$

The predicate $e \succ\!\!- x \to P(x)$ describes the behaviour of a process that first simultaneously assigns the values of e to the variables of x and then behaves like P(x). The initial assignment is an internal action, and is therefore wholly unobservable. In more conventional programming notation this would be written

$$x := e; P(x).$$

A simple example of a program that uses assignment is one that implements a double buffer

$$?x \rightarrow \mu\xi \,.\, ((!x \rightarrow ?x \rightarrow \xi) \vee (?y \rightarrow !x \rightarrow (y \succ\!- x \rightarrow \xi)))$$
$$= \text{stable} \wedge \text{out} \in \{\text{in}, \text{in}^{\dagger}, \text{in}^{\dagger\dagger}\}$$
$$= \text{BUFF2}.$$

Conditional

Let b be a propositional formula, i.e. a single expression that for all values of its free variables yields a result that is either true or false. Let P and Q be programs. Define

$$P \not< b \not> Q \triangleq (b \wedge P \vee \bar{b} \wedge Q).$$

This is a process that behaves like P if b is initially true and like Q if b is initially false. The conventional programming notation for a conditional is

if b **then** P **else** Q.

The reason for the infix notation is that this permits elegant expression of algebraic properties such as idempotence, associativity and distributivity, for example

$$P \not< b \not> (Q \not< b \not> R) = (P \not< b \not> Q) \not< b \not> R$$
$$= P \not< b \not> R.$$

A complete set of algebraic laws for $\not< b \not>$ will be given by Hoare (1985).

$$\mu\xi \,.\, (?x \rightarrow ?y \rightarrow$$
$$0, x \succ\!- q, r \rightarrow$$
$$\mu\psi \,.\, ((q+1, r-y \succ\!- q, r \rightarrow \psi)$$
$$\not< r \geqslant y \not> (!q \rightarrow !r \rightarrow \xi)))$$

FIGURE 3. Long division.

A simple example of the use of a conditional is to construct a program (see figure 3) that repeatedly inputs a pair of natural numbers and outputs the quotient and remainder of division of the first by the second. If the divisor is zero, the program breaks. The program uses the simple but slow method of successive subtraction. To emphasize the familiarity of these ideas, figure 4 gives a translation into the notations of a more conventional programming language.

Sequential composition

If P and Q are processes, their sequential composition (P;Q) is a process that behaves like P until P successfully terminates, and then it behaves like Q. If P never terminates successfully, neither does (P;Q). The process that does nothing but terminate successfully will be called 'skip'.

Let us give the algebraic laws that we would expect to govern the behaviour of sequential composition. First it must be continuous and distributive and strict in its first argument. Clearly

```
begin
ξ: input x; input y;
   q: = 0; r: = x;
ψ: if r ⩾ y then begin q: = q+1;
                       r: = r-y;
                       go to ψ
                 end
            else begin output q;
                       output r;
                       go to ξ
                 end
end
```

FIGURE 4. Conventional notation.

it should be associative and have 'skip' as its unit. Finally $(;Q)$, considered as a unary postfix operator, should distribute backward through all other operators of our language (except $\gg$):

$$\begin{aligned}&(!e \to P);Q = !e \to (P;Q),\\ &(?x \to P(x);Q = ?z \to (P(z);Q),\\ &(e \succ\!- x \to P(x));Q = e \succ\!- z \to (P(z);Q), \quad \text{(for z not free in Q)}\\ &(P \not< b \not> R);Q = (P;Q) \not< b \not> (R;Q).\end{aligned}$$

As for $\gg$, we have sufficient laws to eliminate sequential composition from every finite program. The continuity property ensures that the operator is uniquely defined for all programs, provided that it exists. It is quite difficult to formulate the definition in a satisfactory fashion; for further discussion see Hehner (1984). Certainly, successful termination must be an observable event, and the final values of all variables must also be observable.

3. CONCLUSION

This paper has made the claim that a computer program can be identified with the strongest predicate describing all relevant observations that can be made of a computer executing the program. The claim is illustrated by the formal definition of the notations of a very simple programming language. The claim is justified by purely philosophical arguments. A stronger justification would be its promised practical benefits for the specification and development of reliable programs.

Before writing a program, the programmer is recommended to formulate a specification S of what his program is intended to accomplish. S is a description of the observations that are admissible for his program when it is constructed. The major problem in formulating S is to ensure the utmost simplicity and clarity, so that there can remain no doubt that it describes accurately just what is wanted; for if it does not, there is nothing that the mathematician or the programmer can do to remedy the consequences, which may be disastrous. For this reason, there should be no restriction on the range of concepts and notations used to express the specification: the full set of logical and mathematical notations should be available for use in the overriding interests of clarity. If suitable concepts are not yet known, new branches of mathematics must be developed to meet the need.

Once the specification is formulated, the task of the programmer remains to find a predicate P, expressed in the restricted notations of his programming language, such that P logically implies the specification S, i.e.

$$\models P \Rightarrow S.$$

Because of the notational restrictions, and in the pursuit of efficiency, P will in general get much longer and more complicated than S. But in proving the correctness of P, the programmer may use all the familiar techniques and methods of classical mathematics. Consequently, he does not need the cumbersome specialised proof rules that have often been associated with proof-oriented programming language definitions (Hoare 1969). Finally, if the specification is not tautologous, the total correctness of the program will be established.

I certainly do not recommend that a large program be proved correct by expanding all the definitions and translating it explicitly into one gigantic predicate. A far more effective technique is to perform the proofs as necessary during the design and construction of the program. This is known as 'top-down programming', and is now described in five steps.

(1) Suppose the original specification is S. The programmer needs the insight to see that the achievement of S will involve completion of (say) two subtasks. He formulates the specification of these subtasks as predicates T and U.

(2) Using only the notations of his programming language he then constructs a framework $P(\xi,\psi)$, containing the names ξ and ψ to stand for the subtask programs that have not yet been written.

(3) He then slots the specifications T and U in place of these two subprograms, and proves that this satisfies the original specification S, i.e.

$$\models P(T,U) \Rightarrow S.$$

Note that P(T,U) is a predicate expressed in a mixture of conventional and programming notations.

(4) He can now safely delegate to others the subtasks of writing programs Q and R, which satisfy the specifications T and U, i.e.

$$\models Q \Rightarrow T$$

and $$\models R \Rightarrow U.$$

(5) When this is done, he can slot programs Q and R into the original framework P, and he may be sure that the result will meet the original specification S,

$$\models P(Q,R) \Rightarrow S.$$

This assurance is gained not by laborious integration testing after delivery of the components, but by a proof that has been made even before the task of writing the subprograms has started. Since the subprograms have been constructed by use of similar reliable methods, the risk of error should be quite small. And the validity of this method of programming by parts depends only on the fact that all operators of our programming language are monotonic in the sense that they respect implication ordering.

If $\quad S \Rightarrow T$
then $\quad P(S) \Rightarrow P(T)$.

Another effective method of programming is to write first an inefficient program P that meets the specification S. This can be useful as a demonstration or training prototype of the eventual product. Then the algebraic laws can be used to transform P into a more efficient program Q, such that

$$\models Q \Rightarrow P.$$

Clearly Q will meet any specification that P meets. If P is a non-deterministic program, the transformation may use implications as well as equivalences in the pursuit of greater efficiency.

Thus the approach advocated in this paper includes that of the other contributors to this collection, in that it gives a mathematical model for the notations of a simple executable programming language and uses algebraic laws for optimization. It differs from the other contributions in making three recommendations:

(1) Specifications should *not* be confined to the notations of an executable programming language.

(2) Implication, rather than just equivalence, should be used to prove correctness of programs, and to transform them in the interests of efficiency.

(3) These methods need not be confined to applicative programming languages. They should be extended to conventional procedural languages, which can be efficiently executed on computers of the present day.

I am grateful to: A. J. R. G. Milner (1980) for his pioneering work in the mathematical theory of communicating systems; E. C. R. Hehner (1983) for pointing out that programs are predicates; D. S. Scott (1981) for the domain theory that underlies a proper theory of recursion; S. D. Brookes and A. W. Roscoe (1984) and E.-R. Olderog (1984) for construction of the model on which this exposition is based; E. W. Dijkstra (1976) for his realization of the value of non-determinacy, and his insistence on total correctness.

References

Brookes, S. D., Hoare, C. A. R., Roscoe, A. W. 1984 A theory of communicating sequential processes. *J. Ass. comput. Mach.* (In the press.)

Dijkstra, E. W. 1976 *A discipline of programming*, p. 217. Englewood Cliffs, N.J.: Prentice-Hall.

Floyd, R. W. 1967 Assigning meanings to programs. *Proc. Am. math. Soc. Symp. Appl. Math.*, vol. 19, pp. 19–31.

Hehner, E. C. R. 1984 Predicative Programming, part I. *Comm. Ass. comput. Mach.* (In the press.)

Hehner, E. C. R. & Hoare, C. A. R. 1983 A more complete model of communicating processes. *Theor. computer Sci.* **26**, 105–120.

Hoare, C. A. R. 1969 An axiomatic basis for computer programming. *Commun. Ass. comput. Mach.* **12**, 576–580, 583.

Hoare, C. A. R. 1985 A couple of novelties in the propositional calculus. *Z. math. Logik* (In the press.)

Milner, A. J. R. G. 1980 A calculus of communicating systems. *Springer LNCS* vol. 92. Berlin: Springer-Verlag.

Olderog, E.-R. & Hoare, C. A. R. 1984 *Specification-oriented semantics for communicating processes*, *P.R.G.-37*. Oxford University Computing Laboratory.

Scott, D. S. 1981 *Lecture notes on a mathematical theory of computation*, *P.R.G.-19*, p. 148. Oxford University Computing Laboratory.

Discussion

F. K. HANNA (*Electronics Laboratories, University of Kent at Canterbury, U.K.*). Professor Hoare made a valuable point when he noted that a physical system can be characterized by a predicate that describes all possible observations that may be made at the ports of the system. In fact, not only can this be done, but it can very usefully be done.

At Kent University, we have been working for some years on characterizing digital systems in just this way. One may imagine waveforms in digital systems as being described as partial functions, from time to (typically) a two-element set (conventionally called T and F). One can then write down a predicate (on 3-tuples of waveforms) that characterizes (but not overspecifies) the notion of, for instance, 'behaving like an AND gate'. An AND gate is then, by definition, any device, the waveforms at whose ports satisfy this predicate: likewise with other primitive elements.

Complex digital systems are realized by an interconnected network of primitive elements. The predicate satisfied by the complex system may be related to the predicates satisfied by its component parts by the use of combinators. For instance, the behaviour of proposed implementation of a serial binary adder may be expressed in terms of the behaviour of the primitive gates from which it is constructed, and the combinator representing the constraints on the behaviour of these gates imposed by the 'circuit diagram'. Working within a suitable theory, one may then seek to prove, as a theorem, that this behaviour does in fact correspond to doing binary addition.

The ease with which behavioural predicates may be used to characterize, as weakly or as strongly as desired, the behaviour of systems, irrespective of whether they are implemented in either software or hardware, is today an especially valuable one.

C. A. R. HOARE. Thank you for your supportive comment. The advantages of predicate-oriented specifications and proof of digital systems are especially marked. For small components (for example a single chip) the actions of the components are lock-step synchronized, so there is no problem in hiding infinite sequences of internal events; consequently parallel composition can be simply defined as logical conjunction. This approach is currently being pursued by Mike Gordon at Cambridge.

Unfortunately, there remains the problem of a miracle. A device that simply shortcircuits power to ground is represented by the predicate

true = false,

and by propositional calculus, this implies every specification. So one must take care that a device that shortcircuits will degenerate to 'true' instead of 'false'.

Alternatively, one could admit that we are proving only partial correctness (i.e. conditional upon absence of shortcircuit). Yet another alternative is to accept the obligation to prove a circuit *equivalent* to its specification. Some practical experience is needed to judge between these alternatives.

Invariance and non-determinacy

BY E. W. DIJKSTRA

2100 *Main Building, Institute for Computing Science, The University of Texas at Austin, Austin, Texas* 78712, *U.S.A.*

Since the earliest days of proving the correctness of programs, predicates on the program's state space have played a central role. This role became essential when non-deterministic systems were considered. The first (and still best known) source of non-determinacy was provided by operating systems, which had to regulate the cooperation between components that had speed ratios that were beyond our control. Distributed systems have revived our interest in such configurations.

I know of only one satisfactory way of reasoning about such systems: to prove that none of the atomic actions falsifies a special predicate, the so-called 'global invariant'. Once initialized, the global invariant will then be maintained by *any* interleaving of the atomic actions. That solves the problem in principle; in each particular case, however, we have to choose how to write down the global invariant. The choice of notation influences the ease with which we can show that, indeed, none of the atomic actions falsifies the global invariant.

An example will be given and discussed.

An accident introduced me 32 years ago to automatic computing, a topic that has fascinated me ever since. As the years go by, I am beginning to appreciate the length of my involvement more and more, since I owe to it a very lively picture of a sizeable part of the history of the growth of a science. I have observed profound changes in our thinking habits, and I have found those observations interesting and instructive.

I do remember, for instance, one of my first efforts – in the mid 1950s – to come to grips with what we would now call 'repetition'. It was profoundly inadequate, and in the course of this talk I hope to explain to you why. Very operationally, I tried to deal with it as a recurrence relation: one instructs the machine to start with an initial value x_0 and to generate from there enough values from the sequence further defined by the recurrence relation

$$x_{i+1} = f(x_i).$$

Why did I do that? I think because I was glad to recognize something familiar, and in those days familiarity was more important than significance. The knowledge I had at the time was already sufficient to doubt the significance, but I do not remember doing so. You see, a well known concept was the 'order' of a recurrence relation, the Fibonacci sequence being given by the second-order recurrence relation

$$F_{n+2} = F_{n+1} + F_n;$$

but any programmer would implement this by

$$(A, B)_{n+1} = (A+B, A)_n,$$

i.e. a first-order recurrence relation! In short then, I should have already been suspicious. But it *was* the prevailing view in that decade: not only FORTRAN but even ALGOL 60 included only repetitive constructs of which the so-called 'controlled variable' was an essential ingredient.

My estimation is that the introduction of the so-called 'controlled variable' has delayed the development of computing science by almost a decade. I got very suspicious in the late 1960s when I discovered that the 'dyed-in-the-wool' FORTRAN or ALGOL programmer had been conditioned so as to be unable to design the elegant solution to what became known as The Problem of the Dutch National Flag. The fact that, in the 1970s, the Euclid algorithm for the g.c.d. of the positive integers X and Y was widely quoted as a paradigm, I can only explain by the circumstances that it is the simplest program that demonstrates so convincingly the inappropriateness of the notion of the 'controlled variable'.

I now write the Euclid algorithm in the form

```
|[x, y: int
 ; x, y := X, Y
 ; do x > y → x := x − y
    ▯ y > x → y := y − x
  od
]|   .
```

This is evidently a repetition in which there is no place for a 'controlled variable' counting something of relevance or controlling termination, or both.

* * *

Another incident – A. W. Dek's invention of the real-time interrupt – introduced me 25 years ago to non-determinacy. My first major concern was to show that saving register contents at program interruption and restoring them at program resumption could not be corrupted by the occurrence of a next interrupt. The arguments required were very tricky, so tricky as a matter of fact that I was not surprised at all when I found flaws in the designs of the interrupt facilities of later machines such as the CDC 165 and the IBM 360. I experienced the problems caused by the unpredictable interleaving as completely novel ones, not suspecting that, about a decade later, they would be tackled by the same techniques that would then be used for reasoning about repetitions.

I am, of course, referring to the technique of the so-called 'invariant' as illustrated in the following type of annotation of a repetition (assertions being written within braces)

$$\{P\}$$
$$\textbf{do}\ B \rightarrow \{P \wedge B\}\ S\ \{P\}\ \textbf{od}$$
$$\{P \wedge \neg B\}.$$

In words: if assertion P, guard B and statement S are such that the additional validity of B guarantees that execution of S does not destroy the validity of P, then the whole repetition **do** B→S **od** will not destroy the validity of P, *no matter how often* the repeatable statement S is repeated.

Now, if we have several clauses B→S, none of which destroys the validity of P, the validity of P will not be destroyed *no matter how often and in what order* they are repeated. In other words, the pattern appropriate for reasoning about repetitions is straightforwardly able to cope with the non-determinacy that has to be absorbed by the operating system for, say, a multiprogrammed installation.

The technique has been used rather constructively in the design of the THE Multiprogramming System to derive the 'synchronization conditions' (i.e. guards) that would ensure, for instance, that no buffer would become emptier than empty or fuller than full. At the time we did not know the axiom of assignment; we only knew what it entailed for simple assignment statements, such as $n := n+1$, and equally simple predicates, such as $n \leq N$. This was in the first half of the 1960s.

In the second half of the 1960s the method was formalized for deterministic sequential programs by R. W. Floyd (1967) and by C. A. R. Hoare (1969). Floyd included proofs of termination, but addressed himself to programs that could be expressed by arbitrary flow charts. (This latter generality was not too attractive. In the control graph one had to select a set of so-called 'cutting edges', i.e. a set of edges such that their removal would leave a graph with no cycles, and to each cutting edge a proof obligation corresponded. The awkward thing is that for an arbitrary control graph the problem of determining a minimum set of cutting edges is most unattractive.) Hoare's subsequent contribution was twofold: on account of the structure of the axiom of assignment he definitely decided in favour of so-called 'backwards reasoning' – Floyd had left this choice open – and he tied the proof obligations in with the syntactic constructs for the flow of control. (Ironically, he confined himself to partial correctness, though the problem of finding a minimum set of cutting edges – which are required for termination proofs – had been reduced to triviality by the sequencing discipline he had adopted.) All this was synthesized in the early 1970s by myself, and my 'guarded commands', besides forming a basis for a calculus for the derivation of programs, introduced non-determinacy into conventional sequential programming.

Central to this game was the formal expression and manipulation of so-called 'assertions' or 'conditions', i.e. predicates that contained the coordinates of the program's state space as free variables, for example to derive for a program fragment the precondition corresponding to a given post-condition. (It is this direction of the functional dependence to which the term 'backwards reasoning' refers. In addition to a simpler axiom of assignment, the pragmatic advantages of backwards reasoning are twofold. It circumvents undefined values since for any program fragment the pre-condition is a total function of the post-condition, whereas the post-condition is, in general, a partial function of the pre-condition. Furthermore, the calculus includes non-determinacy at no extra cost at all.)

For the formulation and manipulation of these conditions, the predicate calculus became a vital tool; so much so, that during the last decade it became for many programming computing scientists an indispensable tool for their daily reasoning. (In passing I may mention my strong impression that those computing scientists may very well have been the first to *use* the predicate calculus regularly. Mathematicians, and even logicians, for whom, for instance, the facts that equivalence is associative, that disjunction distributes over equivalence, and that conjunction distributes over non-equivalence, belong to their active knowledge, are extremely rare; I have never met one. Without intimate knowledge of such basic properties of the logical connectives one can hardly be expected to be a very effective user of the predicate calculus; hence my strong impression. In retrospect I found rather shocking the conclusion that as far as the mathematical community is concerned George Boole has lived in vain.)

The extensive use of the predicate calculus in program derivation during the last decade has had a profound influence, the consequences of which are still unfathomed. It turned program development into a calculational activity (and the idea of program correctness into a calculational notion). The consequences are unfathomed because suddenly we find ourselves urgently invited to apply formal techniques on a much greater scale than we were used to. It turns out that the predicate calculus only solves the problems 'in princple': without careful choice of our extra-logical primitives and their notation, the formulae to be manipulated have a tendency of becoming unmanageably complicated. As a result, each specific problem may pose a new conceptual and notational challenge. By way of illustration, I shall show an extreme example from the field of distributed programming; the example is extreme in the sense that almost all the manipulations of the derivation belong to the extra-logical calculus of regular expressions.

* * *

We consider a network of machines that can send messages to each other. Each machine is in one of three states, namely

n for 'neutrally engaged',
d for 'delayed', or
c for 'critically engaged'.

The objective is to ensure that at most one machine at a time shall be in state c. A critical engagment lasts for only a finite period and is immediately followed by a neutral engagement of the machine in question. Between a neutral engagement and the subsequent critical engagement a delay may occur in view of the requirement that at any moment at most one machine be critically engaged (called 'mutual exclusion'). The implied synchronization has to be implemented in such a manner that no delay lasts forever (called 'fairness').

We introduce a single **token**, either held by one of the machines or being sent from one machine to another. Mutual exclusion is then achieved by maintaining the truth of the predicate

a critically engaged machine holds the token.

The machines maintain this by (i) not initiating a critical engagement unless holding the token, and (ii) not sending the token to another machine while being critically engaged.

Furthermore each machine maintains

the machine holding the token is not delayed

by (i) skipping the delay upon termination of a neutral engagement while holding the token, and (ii) initiating a critical engagement upon receipt of the token while delayed. Fairness is therefore ensured when each delayed machine receives the token within a finite period of time. Consequently, there must be some means of passing the token from one machine to another. But we do not want the token to pass unless necessary. We therefore also need one or more **signals**, which are sent by delayed processes to indicate interest in obtaining the token.

The rest of this example deals with the control of the movement of the token and signals. To this end the machines are connected by links into a ring, of which the two circular directions are called 'to the left' and 'to the right', respectively. The token is sent to the left and signals are sent to the right. Each link connecting two neighbouring machines in the ring is in one of three states, namely

u for 'unused',
t for 'carrying the token to the left', or
s for 'carrying a signal to the right'.

The last two states are postulated to last for only a finite period of time.

The computation will be broken up into *atomic actions*. (An atomic action is the same type of idealization as the 'point mass' in physics.) Each atomic action is performed by one of the machines and involves a state change for that machine and for one or both of its adjacent links. There are four kinds of atomic action to be designed, those which take place:

(n) upon completion of a neutral engagement,
(c) upon completion of a critical engagement,
(s) upon arrival of a signal,
(t) upon arrival of the token.

(We need not bother about 'completion of a delay' since this will be subsumed by the arrival of the token; similarly the 'completion' of the state 'unused' for a link is subsumed in sending either the token or a signal over that link.)

Our invariant for the whole system is, loosely speaking, 'the ring is in a permissible state', but that is only helpful provided we have a very precise characterization of the set of permissible states. Instead of giving this characterization in advance as an invariant predicate, we shall derive the set of permissible states as the transitive closure of the atomic transitions, starting from a given initial state, namely: all machines neutrally engaged, all the links unused, and the token residing in one of the machines.

Immediately the question arises how to characterize sets of ring states. We shall represent a ring state as a string in which machine states and link states alternate, with the understanding that the left end of the string is adjacent to the right end.

We can now characterize a set of ring states by writing down a grammar for representative strings. In this example we shall use the grammar of 'regular expressions', though in fact we are concerned only with strings of fixed length (twice the number of machines).

It will turn out to be handy to give the machines one of two colours, either black (b) or white (w), and a machine state will be coded by prefixing one of the three states n, d or c, by one of the colours b or w. Blackness of a machine indicates that interest in the token exists to the left. The machine holding the token will be identified by writing its colour with the corresponding capital letter. Initially all machines being white, we can characterize the unique initial state by the regular expression

– (wn u)* Wn u – (0)

(Note: if a regular expression is used to characterize a set of ring states, we shall surround it by a pair of dashes. This implies, for instance, that (0) is equivalent to

– (u wn)* u Wn – .)

In state (0), only completion of neutral engagements is possible. For the time being we confine our attention to the more interesting case of such completions taking place in machines not holding the token and propose the transition

$$\text{wn u} \rightarrow \text{wd s} \quad , \tag{n. 0}$$

i.e. a white machine without the token completes its neutral engagement by becoming delayed and sending a signal over the link to its right. (Transition (n. 0) only caters for the situation that a 'wn' has a 'u' to its right.)

The transitive closure of (0) under (n. 0) is

$$-\ (\text{wn u} \mathbin{\square} \text{wd s})^{*}\ \text{Wn u}\ - \tag{1}$$

in which ▯ (which syntactically has been given the lowest binding power) should be read as 'or'. Note that (1) is equivalent to

$$-\ (\text{wn u} \mathbin{\square} \text{wd s}\ (\text{wn u})^{*})^{*}\ \text{Wn u}\ - \quad .$$

For the arrival of a signal at a white neutral machine we propose the transition

$$\text{s wn u} \rightarrow \text{u bn s} \quad , \tag{s. 0}$$

i.e. the machine transmits the signal and blackens itself. The transitive closure of (0) under (n. 0) and (s. 0) is given by

$$-\ (\text{wn u} \mathbin{\square} \text{wd}\ (\text{u bn})^{*}\ \text{s})^{*}\ \text{Wn u}\ - \quad .$$

Closing this further under

$$\text{u bn} \rightarrow \text{u bd} \tag{n. 1}$$

$$\text{s wd} \rightarrow \text{u bd} \tag{s. 1}$$

yields

$$-\ (\text{wn u} \mathbin{\square} \text{wd}\ (\text{u bn} \mathbin{\square} \text{u bd})^{*}\ \text{s})^{*}\ \text{Wn u}\ - \quad ,$$

which we record as

$$-\ \text{H}^{*}\ \text{Wn u}\ - \quad \text{with} \tag{2}$$

$$\text{H} = \text{wn u} \mathbin{\square} \text{Q s} \quad \text{with} \tag{3}$$

$$\text{Q} = \text{wd}\ (\text{u bn} \mathbin{\square} \text{u bd})^{*} \quad . \tag{4}$$

We note that the grammars H, H H*, H* and H* Q (note the absence of dashes: these grammars correspond to sets of strings) are also closed under the four transitions considered so far. (The reader is not expected to see this at a glance: the formal verification of the above claim requires a short calculation.) Furthermore we note that under the transitions given so far, the transitive closure of the string wn u H* equals H H*.

Let us now look at the more interesting case that a signal arrives at the machine holding the token. The only way in which we can make the substring s Wn explicit in (2) is by adding the superfluous term Q s Wn u

$$-\ \text{H}^{*}\ (\text{Wn u} \mathbin{\square} \text{Q s Wn u})\ - \quad ,$$

which we can close under

$$\text{s Wn u} \rightarrow \text{t wn u} \tag{s. 2}$$

by applying (s. 2) now as rewrite rule:

$$-\ \text{H}^{*}\ (\text{Wn u} \mathbin{\square} \text{Q t wn u})\ - \quad .$$

As a result of the emergence of a new instance of wn u, this is no longer closed under the previous transformations. But because the ring is cyclic, we can rewrite this as

$$- \mathrm{H}^* \,(\mathrm{Wn\ u} \,\square\, \mathrm{Q\ t\ (wn\ u\ H^*)}) -$$

and the closure of this yields

$$- \mathrm{H}^* \,(\mathrm{Wn\ u} \,\square\, \mathrm{Q\ t\ H}) - \quad . \tag{5}$$

Closing (5) under

$$\mathrm{Wn\ u} \rightarrow \mathrm{Wc\ u} \tag{n. 2}$$

obviously yields

$$- \mathrm{H}^* \,(\mathrm{Wn\ u} \,\square\, \mathrm{Wc\ u} \,\square\, \mathrm{Q\ t\ H}) - \quad , \tag{6}$$

which is also closed under the inverse

$$\mathrm{Wc\ u} \rightarrow \mathrm{Wn\ u} \quad . \tag{c. 0}$$

With the introduction of the term Wc u we have created the possibility of a signal arriving at the critically engaged machine (which holds the token). Observing that in (6) the substring s Wc can only occur in Q s Wc u, adding this as a superfluous term, and applying the transition

$$\mathrm{s\ Wc\ u} \rightarrow \mathrm{u\ Bc\ u} \tag{s. 3}$$

as rewrite rule, we derive the closure

$$- \mathrm{H}^* \,(\mathrm{Wn\ u} \,\square\, \mathrm{Wc\ u} \,\square\, \mathrm{Q\ t\ H} \,\square\, \mathrm{Q\ u\ Bc\ u}) - \quad . \tag{7}$$

(Because we lack a full regularity calculus we did not apply it. It is instructive to know that, as a result, grammars (5), (6) and (7) are *not* fully closed.)

The introduction of the term Bc introduces a new form of critical engagement. When this terminates, we require that the token be sent to the left

$$\mathrm{u\ Bc\ u} \rightarrow \mathrm{t\ wn\ u} \quad . \tag{c. 1}$$

Since the resulting Q t wn u is subsumed by the preceding Q t H, (7) is closed under (c. 1) as well.

We leave to the reader the verification that (7) is also closed under the remaining three transitions, which enumerate how the token can arrive:

$$\mathrm{wd\ t} \rightarrow \mathrm{Wc\ u} \tag{t. 0}$$

$$\mathrm{u\ bn\ t} \rightarrow \mathrm{t\ wn\ u} \tag{t. 1}$$

$$\mathrm{u\ bd\ t} \rightarrow \mathrm{u\ Bc\ u} \quad . \tag{t. 2}$$

Since (7) tells us that t has a string Q to its left, which may end only in these three different ways, the construction of the closure and of the list of transitions that might be needed has now been completed.

Inspection of (7) shows that the condition of mutual exclusion is satisfied. It also enables us to convince ourselves that each delay will be of finite duration. For that purpose we associate with a delayed machine the string of (alternating) links and machines to its right, up to and including the machine that holds the token or the link that carries it. For that string we define k by

k = the number of elements in the string + the number of white machines in the string.

To begin with we observe that k $\geqslant 0$ and that none of the transitions increase k. We now convince ourselves that k decreases within a finite period of time, given that the states s, t and c are of finite duration: from (3), (4) and (7) we conclude that the delayed machine occurs in a Q;

(i) for a Q in H, the string contains an s, and (s. 0), (s. 1), (s. 2) or (s. 3) will decrease k;

(ii) for the Q in Q t H, (t. 0), (t. 1) or (t. 2) will decrease k;

(iii) for the Q in Q u Bc u, (c. 0) is inapplicable and (c. 1) will decrease k, and from (7) we conclude that this case analysis has been exhaustive. This concludes (the compact presentation of) our example.

Retrospective remarks

In the calculations presented, the machines themselves have remained anonymous. We could have numbered them from 0 to $N-1$, but invite the reader to try to visualize what our invariant would have looked like, had we used quantifications over machine subscripts! It would have been totally unmanageable. (Not only did we leave the individual machines anonymous, but even their number is not mentioned in the analysis: for a ring of N machines, only the strings of length 2N that belong to the grammar (7) are applicable. A fringe benefit is that very small values of N do not require special analysis. To pay for these benefits, we have the trivial obligation to show that no transition changes the number of machines.)

After the decision to try to use regular expressions, it took me several iterations before I had reached the above treatment. My first efforts contained errors, due to my lack of experience in using the 'regularity calculus' for deriving a transitive closure under rewrite rules. The lack of experience was made more severe by the fact that the same language can be characterized by many different regular expressions: for instance, (a ▯ b)*, (a ▯ b ▯ a b)* and (a ▯ b a*)* are all equivalent. In the beginning I experienced this great freedom as a nuisance, but now I think this was naïve, since precisely these language-preserving transformations enable us to massage a regular expression into a form suitable for our next manipulation. Equivalences lie at the heart of any practical calculus.

Finally, it took me quite some time before I discovered the proper abbreviations to introduce. (H and Q, easy to defend in hindsight, could have been chosen much earlier, had we had more familiarity with the regularity calculus.)

Conclusion

I mentioned that, owing to the calculational approach to program design, each specific problem may pose a new conceptual and notational challenge. The example given has been included to give the reader some feeling for the forms that challenge may take. I called the consequences unfathomed, the reason being that the machines executing our programs are truly worthy of the name 'general purpose equipment' and that, consequently, the area that calls for the effective application of formal techniques seems to have no limit.

The example illustrating the use of the regularity calculus was developed under the critical inspiration of the Tuesday Afternoon Club, and of F. E. J. Kruseman Aretz in particular. It was a privilege to write half of the above with A. J. M. van Gasteren looking over my shoulder.

References

Floyd, R. W. 1967 Assigning meanings to programs. In *Proc. Symp. Appl. Math.* (ed. J. T. Schwartz), vol. **19**, pp. 19–31. Providence, Rhode Island: American Mathematical Society.
Hoare, C. A. R. 1969 An axiomatic basis for computer programming. *Commun. Ass. comput. Mach.* **12**, 576–580.

Discussion

R. S. Bird (*Programming Research Group, Oxford University, U.K.*). What intuitions lay behind the invention of the coloured states black and white?

E. W. Dijkstra. Clearly the receipt of a signal, i.e. the obligation to send or transmit the token, has to be recorded. Under such circumstances I find 'colouring' objects a handy metaphor. It makes it easy to visualize and to talk about, and, furthermore, one can start colouring without knowing how many colours will eventually be needed. I remember the design of a mark-scan garbage collector in which reachable nodes changed during the marking phase from white to black via the intermediate colour grey. I used the same metaphor in the 1950s, when I designed an algorithm for the shortest path. Clearly the metaphor suits me.

M. H. Rogers (*School of Mathematics, University of Bristol, U.K.*). Does Professor Dijkstra hold out any hope for automating the procedure of choosing suitable global invariants, at least for some range of programs?

E. W. Dijkstra. No, not much. The example I showed is in this respect telling: the choice of notation was already critical.

O.-J. Dahl (*Institute of Informatics, Blindern, Oslo, Norway*). I notice that in this development the invariant is an end result, not an initial idea. Can Professor Dijkstra comment on that? When is this an appropriate mode of development?

E. W. Dijkstra. The reason to derive the invariant as I went along was probably twofold. First, it was too complicated to be guessed or postulated. Second, I wanted this time to have the strongest invariant so as not to have the program cater for situations that could not arise.

Constructive mathematics and computer programming†

BY P. MARTIN-LÖF

Department of Mathematics, University of Stockholm, Box 6701, *S*-113 85 *Stockholm, Sweden*

If programming is understood not as the writing of instructions for this or that computing machine but as the design of methods of computation that it is the computer's duty to execute (a difference that Dijkstra has referred to as the difference between computer science and computing science), then it no longer seems possible to distinguish the discipline of programming from constructive mathematics. This explains why the intuitionistic theory of types (Martin-Löf 1975 In *Logic Colloquium 1973* (ed. H. E. Rose & J. C. Shepherdson), pp. 73–118. Amsterdam: North-Holland), which was originally developed as a symbolism for the precise codification of constructive mathematics, may equally well be viewed as a programming language. As such it provides a precise notation not only, like other programming languages, for the programs themselves but also for the tasks that the programs are supposed to perform. Moreover, the inference rules of the theory of types, which are again completely formal, appear as rules of correct program synthesis. Thus the correctness of a program written in the theory of types is proved formally at the same time as it is being synthesized.

During the period of just over thirty years that has elapsed since the first electronic computers were built, programming languages have developed from various machine codes and assembly languages, now referred to as low level languages, to high level languages, like FORTRAN, ALGOL 60 and 68, LISP and PASCAL. The virtue of a machine code is that a program written in it can be directly read and executed by the machine. Its weakness is that the structure of the code reflects the structure of the machine so closely as to make it unusable for the instruction of any other machine and, what is more serious, very difficult to understand for a human reader, and therefore error prone. With a high level language, it is the other way round. Its weakness is that a program written in it has to be compiled, that is, translated into the code of a particular machine, before it can be executed by it. But there is ample compensation for this by having a language in which the thought of the programmer can be expressed without too much distortion and understood by someone who knows very little about the structure of the hardware, but does know some English and mathematics. The distinction between low and high level programming languages is of course related to available hardware. It may well be possible to turn what is now regarded as a high level programming language into machine code by the invention of new hardware.

Parallel to the development from low to high level programming languages, there has been a change in one's understanding of the programming activity itself. It used to be looked (down) upon as the rather messy job of instructing this or that physically existing machine, by cunning tricks, to perform computational tasks widely surpassing our own physical powers, something

† This paper was previously published in *Proceedings of the Sixth International Congress for Logic, Methodology and Philosophy of Science* (ed. L. J. Cohen, J. Łos, H. Pfeiffer & K.-P. Podewski), pp. 153–175 (1982). It is reprinted here by permission of the North-Holland Publishing Company, Amsterdam.

that might appeal to people with a liking for crossword puzzles or chess problems. But it has grown into the discipline of designing programs for various (numerical as well as non-numerical) computational tasks, programs that have to be written in a formally precise notation to make automatic execution possible. Whether or not machines have been built or compilers have been written by means of which they can be physically implemented is of no importance as long as questions of efficiency are ignored. What matters is merely that it has been laid down precisely how the programs are to be executed or, what amounts to the same, that it has been specified how a machine for the execution of the programs would have to function. This change of programming, which made Dijkstra (1976) change the terminology from computer science to computing science, would not have been possible without the creation of high level languages of a sufficiently clean logical structure. It has made programming an activity akin in rigour and beauty to that of proving mathematical theorems. (This analogy is actually exact in a sense that will become clear later.)

While maturing into a science, programming has developed a conceptual machinery of its own in which, besides the notion of program itself, the notions of data structure and data type occupy central positions. Even in FORTRAN, there were two types of variables, namely integer and floating point variables, the type of a variable being determined by its initial letter. In ALGOL 60, there was added to the two types **integer** and **real** the third type **Boolean**, and the association of the types with the variables was made both more practical and logical by means of type declarations. However, it was only through Professor Hoare's Notes on Data Structuring (Dahl *et al.* 1972) that the notion of type was introduced into programming in a systematic way. In addition to the three types of ALGOL 60, there now appeared types defined by enumeration, Cartesian products, discriminated unions, array types, power types and various recursively defined types. All these new forms of data types were subsequently incorporated into the programming language PASCAL by Wirth (1971). The left column of table 1, which shows some of the key notions of programming together with their mathematical counterparts, uses notation from ALGOL 60 and PASCAL.

TABLE 1. KEY NOTIONS OF PROGRAMMING WITH MATHEMATICAL COUNTERPARTS

programming	mathematics
program, procedure, algorithm	function
input	argument
output, result	value
$x := e$	$x = e$
$S_1; S_2$	composition of functions
if B **then** S_1 **else** S_2	definition by cases
while B **do** S	definition by recursion
data structure	element, object
data type	set, type
value of a data type	element of a set, object of a type
$a : A$	$a \in A$
integer	Z
real	R
Boolean	$\{0, 1\}$
$(c_1, \ldots, c_n)$	$\{c_1, \ldots, c_n\}$
array [I] **of** T	T^I, $I \to T$
record $s_1 : T_1; s_2 : T_2$ **end**	$T_1 \times T_2$
record case $s:(c_1, c_2)$ **of** $c_1 : (s_1 : T_1); c_2 : (S_2 : T_2)$ **end**	$T_1 + T_2$
set of T	$\{0, 1\}^T$, $T \to \{0, 1\}$

As can be seen from table 1, or from recent programming texts with their snippets of set theory prefaced to the corresponding programming language constructions, the whole conceptual apparatus of programming mirrors that of modern mathematics (set theory, that is, not geometry) and yet is supposed to be different from it. The reason for this curious situation is, I think, that the mathematical notions have gradually received an interpretation, the interpretation that we refer to as classical, which makes them unusable for programming. Fortunately, I do not need to enter the philosophical debate as to whether the classical interpretation of the primitive logical and mathematical notions (proposition, truth, set, element, function, etc.) is sufficiently clear, because this much is at least clear, that if a function is defined as a binary relation satisfying the usual existence and unicity conditions, whereby classical reasoning is allowed in the existence proof, or a set of ordered pairs satisfying the corresponding conditions, then a function cannot be the same type of thing as a computer program. Similarly, if a set is understood in the sense of Zermelo, as a member of the cumulative hierarchy, then a set cannot be the same kind of thing as a data type.

Now, it is the contention of the intuitionists (or constructivists, I shall use these terms synonymously) that the basic mathematical notions, above all the notion of function, ought to be interpreted in such a way that the cleavage between mathematics (classical mathematics, that is) and programming that we are witnessing at present disappears. For the mathematical notions of function and set, it is not so much a question of providing them with new meanings as of restoring old ones, whereas the logical notions of proposition, proof, truth, etc. are given genuinely new interpretations. It was Brouwer who realized the necessity of so doing: the true source of the uncomputable functions of classical mathematics is not the axiom of choice (which *is* valid intuitionistically) but the law of excluded middle and the law of indirect proof. Had it not been possible to interpret the logical notions in such a way as to validate the axiom of choice, the prospects of constructive mathematics would have been dismal.

The difference, then, between constructive mathematics and programming does not concern the primitive notions of the one or the other, because they are essentially the same, but lies in the programmer's insistence that his programs be written in a formal notation so that they can be read and executed by a machine, whereas, in constructive mathematics as practised by Bishop (1967), for example, the computational procedures (programs) are normally left implicit in the proofs, so that considerable further work is needed to bring them into a form that makes them fit for mechanical execution.

What I have just said about the close connection between constructive mathematics and programming explains why the intuitionistic type theory (Martin-Löf 1975), which I began to develop solely with the philosophical motive of clarifying the syntax and semantics of intuitionistic mathematics, may equally well be viewed as a programming language. But for a few concluding remarks, the rest of this paper will be devoted to a fairly complete, albeit condensed, description of this language, with emphasis on its character of programming language. As such, it resembles ALGOL 68 and PASCAL in its typing facilities, whereas the way the programs are written and executed makes it more reminiscent of LISP.

The expressions of the theory of types are formed from variables

$$x, y, z, \ldots$$

by means of various forms of expression

$$(Fx_1, \ldots, x_n)\,(a_1, \ldots, a_m).$$

In an expression of such a form, not all of the variables $x_1, \ldots, x_n$ need become bound in all of the parts $a_1, \ldots, a_m$. Thus, for each form of expression, it must be laid down what variables become bound in what parts. For example,

$$\int_a^b f dx$$

is a form of expression (Ix) (a, b, f), with m = 3 and n = 1, which binds all free occurrences of the single variable x in the third part f, and

$$\frac{df}{dx}(a)$$

is a form of expression (Dx) (a, f), with m = 2 and n = 1, which binds all free occurrences of the variable x in the second part f.

I shall call an expression, in whatever notation, canonical or normal if it is already fully evaluated, which is the same as saying that it has itself as value. Thus, in decimal arithmetic,

$$0, 1, \ldots, 9, 10, 11, \ldots$$

are canonical (normal) expressions, whereas

$$2+2, 2\times 2, 2^2, 3!, 10^{10^{10}}, \ldots$$

are not. An arbitrarily formed expression need not have a value, but, if an expression has a value, then that value is necessarily canonical. This may be expressed by saying that evaluation is idempotent. When you evaluate the value of an expression, you get that value back.

In the theory of types, it depends only on the outermost form of an expression whether it is canonical or not. So there are certain forms of expression, which I shall call canonical forms, such that an expression of one of those forms has itself as value, and there are other, non-canonical forms for which it is laid down in some other way how an expression of such a form is evaluated. What I call canonical and non-canonical forms of expression correspond to the constructors and selectors, respectively, of Landin (1964). In the context of programming, they might also aptly be called data and program forms, respectively. Table 2 displays the primitive forms of expression used in the theory of types. New primitive forms of expression may of course be added when there is need of them.

The conventions as to what variables become bound in what parts are as follows. Free occurrences of x in B become bound in $(\Pi x \in A)\, B$, $(\Sigma x \in A)\, B$ and $(Wx \in A)\, B$. Free occurrences

TABLE 2. PRIMITIVE FORMS OF EXPRESSION USED IN THE THEORY OF TYPES

canonical	non-canonical
$(\Pi x \in A)\, B$, $(\lambda x)\, b$	$c(a)$
$(\Sigma x \in A)\, B$, (a, b)	$(Ex, y)\,(c, d)$
$A+B$, $i(a)$, $j(b)$	$(Dx, y)\,(c, d, e)$
$I(A, a, b)$, r	$J(c, d)$
N_0	$R_0(c)$
N_1, 0_1	$R_1(c, c_0)$
N_2, 0_2, 1_2	$R_2(c, c_0, c_1)$
$\vdots$	$\vdots$
N, 0, a'	$(Rx, y)\,(c, d, e)$
$(Wx \in A)\, B$, $\sup(a, b)$	$(Tx, y, z)\,(c, d)$
U_0, U_1, $\ldots$	

of x in b become bound in (λx) b. Free occurrences of x and y in d become bound in (Ex, y) (c, d). Free occurrences of x in d and y in e become bound in (Dx, y) (c, d, e). Free occurrences of x and y in e become bound in (Rx, y) (c, d, e). And, finally, free occurrences of x, y and z in d become bound in (Tx, y, z) (c, d).

Expressions of the various forms displayed in table 2 are evaluated according to the following rules. I use

$$b(a_1, \ldots, a_n/x_1, \ldots, x_n)$$

to denote the result of simultaneously substituting the expressions $a_1, \ldots, a_n$ for the variables $x_1, \ldots, x_n$ in the expression b. Substitution is the process whereby a program is supplied with its input data, which need not necessarily be in evaluated form.

An expression of canonical form has itself as value. This has already been intimated.

To execute c(a), first execute c. If you get (λx) b as result, then continue by executing b(a/x). Thus c(a) has value d if c has value (λx) b and b(a/x) has value d.

To execute (Ex, y) (c, d), first execute c. If you get (a, b) as result, then continue by executing d(a, b/x, y). Thus (Ex, y) (c, d) has value e if c has value (a, b) and d(a, b/x, y) has value e.

To execute (Dx, y) (c, d, e), first execute c. If you get i(a) as result, then continue by executing d(a/x). If, on the other hand, you get j(b) as result of executing c, then continue by executing e(b/y) instead. Thus (Dx, y) (c, d, e) has value f if either c has value i(a) and d(a/x) has value f, or c has value j(b) and e(b/y) has value f.

To execute J(c, d), first execute c. If you get r as result, then continue by executing d. Thus J(c, d) has value e if c has value r and d has value e.

To execute $R_n(c, c_0, \ldots, c_{n-1})$, first execute c. If you get m_n as result for some $m = 0, \ldots, n-1$, then continue by executing c_m. Thus $R_n(c, c_0, \ldots, c_{n-1})$ has value d if c has value m_n and c_m has value d for some $m = 0, \ldots, n-1$. In particular, $R_0(c)$ has no value. It corresponds to the statement

abort

introduced by Dijkstra (1976). The pair of forms 0_1 and $R_1(c, c_0)$ together operate in exactly the same way as the pair of forms r and J(c, d). To have them both in the language constitutes a redundancy. $R_2(c, c_0, c_1)$ corresponds to the usual conditional statement

if B **then** S_1 **else** S_2

and $R_n(c, c_0, \ldots, c_{n-1})$ for arbitrary $n = 0, 1, \ldots$ to the statement

with e **do** $\{c_1 : S_1, \ldots, c_n : S_n\}$;

introduced by Hoare (Dahl *et al.* 1972, p. 113) and realized by Wirth in PASCAL as the case statement

case e **of** $c_1 : S_1; \ldots; c_n : S_n$ **end.**

To execute (Rx, y) (c, d, e), first execute c. If you get 0 as result, then continue by executing d. If, on the other hand, you get a′ as result, then continue by executing e(a, (Rx, y) (a, d, e)/x, y) instead. Thus (Rx, y) (c, d, e) has value f if either c has value 0 and d has value f, or c has value a′ and e(a, (Rx, y) (a, d, e)/x, y) has value f. The closest analogue of the recursion form (Rx, y) (c, d, e) in traditional programming languages is the repetitive statement form

while B **do** S.

To execute $(Tx, y, z)(c, d)$, first execute c. If you get $\sup(a, b)$ as result, then continue by executing $d(a, b, (\lambda v)(Tx, y, z)(b(v), d)/x, y, z)$. Thus $(Tx, y, z)(c, d)$ has value e if c has value $\sup(a, b)$ and $d(a, b, (\lambda v)(Tx, y, z)(b(v), d)/x, y, z)$ has value e. The transfinite recursion form $(Tx, y, z)(c, d)$ has not yet found any applications in programming. It has, as far as I know, no counterpart in other programming languages.

The traditional way of evaluating an arithmetical expression is to evaluate the parts of the expression before the expression itself is evaluated, as shown in the example

$$\underbrace{\underbrace{\underbrace{(3+2)}_{5}!}_{120}\times 4}_{480}.$$

Thus, traditionally, expressions are evaluated from within, which in programming has come to be known as the applicative order of evaluation. When expressions are evaluated in this way, it is obvious that an expression cannot have a value unless all its parts have values. Moreover, as was explicitly stated as a principle by Frege, the value (Ger.: Bedeutung) of an expression depends only on the values of its parts. In other words, if a part of an expression is replaced by one that has the same value, the value of the whole expression is left unaffected.

When variable binding forms of expression are introduced, as they are in the theory of types, it is no longer possible, in general, to evaluate the expressions from within. To evaluate $(\lambda x)\, b$, for example, we would first have to evaluate b. But b cannot be evaluated, in general, until a value has been assigned to the variable x. In the theory of types, this difficulty has been overcome by reversing the order of evaluation: instead of evaluating the expressions from within, they are evaluated from without. This is known as head reduction in combinatory logic and normal order or lazy evaluation in programming. For example, $(\lambda x)\, b$ is simply assigned itself as value. The term lazy is appropriate because only as few computation steps are made as are absolutely necessary to bring an expression into canonical form. However, what turns out to be of no significance, it is no longer the case that an expression cannot have a value unless all its parts have values. For example, a' has itself as value even if a has no value. What is significant, though, is that the principle of Frege's referred to earlier, namely that the value of an expression depends only on the values of its parts, is irretrievably lost. To make the language work in spite of this loss has been one of the most serious difficulties in the design of the theory of types.

So far, I have merely displayed the various forms of expression used in the theory of types and explained how expressions composed out of those forms are evaluated. The inferential or, as termed in combinatory logic, illative part of the language consists of rules for making judgments of the four forms

A is a type,

A and B are equal types,

a is an object of type A,

a and b are equal objects of type A,

abbreviated

$$A \text{ type},$$

$$A = B,$$

$$a \in A,$$

$$a = b \in A,$$

respectively. A judgment of any one of these forms is in general hypothetical, that is, made under assumptions or, to use the terminology of AUTOMATH (de Bruijn 1970), in a context

$$x_1 \in A_1, \ldots, x_n \in A_n.$$

In such a context, it is always the case that A_1 is a type, ..., A_n is a type under the preceding assumptions $x_1 \in A_1, \ldots, x_{n-1} \in A_{n-1}$. When there is a need to indicate explicitly the assumptions of a hypothetical judgment, it will be written

$$A \text{ type } (x_1 \in A_1, \ldots, x_n \in A_n),$$

$$A = B(x_1 \in A_1, \ldots, x_n \in A_n),$$

$$a \in A(x_1 \in A_1, \ldots, x_n \in A_n),$$

$$a = b \in A(x_1 \in A_1, \ldots, x_n \in A_n).$$

These, then, are the full forms of judgment of the theory of types.

The first form of judgment admits not only the readings

A is a type (set),

A is a proposition,

but also, and this is the reading that is most natural when the language is thought of as a programming language,

A is a problem (task).

Correlatively, the third form of judgment may be read not only

a is an object of type (element of the set) A,

a is a proof of the proposition A,

but also

a is a program for the problem (task) A.

The equivalence of the first two readings is the, by now well known, correspondence between propositions and types discovered by Curry (1958) and Howard (1969), whereas the transition from the second to the third is Kolmogorov's (1932) interpretation of propositions as problems or tasks (Ger.: Aufgabe).

The four forms of judgment used in the theory of types should be compared with the three forms of judgment used (although usually not so called) in standard presentations of first order predicate calculus, whether classical or intuitionistic, namely

A is a formula,

A is true,

a is an individual term.

The first of these corresponds to the form A is a type (proposition), the second is obtained from the form a is an object of type (a proof of the proposition) A by suppressing a, and the third is again obtained from the form a is an object of type A, this time by choosing for A the type of individuals.

In explaining what a judgment of one of the above four forms means, I shall first limit myself to assumption-free judgments. Once it has been explained what meanings they carry, the explanations can readily be extended so as to cover hypothetical judgments as well.

A canonical type A is defined by prescribing how a canonical object of type A is formed as well as how two equal canonical objects of type A are formed. There is no limitation on this prescription except that the relation of equality that it defines between canonical objects of type A must be reflexive, symmetric and transitive. If the rules for forming canonical objects as well as equal canonical objects of a certain type are called the introduction rules for that type, we may thus say with Gentzen (1934) that a canonical type (proposition) is defined by its introduction rules. For non-canonical A, a judgment of the form

$$A \text{ is a type}$$

means that A has a canonical type as value.

Two canonical types A and B are equal if a canonical object of type A is also a canonical object of type B and, moreover, equal canonical objects of type A are also equal canonical objects of type B, and vice versa. For arbitrary (not necessarily canonical) types A and B, a judgment of the form

$$A = B$$

means that A and B have equal canonical types as values. This finishes the explanations of what a type is and what it means for two types to be equal.

Let A be a type. Remember that this means that A denotes a canonical type, that is, has a canonical type as value. Then a judgment of the form

$$a \in A$$

means that a has a canonical object of the canonical type denoted by A as value. Of course, this explanation is not comprehensible unless we know that A has a canonical type as value as well as what a canonical object of that type is. But we do know this because of the presupposition that A is a type: it is part of the definition of a canonical type how a canonical object of that type is formed, and hence we cannot know a canonical type without knowing what a canonical object of that type is.

Let A be a type and a and b be objects of type A. Then a judgment of the form

$$a = b \in A$$

means that a and b have equal canonical objects of the canonical type denoted by A as values. This explanation makes sense since A was presupposed to be a type, that is, to have a canonical type as value, and it is part of the definition of a canonical type how equal canonical objects of that type are formed.

These meaning explanations are extended to hypothetical judgments by an induction on the number of assumptions. Let it be given as premises for all of the following four explanations that $x_1 \in A, \ldots, x_n \in A_n$ is a context, that is, that A_1 is a type, ..., A_n is a type under the assumptions $x_1 \in A_1, \ldots, x_{n-1} \in A_{n-1}$. By induction hypothesis, we know what this means.

A judgment of the form

$$A \text{ type } (x_1 \in A_1, \ldots, x_n \in A_n)$$

means that

$$A(a_1, \ldots, a_n/x_1, \ldots, x_n) \text{ type}$$

provided

$$a_1 \in A_1, \ldots, a_n \in A_n(a_1, \ldots, a_{n-1}/x_1, \ldots, x_{n-1}),$$

and, moreover,

$$A(a_1, \ldots, a_n/x_1, \ldots, x_n) = A(b_1, \ldots, b_n/x_1, \ldots, x_n)$$

provided

$$a_1 = b_1 \in A_1, \ldots, a_n = b_n \in A_n(a_1, \ldots, a_{n-1}/x_1, \ldots, x_{n-1}).$$

Thus it is in the nature of a family of types (propositional function) to be extensional in the sense just described.

Suppose that A and B are types under the assumptions $x_1 \in A_1, \ldots, x_n \in A_n$. Then

$$A = B(x_1 \in A_1, \ldots, x_n \in A_n)$$

means that

$$A(a_1, \ldots, a_n/x_1, \ldots, x_n) = B(a_1, \ldots, a_n/x_1, \ldots, x_n)$$

provided

$$a_1 \in A_1, \ldots, a_n \in A_n(a_1, \ldots, a_{n-1}/x_1, \ldots, x_{n-1}).$$

From this definition, the extensionality of a family of types and the evident transitivity of equality between types, it also follows that

$$A(a_1, \ldots, a_n/x_1, \ldots, x_n) = B(b_1, \ldots, b_n/x_1, \ldots, x_n)$$

provided

$$a_1 = b_1 \in A_1, \ldots, a_n = b_n \in A_n(a_1, \ldots, a_{n-1}/x_1, \ldots, x_{n-1}).$$

Let A be a type under the assumptions $x_1 \in A_1, \ldots, x_n \in A_n$. Then

$$a \in A(x_1 \in A_1, \ldots, x_n \in A_n)$$

means that

$$a(a_1, \ldots, a_n/x_1, \ldots, x_n) \in A(a_1, \ldots, a_n/x_1, \ldots, x_n)$$

provided

$$a_1 \in A_1, \ldots, a_n \in A_n(a_1, \ldots, a_{n-1}/x_1, \ldots, x_{n-1}),$$

and, moreover,

$$a(a_1, \ldots, a_n/x_1, \ldots, x_n) = a(b_1, \ldots, b_n/x_1, \ldots, x_n) \in A(a_1, \ldots, a_n/x_1, \ldots, x_n)$$

provided

$$a_1 = b_1 \in A_1, \ldots, a_n = b_n \in A_n(a_1, \ldots, a_{n-1}/x_1, \ldots, x_{n-1}).$$

Thus, just as for a family of types, it is in the nature of a function to be extensional in the sense of yielding equal objects of the range type when equal objects of the domain types are substituted for the variables of which it is a function.

Let A be a type and a and b objects of type A under the assumptions $x_1 \in A_1, \ldots, x_n \in A_n$. Then

$$a = b \in A(x_1 \in A_1, \ldots, x_n \in A_n)$$

means that

$$a(a_1, \ldots, a_n/x_1, \ldots, x_n) = b(a_1, \ldots, a_n/x_1, \ldots, x_n) \in A(a_1, \ldots, a_n/x_1, \ldots, x_n)$$

provided

$$a_1 \in A_1, \ldots, a_n \in A_n(a_1, \ldots, a_{n-1}/x_1, \ldots, x_{n-1}).$$

Again, from this definition, the extensionality of a function and the transitivity of equality between objects of whatever type, there follows the stronger property that

$$a(a_1, \ldots, a_n/x_1, \ldots, x_n) = b(b_1, \ldots, b_n/x_1, \ldots, x_n) \in A(a_1, \ldots, a_n/x_1, \ldots, x_n)$$

provided

$$a_1 = b_1 \in A_1, \ldots, a_n = b_n \in A_n(a_1, \ldots, a_{n-1}/x_1, \ldots, x_{n-1}).$$

This finishes my explanations of what judgments of the four forms used in the theory of types mean in the presence of assumptions.

Now to the rules of inference or proof rules, as they are called in programming. They will be presented in natural deduction style, suppressing as usual all assumptions other than those that are discharged by an inference of the particular form under consideration. Moreover, in those rules whose conclusion has one of the forms $a \in A$ and $a = b \in A$, only those premises will be explicitly shown that have these very same forms. This is in agreement with the practice of writing, say, the rules of disjunction introduction in predicate calculus simply

$$\frac{A \text{ true}}{A \vee B \text{ true}} \qquad \frac{B \text{ true}}{A \vee B \text{ true}}$$

without showing explicitly the premises that A and B are formulas. For each of the rules of inference, the reader is asked to try to make the conclusion evident to himself on the presupposition that he knows the premises. This does not mean that further verbal explanations are of no help in bringing about an understanding of the rules, only that this is not the place for such detailed explanations. But there are also certain limits to what verbal explanations can do when it comes to justifying axioms and rules of inference. In the end, everybody must understand for himself.

General rules

Reflexivity

$$\frac{a \in A}{a = a \in A} \qquad \frac{A \text{ type}}{A = A}$$

Symmetry

$$\frac{a = b \in A}{b = a \in A} \qquad \frac{A = B}{B = A}$$

Transitivity

$$\frac{a = b \in A \quad b = c \in A}{a = c \in A} \qquad \frac{A = B \quad B = C}{A = C}$$

Equality of types

$$\frac{a \in A \quad A = B}{a \in B} \qquad \frac{a = b \in A \quad A = B}{a = b \in B}$$

Substitution

$$\frac{a \in A \quad \begin{matrix}(x \in A)\\ B \text{ type}\end{matrix}}{B(a/x) \text{ type}} \qquad \frac{a = c \in A \quad \begin{matrix}(x \in A)\\ B = D\end{matrix}}{B(a/x) = D(c/x)}$$

$$\frac{a \in A \quad \begin{matrix}(x \in A)\\ b \in B\end{matrix}}{b(a/x) \in B(a/x)} \qquad \frac{a = c \in A \quad \begin{matrix}(x \in A)\\ b = d \in B\end{matrix}}{b(a/x) = d(c/x) \in B(a/x)}$$

Assumption

$$x \in A$$

Cartesian product of a family of types

Π-formation

$$\frac{A \text{ type} \quad \begin{matrix}(x \in A)\\ B \text{ type}\end{matrix}}{(\Pi x \in A)\, B \text{ type}} \qquad \frac{A = C \quad \begin{matrix}(x \in A)\\ B = D\end{matrix}}{(\Pi x \in A)\, B = (\Pi x \in C)\, D}$$

Π-introduction

$$\frac{\begin{matrix}(x \in A)\\ b \in B\end{matrix}}{(\lambda x)\, b \in (\Pi x \in A)\, B} \qquad \frac{\begin{matrix}(x \in A)\\ b = d \in B\end{matrix}}{(\lambda x)\, b = (\lambda x)\, d \in (\Pi x \in A)\, B}$$

Π-elimination

$$\frac{c \in (\Pi x \in A)\, B \quad a \in A}{c(a) \in B(a/x)} \qquad \frac{c = f \in (\Pi x \in A)\, B \quad a = d \in A}{c(a) = f(d) \in B(a/x)}$$

Π-equality

$$\frac{a \in A \quad \begin{matrix}(x \in A)\\ b \in B\end{matrix}}{((\lambda x)\, b)\, (a) = b(a/x) \in B(a/x)} \qquad \frac{c \in (\Pi x \in A)\, B}{(\lambda x)\, (c(x)) = c \in (\Pi x \in A)\, B}$$

Disjoint union of a family of types

Σ-formation

$$\frac{A \text{ type} \quad \begin{matrix}(x \in A)\\ B \text{ type}\end{matrix}}{(\Sigma x \in A)\, B \text{ type}} \qquad \frac{A = C \quad \begin{matrix}(x \in A)\\ B = D\end{matrix}}{(\Sigma x \in A)\, B = (\Sigma x \in C)\, D}$$

Σ-introduction

$$\frac{a \in A \quad b \in B(a/x)}{(a, b) \in (\Sigma x \in A)\, B} \qquad \frac{a = c \in A \quad b = d \in B(a/x)}{(a, b) = (c, d) \in (\Sigma x \in A)\, B}$$

Σ-elimination

$$\frac{c \in (\Sigma x \in A)\, B \quad \begin{matrix}(x \in A, y \in B)\\ d \in C((x, y)/z)\end{matrix}}{(Ex, y)\, (c, d) \in C(c/z)}$$

$$\frac{c = e \in (\Sigma x \in A)\, B \quad \begin{matrix}(x \in A, y \in B)\\ d = f \in C((x, y)/z)\end{matrix}}{(Ex, y)\, (c, d) = (Ex, y)\, (e, f) \in C(c/z)}$$

Σ-equality

$$\frac{a \in A \quad b \in B(a/x) \quad \begin{matrix}(x \in A, y \in B)\\ d \in C((x, y)/z)\end{matrix}}{(Ex, y)\, ((a, b), d) = d(a, b/x, y) \in C((a, b)/z)}$$

Disjoint union of two types

+-formation

$$\frac{A \text{ type} \quad B \text{ type}}{A + B \text{ type}} \qquad \frac{A = C \quad B = D}{A + B = C + D}$$

+-introduction

$$\frac{a \in A}{i(a) \in A + B} \qquad \frac{a = c \in A}{i(a) = i(c) \in A + B}$$

$$\frac{b \in B}{j(b) \in A + B} \qquad \frac{b = d \in B}{j(b) = j(d) \in A + B}$$

+-elimination

$$\frac{c \in A+B \quad \begin{matrix}(x\in A)\\ d \in C(i(x)/z)\end{matrix} \quad \begin{matrix}(y\in B)\\ e \in C(j(y)/z)\end{matrix}}{(Dx, y)\,(c, d, e) \in C(c/z)}$$

$$\frac{c = f \in A+B \quad \begin{matrix}(x\in A)\\ d = g \in C(i(x)/z)\end{matrix} \quad \begin{matrix}(y\in B)\\ e = h \in C(j(y)/z)\end{matrix}}{(Dx, y)\,(c, d, e) = (Dx, y)\,(f, g, h) \in C(c/z)}$$

+-equality

$$\frac{a \in A \quad \begin{matrix}(x\in A)\\ d \in C(i(x)/z)\end{matrix} \quad \begin{matrix}(y\in B)\\ e \in C(j(y)/z)\end{matrix}}{(Dx, y)\,(i(a), d, e) = d(a/x) \in C(i(a)/z)}$$

$$\frac{b \in B \quad \begin{matrix}(x\in A)\\ d \in C(i(x)/z)\end{matrix} \quad \begin{matrix}(y\in B)\\ e \in C(j(y)/z)\end{matrix}}{(Dx, y)\,(j(b), d, e) = e(b/y) \in C(j(b)/z)}$$

Identity relation

I-*formation*

$$\frac{A \text{ type} \quad a \in A \quad b \in A}{I(A, a, b) \text{ type}} \qquad \frac{A = C \quad a = c \in A \quad b = d \in A}{I(A, a, b) = I(C, c, d)}$$

I-*introduction*

$$\frac{a = b \in A}{r \in I(A, a, b)} \qquad \frac{a = b \in A}{r = r \in I(A, a, b)}$$

I-*elimination*

$$\frac{c \in I(A, a, b)}{a = b \in A}$$

$$\frac{c \in I(A, a, b) \quad d \in C(r/z)}{J(c, d) \in C(c/z)} \qquad \frac{c = e \in I(A, a, b) \quad d = f \in C(r/z)}{J(c, d) = J(e, f) \in C(c/z)}$$

I-*equality*

$$\frac{a = b \in A \quad d \in C(r/z)}{J(r, d) = d \in C(r/z)}$$

Finite types

N_n-*formation*

$$N_n \text{ type} \qquad N_n = N_n$$

N_n-*introduction*

$$m_n \in N_n \;(m = 0, \ldots, n-1) \qquad m_n = m_n \in N_n \;(m = 0, \ldots, n-1)$$

N_n-*elimination*

$$\frac{c \in N_n \quad c_m \in C(m_n/z)\ (m = 0, \ldots, n-1)}{R_n(c, c_0, \ldots, c_{n-1}) \in C(c/z)}$$

$$\frac{c = d \in N_n \quad c_m = d_m \in C(m_n/z)\ (m = 0, \ldots, n-1)}{R_n(c, c_0, \ldots, c_{n-1}) = R_n(d, d_0, \ldots, d_{n-1}) \in C(c/z)}$$

N_n-*equality*

$$\frac{c_m \in C(m_n/z)\ (m = 0, \ldots, n-1)}{R_n(m_n, c_0, \ldots, c_{n-1}) = c_m \in C(m_n/z)}\ (m = 0, \ldots, n-1)$$

Natural numbers

N-*formation*

$$N \text{ is a type} \qquad N = N$$

N-*introduction*

$$0 \in N \qquad 0 = 0 \in N$$

$$\frac{a \in N}{a' \in N} \qquad \frac{a = b \in N}{a' = b' \in N}$$

N-*elimination*

$$\frac{c \in N \quad d \in C(0/z) \quad \begin{matrix}(x \in N, y \in C(x/z)) \\ e \in C(x'/z)\end{matrix}}{(Rx, y)\,(c, d, e) \in C(c/z)}$$

$$\frac{c = f \in N \quad d = g \in C(0/z) \quad \begin{matrix}(x \in N, y \in C(x/z)) \\ e = h \in C(x'/z)\end{matrix}}{(Rx, y)\,(c, d, e) = (Rx, y)\,(f, g, h) \in C(c/z)}$$

N-*equality*

$$\frac{d \in C(0/z) \quad \begin{matrix}(x \in N, y \in C(x/z)) \\ e \in C(x'/z)\end{matrix}}{(Rx, y)\,(0, d, e) = d \in C(0/z)}$$

$$\frac{a \in N \quad d \in C(0/z) \quad \begin{matrix}(x \in N, y \in C(x/z)) \\ e \in C(x'/z)\end{matrix}}{(Rx, y)\,(a', d, e) = e(a, (Rx, y)\,(a, d, e)/x, y) \in C(a'/z)}$$

Wellorderings

W-*formation*

$$\frac{A \text{ type} \quad \begin{matrix}(x \in A) \\ B \text{ type}\end{matrix}}{(Wx \in A)\,B \text{ type}} \qquad \frac{A = C \quad \begin{matrix}(x \in A) \\ B = D\end{matrix}}{(Wx \in A)\,B = (Wx \in C)\,D}$$

W-*introduction*

$$\frac{a \in A \quad b \in B(a/x) \to (Wx \in A)\, B}{\sup(a, b) \in (Wx \in A)\, B}$$

$$\frac{a = c \in A \quad b = d \in B(a/x) \to (Wx \in A)\, B}{\sup(a, b) = \sup(c, d) \in (Wx \in A)\, B}$$

W-*elimination*

$$\frac{c \in (Wx \in A)\, B \qquad \begin{matrix}(x \in A, y \in B \to (Wx \in A)\, B, z \in (\Pi v \in B)\, C(y(v)/w)) \\ d \in C(\sup(x, y)/w)\end{matrix}}{(Tx, y, z)\,(c, d) \in C(c/w)}$$

$$\frac{c = e \in (Wx \in A)\, B \qquad \begin{matrix}(x \in A, y \in B \to (Wx \in A)\, B, z \in (\Pi v \in B)\, C(y(v)/w)) \\ d = f \in C(\sup(x, y)/w)\end{matrix}}{(Tx, y, z)\,(c, d) = (Tx, y, z)\,(e, f) \in C(c/w)}$$

W-*equality*

$$\frac{a \in A \qquad b \in B(a/x) \to (Wx \in A)\, B \qquad \begin{matrix}(x \in A, y \in B \to (Wx \in A)\, B, z \in (\Pi v \in B)\, C(y(v)/w)) \\ d \in C(\sup(x, y)/w)\end{matrix}}{(Tx, y, z)\,(\sup(a, b), d) = d(a, b, (\lambda v)\,(Tx, y, z)\,(b(v), d)/x, y, z) \in C(\sup(a, b)/w)}$$

Universes

U_n-*formation*

$$U_n \text{ is a type} \qquad U_n = U_n$$

U_n-*introduction*

$$\frac{A \in U_n \quad \begin{matrix}(x \in A) \\ B \in U_n\end{matrix}}{(\Pi x \in A)\, B \in U_n} \qquad \frac{A = C \in U_n \quad \begin{matrix}(x \in A) \\ B = D \in U_n\end{matrix}}{(\Pi x \in A)\, B = (\Pi x \in C)\, D \in U_n}$$

$$\frac{A \in U_n \quad \begin{matrix}(x \in A) \\ B \in U_n\end{matrix}}{(\Sigma x \in A)\, B \in U_n} \qquad \frac{A = C \in U_n \quad \begin{matrix}(x \in A) \\ B = D \in U_n\end{matrix}}{(\Sigma x \in A)\, B = (\Sigma x \in C)\, D \in U_n}$$

$$\frac{A \in U_n \quad B \in U_n}{A + B \in U_n} \qquad \frac{A = C \in U_n \quad B = D \in U_n}{A + B = C + D \in U_n}$$

$$\frac{A \in U_n \quad a \in A \quad b \in A}{I(A, a, b) \in U_n} \qquad \frac{A = C \in U_n \quad a = c \in A \quad b = d \in A}{I(A, a, b) = I(C, c, d) \in U_n}$$

$$N_0 \in U_n \qquad N_0 = N_0 \in U_n$$

$$N_1 \in U_n \qquad N_1 = N_1 \in U_n$$

$$\vdots \qquad\qquad \vdots$$

$$N \in U_n \qquad N = N \in U_n$$

$$\frac{A \in U_n \quad \overset{(x \in A)}{B \in U_n}}{(Wx \in A)\, B \in U_n} \qquad \frac{A = C \in U_n \quad \overset{(x \in A)}{B = D \in U_n}}{(Wx \in A)\, B = (Wx \in C)\, D \in U_n}$$

$$U_0 \in U_n \qquad U_0 = U_0 \in U_n$$

$$\vdots \qquad\qquad \vdots$$

$$U_{n-1} \in U_n \qquad U_{n-1} = U_{n-1} \in U_n$$

U_n-*elimination*

$$\frac{A \in U_n}{A \text{ type}} \qquad \frac{A = B \in U_n}{A = B}$$

$$\frac{A \in U_n}{A \in U_{n+1}} \qquad \frac{A = B \in U_n}{A = B \in U_{n+1}}$$

An example will demonstrate how the language-works. Let the premises

$$A \text{ type},$$

$$B \text{ type } (x \in A),$$

$$C \text{ type } (x \in A, y \in B)$$

be given. Make the abbreviation

$$\underbrace{(\Pi x \in A)\, B}_{A \to B}$$

provided the variable x does not occur free in B. Then

$$(\Pi x \in A)\, (\Sigma y \in B)\, C \to (\Sigma f \in (\Pi x \in A)\, B)\, (\Pi x \in A)\, C(f(x)/y)$$

is a type which, when read as a proposition, expresses the axiom of choice. I shall construct an object of this type, an object that may at the same time be interpreted as a proof of the axiom of choice. Assume

$$x \in A,$$

$$z \in (\Pi x \in A)\, (\Sigma y \in B)\, C.$$

By Π-elimination,

$$z(x) \in (\Sigma y \in B)\, C.$$

Make the abbreviations

$$\underbrace{(Ex, y)\, (c, x)}_{p(c)}, \quad \underbrace{(Ex, y)\, (c, y)}_{q(c)}.$$

By Σ-elimination,

$$p(z(x)) \in B,$$

$$q(z(x)) \in C(p(z(x))/y).$$

By Π-introduction,

$$(\lambda x)\, p(z(x)) \in (\Pi x \in A)\, B,$$

and, by Π-equality,

$$((\lambda x)\, p(z(x)))\, (x) = p(z(x)) \in B.$$

By symmetry,

$$p(z(x)) = ((\lambda x)\, p(z(x)))\, (x) \in B,$$

and, by substitution,

$$C(p(z(x))/y) = C(((\lambda x)\, p(z(x)))\, (x)/y).$$

By equality of types,

$$q(z(x)) \in C(((\lambda x)\, p(z(x)))\, (x)/y),$$

and, by Π-introduction,

$$(\lambda x)\, q(z(x)) \in (\Pi x \in A)\, C(((\lambda x)\, p(z(x)))\, (x)/y).$$

By Σ-introduction,

$$((\lambda x)\, p(z(x)), (\lambda x)\, q(z(x))) \in (\Sigma f \in (\Pi x \in A)\, B)\, (\Pi x \in A)\, C(f(x)/y).$$

Finally, by Π-introduction,

$$(\lambda z)\, ((\lambda x)\, p(z(x)), (\lambda x)\, q(z(x))) \in (\Pi x \in A)\, (\Sigma y \in B)\, C \rightarrow (\Sigma f \in (\Pi x \in A)\, B)\, (\Pi x \in A)\, C(f(x)/y).$$

Thus

$$(\lambda z)\, ((\lambda x)\, p(z(x)), (\lambda x)\, q(z(x)))$$

is the sought for proof of the axiom of choice.

To conclude, relating constructive mathematics to computer programming seems to me to have a beneficial influence on both parties. Among the benefits to be derived by constructive mathematics from its association with computer programming, one is that you see immediately why you cannot rely upon the law of excluded middle: its uninhibited use would lead to programs that you did not know how to execute. Another is that you see the point of introducing a formal notation not only for propositions, as in propositional and predicate logic, but also for their proofs: this is necessary to make the methods of computation implicit in intuitionistic (constructive) proofs fit for automatic execution. And a third is that you see the point of formalizing the process of reasoning: this is necessary to have the possibility of automatically verifying the programs' correctness. In fact, if the AUTOMATH proof checker had been written for the theory of types instead of the language AUTOMATH, we would already have a language with the facility of automatic checking of the correctness of the programs formed according to its rules.

In the other direction, by choosing to program in a formal language for constructive mathematics, like the theory of types, one gets access to the whole conceptual apparatus of pure mathematics, neglecting those parts that depend critically on the law of excluded middle, whereas even the best high level programming languages so far designed are wholly inadequate as mathematical languages (and, of course, nobody has claimed them to be so). In fact, I do not think that the search for high level programming languages that are more and more satisfactory from a logical point of view can stop short of anything but a language in which (constructive) mathematics can be adequately expressed.

References

Bishop, E. 1967 *Foundations of constructive analysis*. New York: McGraw-Hill.
de Bruijn, N. G. 1970 The mathematical language AUTOMATH, its usage, and some of its extensions. In *Symposium on automatic demonstration, lecture notes in mathematics*, vol. 125, pp. 29–61. Berlin: Springer-Verlag.
Curry, H. B. 1958 *Combinatory logic*, vol. 1, pp. 312–315. Amsterdam: North Holland.
Dahl, O.-J., Dijkstra, E. W. & Hoare, C. A. R. 1972 *Structured programming*, pp. 83–174. London: Academic Press.
Dijkstra, E. W. 1976 *A discipline of programming*, pp. 26, 201. Englewood Cliffs. N.J.: Prentice-Hall.
Gentzen, G. 1934 Untersuchungen über das logische Schliessen. *Math. Z.* **39**, 176–210, 405–431.
Howard, W. A. 1969 The formulae-as-types notion of construction. In *To H. B. Curry: Essays on combinatory logic, lambda calculus and formalism* (ed. J. P. Seldin & J. R. Hindley), pp. 479–490. London: Academic Press.
Kolmogorov, A. N. 1932 Zur Deutung der intuitionistischen Logik. *Math. Z.* **35**, 58–65.
Landin, P. J. 1964 The mechanical evaluation of expressions. *Computer J.* **6**, 308–320.
Martin-Löf, P. 1975 An intuitionistic theory of types: predicative part. In *Logic colloquium 1973* (ed. H. E. Rose & J. C. Shepherdson), pp. 73–118. Amsterdam: North Holland.
Wirth, N. 1971 The programming language Pascal. *Acta informatica* **1**, 35–63.

Discussion

Z. A. LOZINSKI (*Department of Computing, Imperial College, London, U.K.*). Does Professor Martin-Löf's emphasis on terminating programs come about because of his interest in intuitionistic type theory; or does his use of intuitionistic type theory arise from a belief in termination, i.e. total correctness?

P. MARTIN-LÖF. At the time I designed intuitionistic type theory, I was committed to the interpretation of propositions as types, truth as non-emptiness, absurdity as the empty type, conjunction as the Cartesian product and disjunction as the disjoint union of two types, and so on. Therefore there was no question of having but total elements and functions (that is, hereditarily terminating programs) in the theory. Thus I was in the same predicament as Kreisel in his work on a theory of constructions adequate for the interpretation of intuitionistic logic and Scott in his constructive validity paper. If types are interpreted as domains and elements and functions are taken to be partial, as they are in Scott's mathematical theory of computation, then it is no longer possible to interpret propositions as types, because every type contains an element, namely the bottom element. Hence, if propositions were interpreted as domains and truth as non-emptiness, every proposition would come out true. This is why I could not think of dealing with partial elements and functions, that is, possibly non-terminating programs, before I had freed myself from the interpretation of propositions as types.